# WILDLIFE OF GREATER BRISBANE

# WILDLIFE
## OF GREATER
# BRISBANE

museum

Published by the Queensland Museum with the
support of the Environment Management Branch
of Brisbane City Council

Brisbane City

Requests for this book should be made to:

Queensland Museum
PO Box 3300
SOUTH BRISBANE Q 4101
Australia
Fax (07) 3846 1918

National Library of Australia
Cataloguing–in–Publication data:

**Wildlife of Greater Brisbane**

Includes index.

ISBN 0 7242 6447 7.

1. Animals — Identification.
2. Zoology — Queensland — Brisbane Region.
I. Queensland Museum.

591.099431

Edited by Michelle Ryan
Designed by Andrew Ness
Illustrated by Robert Allen and
Mary-Anne Venables

With thanks to Bruce Campbell, Greg Czechura, Audra Douglas and Derek Griffin.

Set in 8.75 pt Utopia
Printed on Impress Satin by
Prestige Litho, Brisbane

Published by the Queensland Museum with the support of the Environment Management Branch of Brisbane City Council.

First printed 1995

# Foreword

For more than 125 years the Queensland Museum has been at the forefront of natural history research. In that time Museum biologists have been collecting, studying and documenting the unique animals for which Australia is famous.

From this on-going work, the Museum's collections have been expanded to form a rich repository of more than 25,000 specimens of fish, 40,000 reptiles, 30,000 birds, 19,000 amphibians, 18,000 mammals, 300,000 insects and countless other invertebrates. These collections are a permanent reference for research by individual scientists, groups and other institutions and for the education and benefit of the whole community.

This book, *Wildlife of Greater Brisbane*, reflects the Museum's continuing quest for knowledge and understanding of our natural environment and its commitment to disseminating this information to the wider public. The book's publication is especially appropriate at a time when so much of the natural environment is under threat from the pressures of modern living.

Cities, by their very nature, are seldom sympathetic to wildlife. The Greater Brisbane Region is indeed fortunate to have retained so many different types of animals and every effort must be made to ensure their survival for the enjoyment and pleasure of future generations.

*Wildlife of Greater Brisbane* provides identification information not only about animals with which we are all familiar, but also about many less well known groups. For example, invertebrates — those often small and easily overlooked inhabitants of soils and waterways — are rarely included in environmental studies or debate, yet their ecological value is no less profound than many of the higher profile, furred and feathered animals.

Acknowledgment must be made of the many individuals and organisations who co-operated and assisted with this project. I would like to extend my personal thanks to each of them — especially the authors, all experts in their fields, who so generously contributed their time, knowledge and goodwill to this long-term project.

The Environment Management Branch of Brisbane City Council provided significant financial support and text and photographic assistance. The CSIRO, Department of Primary Industries, Department of Environment and Heritage, Department of Education, NatureSearch, Brisbane Forest Park, Lone Pine Sanctuary, Currumbin Bird Sanctuary, Nature Focus (Australian Museum), Peter and Lil Frater, and Rod Hobson, all assisted with information or photographs.

Special thanks are owed to Phil Ryan and Jean Tilly for their valuable advice.

The following individuals assisted with photographs: Neil Armstrong, Robert Ashdown, John Cann, John Clatworthy, Peter Corkeron, Bruce Cowell,

Greg Daniels, Tony Ewart, Ivan Fien, Rodger Fiddler, Andrew Flowers, Ian Gynther, Clancy Hall, Les Hall, Robin Hill, Heather Janetzki, Owen Kelly, Joy Luke, Leslie Newman, Vic Perren, Jack Pettigrew, Chris Pollitt, Stephen Poole, Anthony Preen, Robert Raven, Deniss Reeves, Gunther Schmida, John Short, R. Slade, Peter Slater, Raoul Slater, Eric Vanderduys, Ray Viljoen, Jeffrey Willmer, Steve Wilson, Leigh Winsor and Jeff Wright. Several photographs are from the collection of the late Dr Garth May.

It is my hope that this book will alert residents of the Greater Brisbane Region to the importance of their natural heritage and become an essential reference for those attempting to protect and maintain the region's biodiversity.

**Dr Alan Bartholomai**
DIRECTOR, QUEENSLAND MUSEUM

# Contents

# A message from David Bellamy

I have been truly fortunate to travel extensively around the world and experience the wonders of this planet's biodiversity, in all its glory.

While the damage that humankind is doing to our fragile terrestrial and marine ecosystems continues to cause me dismay, I take heart at the growing number of initiatives aimed at redressing such damage and increasing public awareness of our precious environment.

Initiatives such as community-based environment management groups, bushland buy-back, local nature reserves and information centres and now, this book, are the key to protection and sensitive management of our ecological assets.

How can people appreciate and support sustainable use and conservation of our environment if they do not know what is out there? This book is the "Actual Reality Time Out Guide" to the wildlife of Greater Brisbane.

From now on everyone will be able to look out of their windows or take a walk in the city or out in the bush and say hello to a bird, a possum, a fish — yes, even an insect — calling it by name.

I commend this field guide to you and look forward to sharing the wildlife experience of Greater Brisbane in my future visits to your city.

**Professor David Bellamy**

THE CONSERVATION FOUNDATION, May 1995.

# How to use this book

This field guide is designed to help residents and visitors in the Greater Brisbane Region identify some of the animals they may encounter here.

More than 600 animals are listed in the species descriptions that follow. Even so, these represent only a fraction of the animals found within the region. It is not possible to include every species in a small book like this. The known insects alone would fill many much larger volumes. Selection has been based on public inquiries to the Queensland Museum and covers the most common animals in most major groups.

The animals are listed either in their taxonomic order or alphabetically by scientific name. There are a few exceptions. **Spiders**, for example, are listed alphabetically by their common names, which are the names more frequently used in the many public inquiries received at the Museum.

The information presented in each species description is intended as a concise, accurate guide to the physical appearance of each animal. It details how they are most often seen and includes:

**Common Name:** The name by which the animal is most widely known to the general community.

**Scientific Name:** The Latin-based name by which, despite variations in common names, the species can be recognised internationally, and which assigns each animal to a particular grouping.

**Other Names:** Often an animal will have more than one name in colloquial use.

**Identification:** Includes a general body length (unless otherwise specified); average weight where appropriate; colour details; and any other physical characteristic which distinguishes the animal.

**Habitat and Range:** Briefly outlines the type of environment in which the animal lives and where it is found. Locality records have been included where such information is available, accurate and up-to-date, and provided there are no conservation considerations.

**Similar species:** Other species, related or not, which may closely resemble the particular animal.

**Notes:** Any other points which make identification easier or brief general information of interest.

Where relevant, the standard descriptions also include several other sub-categories — eg Web Type and Bite for **Spiders**; Flight Pattern for **Dragonflies and Damselflies**; Traces for **Monotremes and Marsupials**.

In a few instances, technical detail — such as scale counts for snakes — is included as a cross-reference to identification. The reasons for this are discussed more fully where it occurs in the text.

The standard format has occasionally been enlarged to include information that is new, not easily accessible or not generally available to a wide audience, as is the case with the chapter on birds of prey, **Hawks, Eagles and Falcons**. Similarly, in a few chapters the species descriptions have been expanded beyond the "most common" to a comprehensive listing because of high public interest. **Frogs**, for example, includes a list of species which, although not officially from the region, are being more frequently reported. The section on **Land Snakes** is preceded by a general essay which briefly answers some of the most frequently asked questions from the general public.

General biological and life cycle details, unless of assistance to identification, have been omitted. Information considered sensitive in relation to conservation issues has also been left out. For example, no details are given about bird nesting because of the possible associated problems of egg collecting and nest disturbance.

Sometimes information is difficult to present in a meaningful form — as in rendering bird calls into human language. Bird calls are a pleasure amateur naturalists must discover for themselves.

Every attempt has been made to ensure that the information in this field guide is as current as possible; however scientific research is constantly expanding our knowledge of the natural world. As well, there are many animals regarded as "common" about which little is known because formal studies have not been undertaken. Lacewings are frequent visitors to Brisbane gardens, but in Australia there are only a few researchers investigating these beautiful insects.

This is the first time many of the animals — particularly invertebrates — have been publicly documented. Because of this, and the reason given above, not all the photographs are of live animals in natural habitats. Many are Queensland Museum collection specimens. This book may inspire amateur naturalists to study and photograph more species.

Users of this guide should be aware that animals in the wild may look different to captive or "domesticated" species. Guppies are common aquarium fish, but in rivers and creeks their bright colouring fades. The reasons for this are unclear. A wild animal's appearance is also affected by its age, breeding condition, and the physical environment in which it is seen.

This field guide is a first step to identification. Readers are encouraged to consult other books or to use the services of the Queensland Museum (Reference Centre: (07) 3840 7635) and similar organisations to further their knowledge of wildlife in the Greater Brisbane Region.

# The Greater Brisbane Region

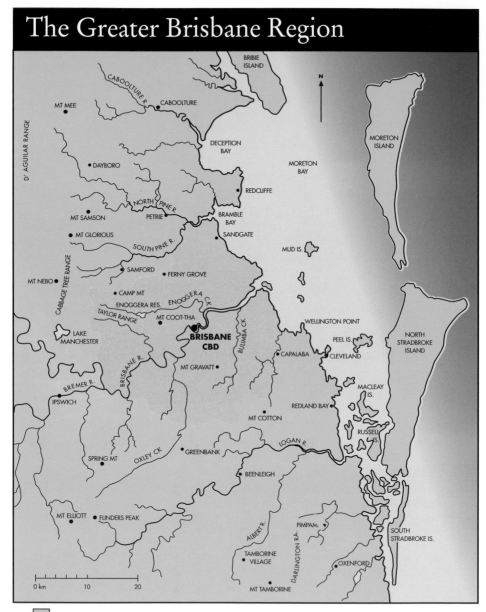

Brisbane Metropolitan Area

# Wildlife of the Greater Brisbane Region — An Overview

**Stephen Poole,** Environment Officer (Bushland Acquisition, Ecotourism and Fauna) Environment Management Branch, Brisbane City Council

The Greater Brisbane Region[1] covering some 3000 square kilometres contains one of the largest and fastest growing urban areas in the world. Brisbane City itself accounts for a staggering 1220 sq km or 122,000 hectares (including Moreton Island) and supports a population of more than 1 million.

However, despite this, the region has a rich diversity of plants and animals not found in similar sized cities elsewhere. Thousands of invertebrate and more than 400 vertebrate animals have so far been recorded.

It is unusual for so many animal species to exist in such close proximity to a major city  and their existence is due to a myriad of factors, not the least of which has been the pattern of human settlement and urban development over time. Widespread development has occurred only relatively recently in the region's history and most of the elevated areas escaped clearing. Although pastoral, logging and mining activities accompanied European settlement, relatively large tracts (compared to present coverage) of lowland forest remained until early this century.

Physical constraints such as the rugged terrain of Mt Coot-tha and the D'Aguilar Range in the west blocked the expansion of settlement and contributed greatly to maintaining vegetation, as have land tenure and land use in other areas. For example, the hundreds of hectares of bushland used as safety buffers around the Greenbank and Enoggera military reserves and the Belmont Rifle Range have unintentionally created wildlife havens.

**Mangroves**  Bruce Cowell

Although the climate is primarily sub-tropical, temperature and rainfall vary widely across the Greater Brisbane Region, as does the topography. The outcome of this is a complex mosaic of wildlife habitats — from sub-tropical rainforest on the wetter upland areas on the rim of the Brisbane Valley, down through dry eucalypt forest and riverine pockets to the lowlands with more dry eucalypt forest, woodlands and some coastal (wallum) heath. Wetland areas and mangrove and intertidal zones fringing Moreton Bay complete the ecological cross section.

The Greater Brisbane Region also forms part of what is known as the Macleay-McPherson Overlap. Animals generally regarded as belonging to either northern Australian (Torresian) or southern Australian (Bassian) faunas reach their distribution limits within the Overlap.[2] Certain species of vegetation also have their known geographic limits within the Overlap. One of the best examples is the Antarctic Beech of the high McPherson Ranges. It may well be established that Moreton Bay experiences the same phenomenon. The Dugong, a marine mammal of warm tropical seas, is at its most southerly limit in Moreton Bay.

There is still debate as to the exact extent of the Macleay-McPherson phenomenon but it is certain that the natural areas of the Greater Brisbane Region form part of, and are influenced by, the Overlap. There is not only a very large number of species, but some groups of animals found Australia-wide have their highest diversity here.

Within the Overlap area several ecological and climatic factors converge to again produce many different types of wildlife habitats. Within these broad habitats, there may also occur localised microhabitats (eg, a protected gully). The existence of so many varied habitats gives rise to a higher number of animal species than would normally be found in such a relatively confined area.

The region is also fortunate in having nearby several natural assets which continue to support this wonderful diversity of wildlife. The most important of these is arguably Brisbane Forest Park which covers 26,500 hectares on and around the D'Aguilar Range. When combined with surrounding bushland, the park provides an extended ecological reservoir nearly 50 km long. Without this area, which supports almost every animal species found in the Greater Brisbane Region, the long term viability of many species would be threatened.

The close proximity of Moreton Bay and its associated intertidal and wetland areas provides not just an important recreational reserve for the region's populace, but breeding habitats for fish, birds and a variety of marine animals. Wetland areas also remain at Pine River, Deagon, Boondall, Nudgee and Carbrook.

The Bay sand islands (particularly Moreton Island) provide diverse wildlife habitats which tend to be more secure than those on the mainland and which have allowed some species to survive in isolation. For example, a golden colour phase of the Swamp Wallaby can be found on Stradbroke Island.[3]

In all, this unique combination of environmental circumstances has given those of us who live in the Greater Brisbane Region a remarkable opportunity to still appreciate our "wild" animals and the habitats in which they are found.

The region contains a nationally significant — perhaps the most important — koala population based on high quality eucalypt forest habitat overlapping the boundaries of Brisbane and Logan Cities and the Redland Shire. This area is notable not only for the quality of the habitat, but also the density of the koalas and its proximity to a capital city — Brisbane can justly be called the "Koala Capital" of Australia.

The sheltered waters of Moreton Bay are strongholds for turtles, dugongs and dolphins and its international significance as a wetland in relation to migratory wading birds — such as the Bar-tailed Godwit, Eastern Curlew and Mongolian Plover — has recently been recognised by the Ramsar Convention.[4] In terms of spectacle, the world's largest Cattle Egret rookery is found at Doboy, near the mouth of the Brisbane River.

Species under threat elsewhere in Queensland and Australia survive within the Greater Brisbane Region. The Ornate (or Soft-spined) Rainbow Fish is rated as vulnerable to extinction at State level and was thought to be extinct within the Greater Brisbane Region (except for Moreton Island). However this fish has now been found in Upper Buhot and Tingalpa Creeks within the Leslie Harrison Reservoir catchment.[5]

**Sugar Glider**  Brisbane City Council

Squirrel Gliders, rare to endangered across the rest of Australia,[6] are found nowhere else in such prolific numbers as in Brisbane. The southernmost population of the Brown Soldier Butterfly occurs around Brisbane[7] and the Richmond Birdwing Butterfly is also found here. Brisbane was once the centre of the Richmond Birdwing's distribution and, ironically, is now the centre of activity to save it from extinction.

The Greater Brisbane Region still has platypus (Pullen Pullen Creek),[8] Greater Gliders (Burbank and Daisy Hill) and Bobuck or Mountain Brushtail Possums (Mt Cotton and Cornubia).[9] Other significant species include the Powerful and Eastern Grass Owls, Black Cockatoo, Wallum Froglet and Green-stripe Frog, Stephen's Banded Snake, Elf Skink (southernmost population),[10] Yellow-bellied Glider, Brush-tailed Phascogale and the False Water Rat.

However, while many animals have survived and even adapted to the environmental changes that accompany the growth of cities others have not fared so well. Among the species that have declined or disappeared from the region are the Frilled Lizard (which used to be common, appeared to be lost, but has recently been reported from Greenbank, its southernmost occurrence), the Tiger Quoll and Death Adder.[11] More are under threat

**Giant Fig — Fig Tree Pocket. Note the figure, centre foreground, among the buttresses.** John Oxley Library

Before European settlement, the Greater Brisbane Region was a wondrous place for ecological investigation. Of the historical photographs of Brisbane, none is perhaps more striking than that of the huge Moreton Bay Fig which used to stand at Fig Tree Pocket. Such marvels illustrate what treasures have been lost since free settlers entered the area in the 1840s.

In the past 150 years, much of the natural environment has given way to the urban fabric of roads, homes, factories and the like. The Brisbane metropolitan area is continuing to spread — north to Noosa; south towards the Gold Coast and New South Wales Border (east of the Darlington Range); south-west towards Beaudesert; and in the west, beyond Ipswich with outliers towards the foot of the Great Dividing Range. The developed areas of Logan City, Pine Rivers Shire, Ipswich, northern Gold Coast and parts of the Redland Shire are all extending, resulting in a near continuous urban sprawl centred on Brisbane.

As the development pushes outward, the remaining natural environments are coming under increasing pressure. It has been calculated that in South-East Queensland, 39 percent of existing freehold bushland was cleared between 1974 and 1989.[12] If these rates continue, all freehold bushland will be gone by the year 2012. Lowland rainforests, eucalypt forests and wetlands have also been drastically reduced. Between 1974 and 1989, eucalypt forest on the South-East Queensland coastal strip declined by 28 percent, *Melaleuca quinquinerva* forest by 39 percent and heathland by 15 percent. In hinterland areas, the vegetation loss has been more severe.

Within the City of Brisbane, about 4500 hectares or 22 percent of remnant bushland was replaced by urban development in the period 1982–1990.[13] This translates to an average bushland loss of approximately three football fields per day. For the rest of South-East Queensland, bushland is still being cleared at average rates equivalent to 21 football fields per day. Unless this trend is slowed or reversed, only tiny fragments will remain.

It is not only land clearing which poses a problem. Other forms of human interference can have a devastating effect on native animals. Toohey Forest, a green buffer bordering the Brisbane suburbs of Mt Gravatt, Nathan and Tarragindi, has lost almost all the native ground mammals that were once present. This may be due to a range of human activities which together impact on ground mammals. The most obvious of these activities are the surrounding major road networks and the South-East Freeway which runs through the forest.

Stephen Poole

Road traffic, an inescapable part of city life, impacts on many other types of fauna including arboreal (tree-dwelling) animals such as koalas which are vulnerable while on the ground. It has been estimated that up to 60 koalas a year are killed on the southern section of the Gateway Arterial Road.[14] Such estimates are probably conservative due to a lack of systematic reporting and deaths that occur away from the road, as in the case of an animal with internal injuries or an animal with a broken jaw which subsequently dies of starvation.

Examples such as Toohey Forest, considered large in relation to its urban surroundings, demonstrate the threats humans impose on wildlife by fragmenting natural habitats into what are, in effect, small islands of vegetation. There is still debate as to how large a natural area needs to be to maintain native fauna and how requirements for each species vary, but it is safe to say that large animals need extensive, connected habitats.

It has been suggested that for macropods (such as the Swamp and Red-necked Wallabies) to survive in the long term in Daisy Hill State Forest and its surrounds, the area needed to remain connected to what was approximately 10,000 hectares of remnant vegetation centred on the Leslie Harrison Reservoir catchment area.[15] However much fragmentation has occurred in the past 20 years and it is uncertain which large fauna populations will be viable over time. It is clear that in urban and near urban growth areas (where threatening and high impact processes occur), thousands of hectares of predominantly natural habitats are required to provide a stronger likelihood of long term viability for large mammals.

Those of us who live in the Greater Brisbane Region are very fortunate to still have special remnants of the natural environment that we can experience, learn from and marvel at. Such natural assets should be treasured. They serve three main purposes: they are monuments to the region's ecological history, they provide and maintain biodiversity, and they serve as small green buffers, important for our well-being and lifestyle within an increasingly artificial urban expanse.

The Greater Brisbane Region, and indeed South-East Queensland, is at a crossroads. One path will lead to unrestrained and poorly planned, nearly continuous urban sprawl. The alternative path will lead to an accommodation of urban growth while still retaining the "green" zones essential not only for wildlife, but for humans too. There is a responsibility on all levels of government and the community to realise that "development at all costs" is not an ecologically sustainable option and to work towards securing the future of wildlife in the region.

The time has come for all relevant agencies and authorities to co-operate and develop initiatives to maintain and enhance the region's biodiversity. It is important to remember that, while on a national or state basis certain species may not be threatened or endangered, there is no reason why such species should not be conserved at the local or regional level. Localised extinctions contribute to overall decline. We should not wait for a species to become endangered or rare before moving to protect it.

The wildlife of the Greater Brisbane Region is a unique natural asset which is now being appreciated as never before. For example, boat trips to Indooroopilly Island in the Brisbane River allow people to witness the dusk spectacle of hundreds of thousands of flying foxes departing their daytime roosts. Alternatively, the potential of whale watching off Brisbane is yet to be fully appreciated with only a small operation in place.

The increasing commercial activity generally called ecotourism provides for a greater awareness and appreciation of these precious natural assets while at the same time identifying them as economically valuable and providing a financial justification to protect and augment. It is quite likely that compatible and sustainable ecotourism provides the linchpin for the long-term maintenance of wildlife in the Greater Brisbane Region.

1    The Greater Brisbane Region, although not officially defined, is usually regarded as the Brisbane Statistical Division and a further 60–100 km. See map.

2    Paul Adam, *New South Wales Rainforests — The Nomination for the World Heritage List*, NSW NPWS, Sydney, 1987.

3    Ironically, these wallabies are now often killed by road traffic, a distinct threat to some fauna populations on the mainland.

4    The International Convention for the Protection of Wetlands. Such recognition will also lead to better protection of Moreton Bay's marine species.

5    *Eastern Corridor Report, Draft Impact Assessment Study for the South Coast Motorway*, Kinhill, Cameron, Macnamara, February 1995.

6    Tim Low, Fauna of Brisbane, unpublished report to Brisbane City Council, 1993.

7    Low, 1993.

8    Frank Carrick, Platypus Survey of Brisbane, unpublished report to Brisbane City Council, 1995.

9    All three species are locally threatened and likely to become locally rare.

10   Low, 1993.

11   Low, 1993.

12   Carla Catterall, *A Natural Area Conservation Strategy for Brisbane City*, Brisbane City Council, 1990.

13   Catterall, 1990.

14   Ric Natrass, verbal communication with the author, 1994.

15   Wally Davies, *Wildlife of the Brisbane Area*, Jacaranda, Brisbane, 1983.

# Worms

Dr Lester Cannon

"Worms" is a descriptive term that refers to animals which are "worm-like" in appearance. Worms actually comprise about 20 groups of animals. Only a few are recognisable to most people and many are not well known or understood, although some such as roundworms are among the most abundant animals on Earth. As many as 3.75 million roundworms may occur in one hectare of beach sand and twice as many in the same area of pasture. In general, free-living roundworms are extremely tiny and cannot be seen without the aid of a microscope. Because of this they are not included in these species descriptions. Similarly, parasitic worms of all kinds have also been omitted.  Many animals popularly referred to as "worms" are not worms at all but the larvae of insects. These include silkworms, glowworms and mealworms.

## Flatworms

As the name suggests most flatworms are flat and leaf-like although some may be spherical or round. Flatworms may be free-living or parasitic.

A. Flowers and L. Newman

### Oyster Leech *Stylochus* spp.

**Identification:** Leaf-like, about 3×2 cm. Slimy, fleshy and brown.

**Habitat and Range:** Marine worm. Found in dead oyster shells. Moreton Bay. Possibly several species; common throughout the world.

**Notes:** These worms eat oysters and are considered a commercial pest.

Leigh Winsor

### Shovel-headed Garden Flatworm
*Bipalium kewense*

**Identification:** Length about 10–20 cm. Thin, brown with dark upper stripes and rounded, shovel-shaped head.

**Habitat and Range:** Under rocks and logs in gardens, particularly in well-treed suburbs. Cosmopolitan; transported around world in pot plant soil.

**Notes:** Predator of earthworms. When attacked, these worms produce copious amounts of mucus. May cause vomiting in cats.

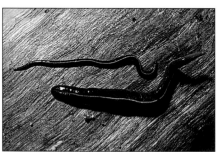

Leigh Winsor

### Blue Garden Flatworm
*Caenoplana coerulea*

**Identification:** Length about 8–10 cm. Thin, dark blue above, lighter below. Narrow head.

**Habitat and Range:** Found under rocks and logs in damp places in well-treed suburbs; native of damp forests. Animal often found coiled, surrounded by a dry, silvery plaque of mucus.

**Notes**: Harmless predator of soil fauna. When attacked, these worms tend to fragment.

## Planarians

**Identification:** There are several species, indistinguishable to the lay person. In general, about 2 cm long, thin; some may have a triangular head. Usually brown; characterised by two small white patches surrounding black eyes.

**Habitat and Range:** Found in permanent freshwater, usually under rocks or floating vegetation such as water lily leaves.

**Notes:** Predators of small freshwater fauna.

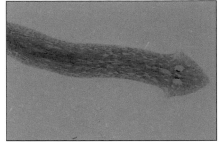

*Girardia tigrina*　　Queensland Museum

## Temnocephala　*Temnocephala* spp.

**Identification:** Length about 1–2 cm. White, grey, brown to black; five tiny tentacles on head and posterior sucker under tail end. Leech-like looping movements.

**Habitat and Range:** Symbiotic — found on surface of freshwater shrimps and crayfish. Numerous species associated with different crayfish. Australia has richest fauna, but also found in South America, South-East Asia and Madagascar.

**Notes:** Opportunistic feeders on microscopic animals; sometimes cannibalistic.

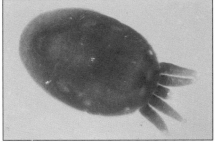

Queensland Museum

# Ribbonworms

Ribbonworms resemble flatworms but have a more complex internal organisation including a vascular system and a long and powerful pharynx. They can be confused with flatworms but are often much more extensible (can be thinly stretched). Most species of ribbonworms are marine and there are no records of terrestrial species from the Greater Brisbane Region.

## Ribbonworm　*Baseodiscus princhii*

**Identification:** Very long, non-segmented, often easily broken. Creamy-white with a dark upper stripe. Generally less than a metre long.

**Habitat and Range:** Marine worm. Found on intertidal mudflats. East coast of Queensland extending to Barrier Reef.

**Notes:** Predator of small mud fauna.

Queensland Museum

## Gordian Worms

Gordian worms are long hair-like or wire-like animals which parasitise insects when in the juvenile phase. The adults are free-living and do not feed but will live for many months seeking a mate. Eggs are laid in water and ingested by the insect when it drinks. Their common name is derived from the Gordian Knot of antiquity because of the complex tangles that these worms form.

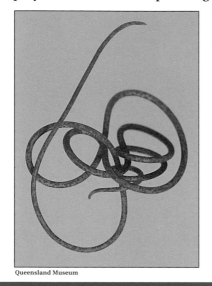

Queensland Museum

### Gordian Worms
*Gordius* spp. *Chordodes* spp.

**Other Names:** Wireworms, Horsehair Worms.

**Identification:** Length to 25–30 cm; up to 1 mm thick. *Gordius* spp. — smooth and golden; *Chordodes* spp. — rough and mottled brown and black.

**Habitat and Range:** Found in freshwater (and swimming pools). More common in summer. Worldwide.

**Notes:** Harmless to humans and other animals. As the juvenile parasitic phase reaches maturity within its host, the worm induces the insect to go to water. How this occurs is not known. The worm breaks through the body wall of the insect and swims free. The insect dies.

## Segmented Worms

Segmented Worms are complex invertebrate animals. They have a true coelom (body cavity) that surrounds the internal organs including those associated with blood supply, nutrition and reproduction. Their bodies are made up of replicate segments that appear ring-like externally. Contraction of the muscles in each successive segment along the body creates peculiar peristaltic (wave-like) movements.  These are the animals to which people often refer when they use the term "worm".

*Digaster longmanii* Queensland Museum

### Earthworms Oligochaeta

Many different species of native and introduced earthworms occur in the region.  Earthworms are hermaphrodites which cross fertilise and lay cocoons from which small worms emerge. Introduced species are the most usual ones found in compost and sold for worm farms.  Native species include the giant *Heteroporodrilus tryoni* which is from 10–50 cm long and is common in Brisbane's western suburbs. Other worms found in gardens include *Digaster* spp. and the introduced *Amynthas* spp. Small red tangles of worms, *Tubifex* spp., occur in freshwater especially in sludge or places with high organic matter.

## Leech *Chtonobdella whitmani*

**Identification:** About 1–5 cm long, up to 1 cm thick. Black-brown above with a distinct central stripe; pale below. Body tapers to narrow head; robust posterior sucker.

**Habitat and Range:** Most common local species. Creeks, wet forest situations. Well-treed suburbs. Northern NSW to southern Qld.

**Notes:** Characteristic looping movement on land; swims with an undulating movement.

Leech Bruce Cowell

# Marine Bristle Worms (Polychaeta)

**These worms are characterised by having many stiff bristles on each of their body segments They display a diversity of body shapes and sizes and fall into two main groups — the wandering (errant), and the sedentary tube worms.**

## Bloodworms *Marphysa sanguinea*

**Other Names:** Mudworms

**Identification:** Length 15–20 cm; less than 1 cm thick. Firm body with many segments. Dark pinky-brown. Pale to golden bristles down both sides. Worms bleed if they break.

**Habitat and Range:** Commonly dug from sand and mud. Intertidal sediments along east coast of Australia.

**Notes:** Good bait, much favoured by fishermen. Unlike earthworms these animals cannot be easily cultured because their planktonic larval stages are dispersed in the ocean.

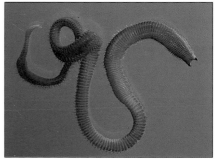
Queensland Museum

## Beach Worm *Australonuphis* sp.

**Identification:** Length to 1 m; around 1 cm thick. Creamy-brown. Pale to golden bristles down both sides.

**Habitat and Range:** Beneath sand of ocean beaches in intertidal zone. Australia-wide.

**Notes:** Good bait. Collection involves dragging dead fish along edge of surf and grabbing head of worm as it surfaces to feed. Has powerful jaws and can bite.

Queensland Museum

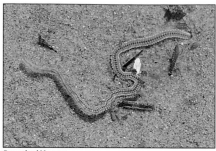

Queensland Museum

## *Phyllodoce* spp.

**Identification:** Length to 12 cm. Bright green. Delicate.

**Habitat and Range:** Found wriggling on sand of intertidal zone. Australia-wide.

**Notes:** Worms leave trails — fine grooves in sand; not to be confused with snail trails which are formed from below the surface.

## Spoonworms

Spoonworms are soft-bodied marine worms. The proboscis of these animals is not retractable and if disturbed, the worm will discard the proboscis. Spoonworms are detritus feeders and gather their food on mucus trails.

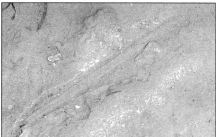

Queensland Museum

## Spoonworm *Listriobolus bulbocaudatus*

**Identification:** Body sausage-shaped to 5–8 cm; red-brown. Only pale proboscis of worm is generally seen, extending over the surface mud.

**Habitat and Range:** Found buried in mud flats. Moreton Bay.

# Land Snails

Dr John Stanisic

The snails and slugs (snails without shells) of the Greater Brisbane Region are a mixture of introduced and native species. With few exceptions, the snails found in suburban gardens are introductions (mainly from Europe) which flourish in the artificially-created, moist microhabitats of backyards and farms. By contrast, native species (about 60 occur in the area) do not adapt well to the environmental changes that human activity brings and are mostly restricted to more natural habitats.

Identification is based on the features of the shell — size, shape, colour and sculpture which can be spiral (in the direction of coiling) or radial (at right angles to the direction of coiling) — and of the animal in the case of slugs.

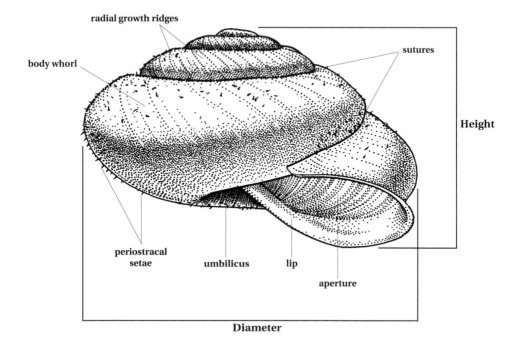

Queensland Museum

## Fastosarion virens

**Identification:** Shell diameter 13–15 mm. Animal length up to 40 mm. Semi-slug with smooth skin. Animal pinkish-grey with diffuse, irregular dark grey to black markings on sides of foot and on tissue surrounding shell. Sole of foot with outer margins pink to red. Shell shiny, yellowy-brown, ear-shaped, fragile; sculpture of weak, fine, spiral grooves, almost smooth.

**Habitat and Range:** Under logs and in discarded palm fronds in rainforest and wet eucalypt forest; sometimes found feeding in low shrubs. Lismore, NSW to Gympie, Qld. Key localities: Mt Mee, suburban Brisbane.

**Notes:** Common species around Brisbane . Family Helicarionidae.

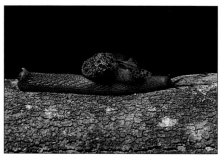

Queensland Museum

## Fastosarion aquila

**Identification:** Shell diameter 14–17 mm. Animal length up to 40 mm. Semi-slug with pimply skin. Animal browny-orange with distinctive black spotting on tissue surrounding shell. Sole of foot with outer margins orange. Shell shiny, yellowy-brown, ear-shaped, fragile; sculpture of fine, spiral grooves, more pronounced than in *F. virens.*

**Habitat and Range:** Habitat similar to *F. virens* (see above). Mullumbimby, NSW to Kenilworth, Qld. Key localities: Tamborine Mountain, Lamington National Park.

**Notes:** Not known from Brisbane suburbs but common in undisturbed rainforest patches such as Mt Glorious. Most readily distinguished from *F. virens* by black spotting on animal. Family Helicarionidae.

Queensland Museum

## Nitor pudibunda

**Identification:** Shell diameter 14 mm; height 10 mm. Shell medium-sized, glassy, angled; sculpture almost smooth; light brown to yellow. Animal pink with yellow markings on shell lappets (tissue overlapping shell); body with darker markings visible through transparent shell. Umbilicus almost closed.

**Habitat and Range:** Under logs and rocks in rainforest. Byron Bay, NSW to Cooloola, Qld.

Key localities: Mt Glorious, Tamborine Mountain.

**Notes:** Confined to rainforest. Family Helicarionidae.

## Hedleyella falconeri

**Identification:** Shell diameter 70 mm. Shell very large, with inflated last whorl; umbilicus present, lip thin; dark brown with interrupted, darker spiral markings. Sculpture almost smooth. Animal brown to grey with black tentacles.

**Habitat and Range:** Under logs in rainforest. Gosford, NSW to Mt Mee, Qld. Key localities: Mt Glorious, Lamington National Park.

**Notes:** Australia's largest land snail. Related species, *H. maconelli*, lives in rainforest south of Gympie. Family Caryodidae.

Queensland Museum

## Pedinogyra rotabilis

**Identification:** Shell diameter up to 50 mm. Shell large, flat-coiled with a very large umbilicus; body whorl angled. Sculpture weak, consisting of thin, radial growth ridges; brown to straw-yellow. Animal grey with darker neck and tentacles.

**Habitat and Range:** In litter and soil among rocks in rainforest. Lismore, NSW to Mt Glorious, Qld. Key localities: Tamborine Mountain, Lamington National Park.

**Notes:** Distinguished by its angled, flat-coiled shell. Larger relatives live around Mt Mee and Gympie areas and in most hoop pine scrubs of south-eastern Qld. Family Caryodidae.

Australian Museum

Queensland Museum

## *Sphaerospira fraseri*

**Identification:** Shell diameter 50 mm. Shell large, spherical, with reflected (bent backward) and thickened lip (in adults); umbilicus closed by reflexion of lip. Sculpture smooth. Shell brown to dark brown with darker, complete spiral bands; lip dark grey to black. Animal grey with dark grey mantle.

**Habitat and Range:** Under logs in rainforest or wet eucalypt forest. Grafton, NSW to Cooloola, Qld. Key localities: Mt Glorious, Mt Mee.

**Notes:** Common species which still survives in moist gullies around Brisbane. Often mistaken for introduced garden snail. Family Camaenidae.

Queensland Museum

## *Sphaerospira mattea*

**Identification:** Shell diameter 26 mm. Shell moderately large, smooth, with reflected (bent backward) and thickened lip (in adults); umbilicus open, small. Colour white to creamy-yellow with dark brown spiral bands. Animal brown with pinky-red mantle.

**Habitat and Range:** Under logs in dry vine thickets. Brisbane to Mackay, Qld. Key locality: Ipswich.

**Notes:** Not common around Brisbane. Family Camaenidae.

Queensland Museum

## *Xanthomelon pachystylum*

**Identification:** Shell diameter 40 mm. Shell large, solid, spherical with a moderately thickened, unreflected lip; umbilicus absent; sculpture of fine, radial growth ridges crossed by irregular, incised spiral furrows; yellow with white apex. Animal light grey.

**Habitat and Range:** Buried in soil under logs in drier areas. Brisbane to Cairns, Qld. Key locality: Gold Scrub at Samsonvale.

**Notes:** Wide ranging species and possible commercial prospect for gourmet food market. Family Camaenidae.

## Thersites richmondiana

Queensland Museum

**Identification:** Shell diameter 50 mm. Shell large, top-shaped with strongly angled body whorl; umbilicus absent; lip thickened and reflected (bent backward); sculpture of fine growth lines; brown to black. Animal brown to black.

**Habitat and Range:** Under logs and bark in rainforest. Lismore, NSW to Conondale Range, Qld. Key localities: Tamborine Mountain, Lamington National Park.

**Notes:** Distinguished from all other land snails in south-eastern Qld by shape of shell. Family Camaenidae.

## Meridolum gilberti

Queensland Museum

**Identification:** Shell diameter 25 mm. Shell moderately large, spherical with weakly re-flected (bent backward) lip; umbilicus absent; sculpture of strong radial growth ridges and crowded pimples. Colour light brown to straw yellow, sometimes with red spiral band near suture and red suffusion surrounding umbilical area. Animal yellowy-brown to grey.

**Habitat and Range:** Under logs in dry wood-land. Coffs Harbour, NSW to Brisbane. Key localities: Tamborine Mountain, suburban Brisbane.

**Notes:** Common in some semi-rural areas around Brisbane. Family Camaenidae.

## Ramogenia challengeri

Queensland Museum

**Identification:** Shell diameter 15 mm. Shell medium-sized with almost flat spire and rounded periphery; umbilicus open; lip reflected (bent backward). Shell surface velvety, sometimes with fine, scattered hair-like extensions; dark brown. Animal black.

**Habitat and Range:** Under logs in rainforest. Mullumbimby, NSW to Cooloola, Qld. Key localities: Tamborine Mountain, Lamington National Park.

**Notes:** One of a number of species character-ised by a "hairy" periostracum (shell cover-ing). Family Camaenidae.

Queensland Museum

## *Papuexul bidwilli*

**Identification:** Shell height 17 mm. Shell medium-sized, smooth, top-shaped with thin, unreflected lip and strongly angled body whorl; umbilicus absent; white to straw yellow with irregular coffee-coloured to black spotting. Animal creamy-white becoming darker in the neck and head region.

**Habitat and Range:** Arboreal in upper canopy of rainforests. Lismore, NSW to Gympie, Qld. Key localities: Mt Nebo, Kondalilla National Park.

**Notes:** Very rare species. Family Camaenidae.

Queensland Museum

## *Posorites fucata*

**Identification:** Shell height 17 mm. Shell medium-sized, smooth, top-shaped with thin unreflected lip and weakly rounded body whorl; umbilicus absent; creamy-white with uninterrupted brown to black, spiral bands. Animal white.

**Habitat and Range:** Arboreal in dry vine forests. Brisbane to Monto, Qld. Key locality: Brookfield, Brisbane.

**Notes:** Distinguished from *Papuexul bidwilli* by rounded body whorl and uninterrupted spiral colour bands. Family Camaenidae.

Queensland Museum

## *Strangesta ramsayi*

**Identification:** Shell diameter 25 mm. Shell moderately large, with almost flat spire and thin, simple lip; umbilicus widely open; sculpture of prominent radial ribs; base smooth. Colour dark brown to yellow. Animal brown with prominent central creamy stripe on neck.

**Habitat and Range:** Under logs in rain-forest. Lismore, NSW to Bundaberg, Qld. Key localities: Mt Glorious, Kenilworth.

**Notes:** Carnivorous on a range of inverte-brates including other land snails. Charact-erised by long neck. Family Rhytididae.

## *Saladelos urarensis*

Queensland Museum

**Identification:** Shell diameter 7mm. Shell small, flattened with a very wide umbilicus; sculpture almost smooth with interrupted spiral grooves; yellow. Animal orange.

**Habitat and Range:** Under logs in rainforest. Port Macquarie, NSW to Gympie, Qld. Key localities: Mt Glorious, Tamborine Mountain, Lamington National Park.

**Notes:** Carnivorous. Family Rhytididae.

## *Prisma australis*

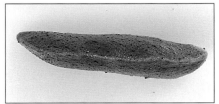
Queensland Museum

**Identification:** Length to 50 mm. Animal slug-like with leathery, minutely pimpled surface and ridged back; foot with narrow central sole. Animal brown to grey with small, dark, circular markings.

**Habitat and Range:** Under logs in rainforest. Dorrigo, NSW to Rockhampton, Qld. Key localities: Mt Mudlo, Lamington National Park.

**Notes:** Carnivorous slug distinguished by triangular cross-section. Family Rathouisiidae.

## *Triboniophorus graeffei*

Queensland Museum

**Identification:** Length 70 mm. Large flattened slug with a single pair of retractile tentacles; upper surface with pronounced creases. Mantle triangular, located mid-line near front of animal; pneumostome (breathing pore) visible on back. Colour white to creamy-white with red markings on edges of mantle (red triangle) and on edges of foot.

**Habitat and Range:** Rainforest and eucalypt woodland; buried in ground under logs during day, crawling on trees at night. Wollongong, NSW to Mossman, Qld. Key localities: Mt Coot-tha, Mt Nebo.

**Notes:** Common in Brisbane area. Feeding tracks (lines of small circular markings) often visible on smooth barked eucalypts. Bright orange and pink forms known from Border Ranges. Family Athoracophoridae.

Queensland Museum

## *Deroceras panormitanum*

**Identification:** Length 30 mm. Small, narrow with saddle-like mantle located on the upper side at front of animal; pneumostome (breathing pore) in posterior half of mantle. Uniform light brown to grey.

**Habitat and Range:** Suburban gardens and semi-rural paddocks. Throughout most of suburban Australia and in nearby rural areas where habitat has been altered.

**Notes:** Introduced. Family Limacidae.

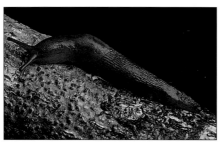

Queensland Museum

## *Lehmannia nyctelia*

**Identification:** Length 50 mm. Moderately large, slender slug with saddle-like mantle situated on the upper side at front of animal; pneumostome (breathing pore) in rear half of mantle. Colour light brown with two dorsal stripes on body and tail and 2–3 stripes on mantle.

**Habitat and Range:** Suburban gardens and semi-rural paddocks. Range as for *D. panormitanum* (see above).

**Notes:** Introduced. Family Limacidae.

Queensland Museum

## *Limax maximus*

**Identification:** Length up to 200 mm. Very large with saddle-like mantle situated on the upper side near front of animal; pneumo-stome (breathing pore) in posterior half of mantle. Colour light brown with dark brown to black bands and irregular black markings on mantle.

**Habitat and Range:** Surburban gardens and semi-rural paddocks. Range as for *D. panormitanum* (see above).

**Notes:** Largest of the introduced European slugs. Family Limacidae.

## Vaginulus plebeius

Queensland Museum

**Identification:** Length to 60 mm. Very large, flattened slug, with leathery upper surface (notum); mantle cavity and pneumostome (breathing pore) absent. Foot with broad sole. Colour light to dark brown.

**Habitat and Range:** Suburban gardens, paddocks and cultivated areas. Eastern Qld to NT and WA.

**Notes:** Species introduced to Pacific region from tropical America. Often seen crawling on lawns after rain. Family Veronicellidae.

## Laevicaulis alte

Queensland Museum

**Identification:** Length to 60 mm. Very large, flattened slug with slightly elevated, leathery upper surface. Mantle cavity and pneumostome (breathing pore) absent. Foot with broad sole. Colour grey to dark grey with a creamy-white median dorsal stripe.

**Habitat and Range:** Suburban gardens, paddocks and cultivated areas. Eastern Qld to NT and WA.

**Notes:** Introduced from southern Asia and now widespread in Pacific region. Distinguished from *V. plebeius* (see above) by darker colour, white stripe on back and more raised body hump. Family Veronicellidae.

## Bradybaena similaris

Queensland Museum

**Identification:** Shell diameter 15 mm. Shell medium-sized, with small umbilicus; lip reflected (bent backward); sculpture almost smooth. Colour creamy-white; often with a dark red band at the periphery. Animal white.

**Habitat and Range:** Suburban gardens. Coastal eastern Australia.

**Notes:** Introduced from Asia and now widespread along east coast. Large numbers have been recorded from Brisbane's market gardens. Family Bradybaenidae.

Queensland Museum

## Helix aspersa

**Identification:** Shell diameter to 40 mm. Shell large, thin with reflected lip (bent backward); umbilicus absent; sculpture of prominent growth ridges and irregular spiral wrinkles. Colour yellow to brown with darker brown interrupted spiral bands. Animal grey.

**Habitat and Range:** Suburban gardens throughout most of Australia.

**Notes:** The common garden snail. Introduced from Europe in early 1800s; an established garden pest. Edible. Family Helicidae.

# Spiders

Dr Robert Raven and Phil Lawless

The known spider fauna of the Greater Brisbane Region includes more than 300 species belonging to 50 families. However, many species remain unknown despite the high urban population.

The accurate identification of spiders often requires a microscope and a considerable knowledge of the animals and their anatomy. The Identification Chart and species descriptions that follow are not intended to be comprehensive, but rather an introduction to spiders. Species selection has been based on the most common public inquiries to the Queensland Museum.

In the Identification Chart, spiders are grouped according to where they are found, their web types, and the shape of their egg sacs. Within each category, spiders appear in descending order of size with a scale comparison to actual size. The species descriptions are arranged alphabetically by common name. Entries marked with an asterisk (*) are not listed in the Identification Chart. The species descriptions also contain a brief summary of bites and known reactions. (Size refers to a spider's body including legs). Two species of water spiders are included at the end of the descriptions.

If, after looking at the chart and reading the descriptions, doubt still exists contact the Museum's Arachnology section.

# SPIDER IDENTIFICATION CHART

| LOCATION | | | | | |
|---|---|---|---|---|---|
| **On wall (no web)** | 0.2 × Life | 0.2 × Life | 0.2 × Life | 0.5 × Life | |
| | Brown Huntsman | Grey Huntsman | Net-casting Spider | Garden Orb-weaver | |
| **Above ground** | 0.3 × Life | 0.3 × Life | 0.8 × Life | Life size | |
| | Trapdoor | Wolf Spider | Swift Ground Spider | White-tailed Spider | |
| **On vegetation** | 0.2 × Life | 0.2 × Life | Life size | 1.5 × Life | |
| | Slender Sac Spider | Net-casting Spider | Slender Sac Spider | Black House Spider | |

| WEB TYPE | | | | | |
|---|---|---|---|---|---|
| **Circular web** | 0.2 × Life | 0.2 × Life | 0.5 × Life | 0.5 × Life | |
| | Golden Orb-weaver | Jewelled Spider | Garden Orb -weaver | St Andrew's Cross | |
| **Tangled web** | 0.2 × Life | 0.1 × Life | 0.4 × Life | 0.5 × Life | |
| | Net-casting Spider | Tent Spider and web | | Daddy -long- legs | |
| **Funnel-shaped web** | 0.1 × Life | 0.4 × Life | 0.5 × Life | 0.5 × Life | |
| | Tent spider and web | | Black House Spider | Funnel-web | |

| EGGS | | | | | |
|---|---|---|---|---|---|
| | 0.2 × Life | 0.3 × Life | 0.3 × Life | 0.5 × Life | |
| | Tent Spider | Magnificent Spider | Wolf Spider | Brown Widow & Redback | |

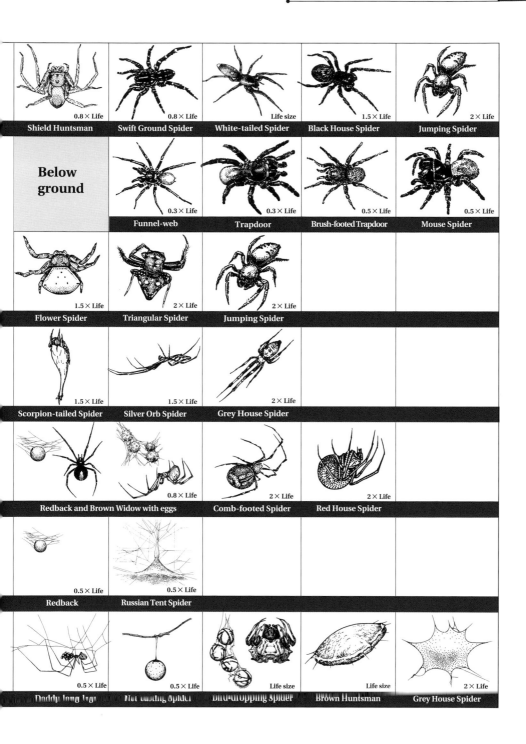

| Shield Huntsman | Swift Ground Spider | White-tailed Spider | Black House Spider | Jumping Spider |
| --- | --- | --- | --- | --- |
| 0.8 × Life | 0.8 × Life | Life size | 1.5 × Life | 2 × Life |

**Below ground**

| Funnel-web | Trapdoor | Brush-footed Trapdoor | Mouse Spider |
| --- | --- | --- | --- |
| 0.3 × Life | 0.3 × Life | 0.5 × Life | 0.5 × Life |

| Flower Spider | Triangular Spider | Jumping Spider |
| --- | --- | --- |
| 1.5 × Life | 2 × Life | 2 × Life |

| Scorpion-tailed Spider | Silver Orb Spider | Grey House Spider |
| --- | --- | --- |
| 1.5 × Life | 1.5 × Life | 2 × Life |

| Redback and Brown Widow with eggs | Comb-footed Spider | Red House Spider |
| --- | --- | --- |
| 0.8 × Life | 2 × Life | 2 × Life |

| Redback | Russian Tent Spider |
| --- | --- |
| 0.5 × Life | 0.5 × Life |

| Daddy-long-legs | Net-casting Spider | Bird-dropping Spider | Brown Huntsman | Grey House Spider |
| --- | --- | --- | --- | --- |
| 0.5 × Life | 0.5 × Life | Life size | Life size | 2 × Life |

Dr G. May

## Bird-dropping Spider
### *Celaenia excavata*

**Identification:** Full size — 20 c piece; leg diameter — pin. Black and white body huddled on a leaf looks like bird dung.

**Habitat and Range:** Garden. Most common summer. Eastern Australia.

**Web:** Single line with drop of special silk spun to attract and stick to moths. Characteristic line of marbled brown egg sacs hung vertically.

**Bite:** None recorded.

Robert Raven

## Black House Spider *Badumna longinqua*

**Identification:** Full size — 50 c piece; leg diameter — pin. Usually seen only at night or males when wandering.

**Habitat and Range:** Cool dark areas — gardens, trees, corners in houses. Most prevalent summer. Australia-wide.

**Web:** Characteristic funnel-shaped web of sail-like panels or lacey web leading to funnel. Young of related species live with adult in colonial nest in bushes.

**Bite:** Nip and run. Mild to severe; considerable disagreement concerning severity; local pain, redness, with systemic involvement. Infection a known problem needing careful medical management.

Queensland Museum

## Brisbane Brush-footed Trapdoor
### *Seqocrypta jakara*

**Identification:** Full size up to 50 c piece; leg diameter — "o". Can climb vertical glass easily.

**Habitat and Range:** Various older Brisbane suburbs. Most common winter.

**Web:** Concealed tube with one or two trapdoors.

**Bite:** None recorded.

## Brown Huntsman Spider
### *Heteropoda jugulans*

Queensland Museum

**Identification:** Full size — hand span; leg diameter — pin to "o". Mottled brown abdomen and legs; carapace (head) with black X. Crab-like legs. Fast. Hunts easily on ceilings or walls.

**Habitat and Range:** Houses, forested areas, gardens, rainforest. Most common summer. Eastern Australia.

**Web:** Rover.

**Bite:** Ready biter; mild local pain.

## Brown Widow Spider
### *Latrodectus geometricus*

Queensland Museum

**Identification:** Full size — 50 c piece; leg diameter — pin. Pale to dark pea-shaped abdomen, no red stripe above but yellow to red hourglass mark below.

**Habitat and Range:** Sedge-like vegetation, seats, buildings. Most common summer. North-eastern Australia.

**Web:** Strong, tangled, fine conical retreat, egg sacs spiky.

**Bite:** Mild to severe local and generalised pain. Redback antivenom effective.

## Comb-footed Spider *Achaearanea* sp.

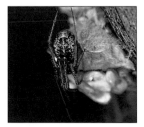

Queensland Museum

**Identification:** Full size — 20 c piece; leg diameter — pin. Mottled pea-shaped abdomen.

**Habitat and Range:** Corners of houses under leaves. Most common summer. Australia-wide.

**Web:** Tangled, fine, exposed "retreat".

**Bite:** Mild local pain.

## Daddy-long-legs *Pholcus phalangiodes*

Queensland Museum

**Identification:** Full size — half hand span; leg diameter — pin. Very long springy legs.

**Habitat and Range:** Dark corners. Most common summer. Australia-wide.

**Web:** Tangled, fine, exposed "retreat".

**Bite:** Venom is harmless to humans.

**Notes:** Easily kills Redback and Huntsman Spiders coming into its web.

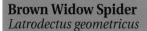

Dr G. May

## Flower Spider *Thomisus spectabilis*

**Other Names:** Crab Spider

**Identification:** Full size — 20 c piece; leg diameter — pin to matchstick. All white or yellow with stout legs held like a crab.

**Habitat and Range:** Flowers, shrubs, clothes lines and thus clothes. Most common summer. Australia-wide.

**Web:** Rover.

**Bite:** Ready biter; mild local pain.

## Funnel-web Spiders *Hadronyche* spp.

**Identification:** Full size — hand; leg diameter — letter "O". Jet black shiny head; black legs and black to grey (when gravid) abdomen; abdomen as large as last joint of adult thumb. Slow moving; does not jump but lunges when aggravated.

**Habitat and Range:** Cool, dark moist places — litter, staghorns, ferns, logs. Rarely found in outer Brisbane suburbs bordering native forest. North of Coffs Harbour tends to occur in cool mountainous areas. Often found in rainforest, can hang on in cleared pastoral areas (eg Maleny, Guyra). Mountain rainforest around Mossman and from rainforest or moist forests along east coastal fringe; west of Gladstone south to Tas. and SA. Males active in light rain in warm months, October–May in Qld.

**Web:** Rover, also sits. Burrows not obviously funnel-shaped; under rocks and in banks the strong lines radiate from broad floppy silk entrance; in trees, web appears like an X or T with 3 or 4 entrances.

**Bite:** Long strong fangs strike vertically like snakes. Bite and stay. Male venom more toxic, severe effects, sometimes death (without antivenom); no deaths recorded from bite of females. Muscular trembling a symptom of bite.

**Funnel-web — female** Bruce Cowell

**Funnel-web — male** Queensland Museum

Robert Raven

## Garden Orb-weaver
*Eriophora transmarina*

**Identification:** Large, fat. Full size — 50 c piece or larger; leg diameter — matchstick. Abdominal pattern highly variable — paired white dots to central brown, yellow or rusty red stripe. Deep red head, hairy legs.

**Habitat and Range:** Trees, shrubs, eaves of houses. Most prevalent summer. Eastern Australia.

**Web:** Sticky circle across open pathways, Silk silver.

**Bite:** Hard, strong, readily delivered. Typically mild local pain for 30 minutes, atypically 3–4 hours strong pain.

Queensland Museum

## Giant Green Huntsman *Typostola* sp. *

**Identification:** Full size can be greater than hand span; leg diameter — pin to "O". Fawn to grey head and abdomen; green "blood" evident through leg joints. Crab-like legs; front legs much longer than back. Fast, hunts easily upside down on ceilings or walls.

**Habitat and Range:** Houses, forested areas, gardens, open forest. Most common summer. Eastern Australia.

**Web:** Rover.

**Bite:** Timid, biter; probably mild local pain.

Queensland Museum

## Golden Orb-weaver *Nephila* sp.

**Identification:** Full size hand plus; leg diameter at mid-point — letter "O". Long yellow and black legs.

**Habitat and Range:** Warm moist areas — gardens, trees, paths. Most prevalent summer. Eastern Australia.

**Web:** Strong orb web; about 1 m; strung between trees, around sunny parts of buildings. Strong golden silk. Large web often traps small animals like Silvereyes.

**Bite:** Only if forced.

Queensland Museum

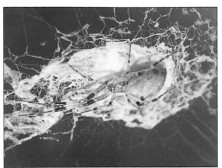

Queensland Museum

## Grey House Spider *Zosis geniculatus*

**Identification:** Full size — 20 c piece; leg diameter — pin. Grey body and legs.

**Habitat and Range:** Dark corners. Most common summer. Australia-wide.

**Web:** Ragged circular web.

**Bite:** Mild local pain; no venom glands present.

Bruce Cowell

## Grey Huntsman Spider
*Holconia immanis*

**Identification:** Full size hand span; leg diameter — pin to "O". Grey head and abdomen; head with brown margin; upper abdomen with brown dagger. Crab-like legs; front legs much longer than back. Fast, hunts easily upside down on ceilings or walls.

**Habitat and Range:** Houses, forested areas, gardens, open forest. Most common summer. Eastern Australia.

**Web:** Rover.

**Bite:** Timid, biter; probably only mild local pain.

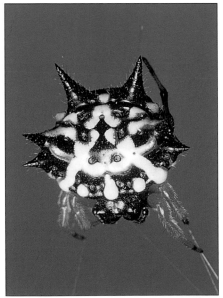

Queensland Museum

## Jewelled Spider *Gasteracantha minax*

**Identification:** Full size — 20 c piece; leg diameter — pin. Abdomen bright yellow and white on black with 6 strong spikes.

**Habitat and Range:** Garden. Most common summer. Australia-wide.

**Web:** Fine circular web.

**Bite:** Mild local pain.

## Jumping Spiders Salticidae

**Identification:** Full size — 20 c piece; leg diameter — pin. Many different species; all jump and turn head separate from body to look at objects.

**Habitat and Range:** House and garden. Most common summer. Australia-wide.

**Web:** Rover, hangs from web lines at night.

**Bite:** Rare biter; mild local pain.

Raoul Slater

## Leaf Curling Spider *Phonognatha* sp. *

**Identification:** Full size — 50 c piece; leg diameter — pin. Brown body with long sac abdomen with pale paired markings.

**Habitat and Range:** Open gardens. Most common summer. Australia-wide.

**Web:** Circular web with curled leaf retreat in upper corner.

**Bite:** Mild local pain.

Dr G. May

## Lynx Spiders Oxyopidae *

**Identification:** Full size — 20 c piece; leg diameter — pin. Colourful abdomen with spiky legs. Springs and leaps.

**Habitat and Range:** Vegetation. Most common summer. Many species Australia-wide.

**Web:** Rover.

**Bite:** None recorded.

Queensland Museum

Dr G. May

## Magnificent Spider
*Ordgarius magnificus*

**Identification:** Full size — 50 c piece; leg diameter — pin/match. Beautifully mottled abdomen and strangely spiked head.

**Habitat and Range:** Garden. Most common summer. Eastern Australia.

**Web:** Single line at night; characteristic spindle-shaped egg sacs.

**Bite:** None recorded.

**Mouse Spider — female** Queensland Museum

**Mouse Spider — male** Queensland Museum

## Mouse Spiders *Missulena* spp.

**Identification:** Full size — 50 c piece; leg diameter— "O". Short stocky legs; black shiny head with distinct "step"; tiny eyes spread widely across head. Fangs strike towards each other diagonally, not vertically. Male of *M. occatoria* (shown) has deep red carapace, dark blue abdomen. Male of second species (*M. bradleyi*) has black head, abdomen with light blue patch in front area. Very aggressive.

**Habitat and Range:** Cool dark areas — gardens. Most prevalent spring-autumn. Australia-wide.

**Web:** Short burrows in ground with floppy door projecting just above ground. Rarely rover.

**Bite:** "Bull-terrier". Very hard and deep but no significant reaction to venom.

Dr G. May

## Net-casting Spider *Deinopis* sp.

**Identification:** Full size — palm of hand; leg diameter — pin. Long slender brown abdomen sometimes with V-shaped markings; long brown legs (first and second often held as one); very large pair of front eyes.

**Habitat and Range:** Cool dark areas — garden, shrubs, low trees. Found among dead twigs and tangles of branches. Most prevalent summer. Australia-wide.

**Web:** Messy, tangle.

**Bite:** No bites recorded.

## Redback Spider *Latrodectus hasseltii*

**Identification:** Full size — 50 c piece; leg diameter — pin. Dark brown to black pea-shaped abdomen and legs with distinct red (rarely orange-yellow) stripe down back.

**Habitat and Range:** Gardens, bark, walls, rubbish, metallic objects. Most prevalent August-May. Most common in dry south and west; rare in urban areas north of Rockhampton. Australia-wide.

**Web:** Strong, untidy tangled web in area with sun exposure.

**Bite:** Nip and run. Effects highly variable, mild to severe (death without antivenom). Typically intense local pain. Early medical attention required (but no tourniquet).

Redback Spider — adult female Queensland Museum

Redback Spider — juvenile female Dr G. May

## Red House Spider *Nesticodes rufipes*

**Identification:** Full size — 20c piece; leg diameter — pin. Mottled, pea-shaped rust-red abdomen and legs.

**Habitat and Range:** Dark corners. Most common summer. Australia-wide.

**Web:** Tangled, fine, exposed "retreat".

**Bite:** Mild to severe local pain.

Queensland Museum

## Scorpion-tailed Spider
*Arachnura higginsi*

**Identification:** Full size — 10–20c piece; leg diameter — pin. Bright colourful abdomen; long, slender, moveable "tail" with 3–4 "spikes".

**Habitat and Range:** Garden, mangroves. Most common summer. Australia-wide.

**Web:** Circular.

**Bite:** None recorded.

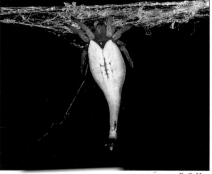

Dr G. May

Queensland Museum

## Shield Huntsman Spider
*Neosparassus* (aka *Olios*) spp.

**Identification:** Full size up to hand span; leg diameter — pin to "O". Pale or fawn; carapace arched, no markings above; below with black, yellow or orange badge. Crab-like legs; front legs much longer than back. Fast, hunts easily upside down on ceilings or walls.

**Habitat and Range:** Houses, forested areas, gardens, rainforest. Most common summer. Eastern Australia.

**Web:** Rover.

**Bite:** Ready biter; large fangs. Mild to severe local pain often with temporary cardiac complications.

## Silver Orb Spider *Leucauge dromedaria*

**Identification:** Full size — 20 c piece; leg diameter — pin. Long, bright silver abdomen, light green legs and dark green head.

**Habitat and Range:** Garden. Most common summer. Australia-wide.

**Web:** Inclined weak circular web.

**Bite:** No bites recorded.

Queensland Museum

Dr G. May

## Slender Sac Spiders *Cheiracanthium* spp.

**Identification:** Full size — 20–50 c piece; leg diameter — pin. Pale slender body with long pale legs. Several species.

**Habitat and Range:** Vegetation. Most common summer. Australia-wide.

**Web:** Night rover.

**Bite:** Mild to severe local pain.

## Spotted Ground Spider *Storena* spp.*

**Identification:** Full size — 20 c piece; leg diameter — pin. Shiny black head and shiny colourful body; legs black. Many species.

**Habitat and Range:** Garden, open ground. Most common summer. Australia-wide.

**Web:** Rover; fast runner.

**Bite:** Mild local pain.

Queensland Museum

## St Andrew's Cross Spider
*Argiope keyserlingi*

**Identification:** Full size — 50 c piece; leg diameter — pin. Flat, ornately coloured abdomen with transverse stripes and silver head and banded legs. Several species.

**Habitat and Range:** Garden. Most common summer. Australia-wide.

**Web:** Tangled, fine, exposed "retreat".

**Bite:** Mild local pain.

**Notes:** Common food of Friar birds.

Queensland Museum

## Swift Ground Spider *Supunna* sp.

**Identification:** Full size — 20 c piece; leg diameter — pin. Spotted black head and body; legs black and orange.

**Habitat and Range:** Gardens, open ground. Most common summer. Many species Australia-wide.

**Web:** Rover; very fast runner.

**Bite:** Mild local pain.

Robert Raven

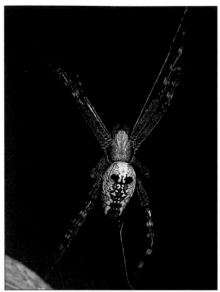

*C. moluccensis* Queensland Museum

## Tent Spiders *Cyrtophora* spp.

**Identification:** Full size — 50 c piece; leg diameter — pin. *C. moluccensis* often has broad, rusty red stripe down back of abdomen. *C. hirta* is a smaller white spider, rarely seen.

**Habitat and Range:** Shaded warm areas — gardens, litter, trees, walls, paths. Most prevalent summer. North from Coffs Harbour, NSW.

**Web:** Quickly recognised by form of webs. *C. moluccensis* builds large webs about 60–90 cm diameter; web consists of low inverted saucer-like dome amongst large tangle. *C. hirta* builds peaked web like a Russian tent, rarely more than 30 cm diameter.

**Bite:** Only if forced. No effects.

## Trapdoor Spider

The name Trapdoor Spider covers several families and many different species. Their correct identification is a matter for experts. Several species occur in bushland areas of Brisbane.

Robert Raven

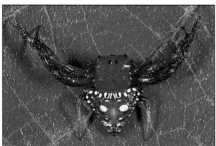

Dr G. May

## Triangular Spider *Arkys lancearius*

**Identification:** Full size — 20 c piece; leg diameter — pin. Abdomen small, flat, triangular to heart-shaped with white circles; front legs with strong spines; spikes going sideways from front of head

**Habitat and Range:** Gardens, trees, shrubs, clothes lines. Most prevalent summer. Australia-wide.

**Web:** Rover.

**Bite:** Nip and run, held in. Mild local pain for about 30 minutes; forms red welt and heat.

## Two-spined Spider*
### *Poecilopachys australasiae*

**Identification:** Full size — 20 c piece; leg diameter — pin. Yellow, brown and white body with two spines that form "eyes".

**Habitat and Range:** Gardens. Most common summer. Australia-wide.

**Web:** Circular web at night.

**Bite:** Mild local pain.

Queensland Museum

## Whip Spider *Ariamnes* sp.*

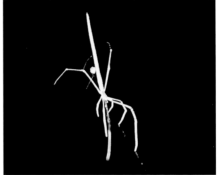

**Identification:** Full size — 50 c piece; leg diameter — hair. Long, worm-like body and short legs.

**Habitat and Range:** Vegetation. Most common summer. Australia-wide.

**Web:** Single thread at night.

**Bite:** No recorded bites.

Queensland Museum

## White-tailed Spider
### *Lampona cylindrata*

**Identification:** Full size — 50 c piece; leg diameter — pin. Grey cigar-shaped abdomen with white spot on end; sometimes legs banded and light transverse marks on abdomen.

**Habitat and Range:** Typically found in cool dark areas — under bark, in gardens, litter, walls, beds. Most prevalent spring-autumn. Many species; Australia and New Zealand.

**Web:** Rover

**Bite:** Nip and run. Bites repeatedly. Usually mild local pain, redness, and small local ulcers that clear up in a few days. More serious reactions claimed in other states. Media reports of alleged bites are typically "spider-less" incidents.

Queensland Museum

Dr G. May

## Wolf Spiders *Lycosa* spp.

**Identification:** Full size — 50 c piece to hand; leg diameter — pin to "O". Black X on head; underside all black. Large front eyes.

**Habitat and Range:** Hot dry areas — gardens, bark, litter. Common in open country and desert. Each species is often restricted to a particular microhabitat (eg *L. lapidosa* mostly occurs on rocks besides water). Many species Australia-wide.

**Web:** Rover. Some build trapdoors, some build retreats in shrubs.

**Bite:** Nip and run. Mild to local effects.

**Notes:** Two species are predators of cane toads. *L. lapidosa* takes small toads and frogs; *L. obscuroides* has been noted biting a large toad on back of head. Toad died in one hour.

Robert Raven

## Giant Water Spider* *Megadolomedes australianus*

**Identification:** Full size — bigger than hand; leg diameter — pin to matchstick, very flexible. Mottled dark abdomen or with long pale broad stripes; head with pale margins.

**Habitat and Range:** Creek banks and streams; hunts on water; eats fish and insects. Most common summer. Australia-wide.

**Web:** Rover, but builds nursery retreat for egg sac.

**Bite:** Timid, but probably causes mild local pain.

Dr G. May

## Water Spider *Dolomedes* sp. *

**Identification:** Full size — 50 c piece; leg diameter — pin to matchstick. Mottled dark abdomen; head with silver or dark gold border.

**Habitat and Range:** Creek banks and streams; hunts on water. Most common summer. Many species Australia-wide.

**Web:** Rover, but builds nursery retreat for egg sac.

**Bite:** Mild local pain.

# Arachnids and Myriapods

Phil Lawless

To many people all arachnids are spiders, but there are animals which — though too oddly shaped to be spiders — are nevertheless arachnids. These other arachnids include scorpions, ticks and mites which may be familiar. Less obvious are the harvestmen and pseudoscorpions. Many of these animals are denizens of the moist forests but some dwell with us in the urban environment and even come into our homes.

The bodies of all arachnids have many segments, grouped into two main regions. The segmentation is not always obvious externally. Generally the head, with its simple eyes and mouthparts, and the trunk, with its eight walking legs, form the forward section. The abdomen with the internal organs forms the hind section.

Unlike insects and crustaceans, arachnids do not possess mandibles for chewing and almost all eat only liquid food. Instead they have a pair of chelicerae — the appendages of the first body segment. These may be chelate (ie have pincers on the end) for grasping and cutting or they may be reduced to piercing fangs.

Similarly arachnids do not possess antennae. To sense their surroundings they use their pedipalps — the appendages of the second body segment. These are also used to manipulate food. In some arachnids they are chelate for grasping and tearing prey. In male spiders they are modified to transfer sperm during mating.

The myriapods — centipedes and millipedes — share some features with the insects and arachnids. Their jointed legs, hard external skeleton and segmented body plan are common to these groups. They possess two antennae and mandibles and are more closely related to the insects than to the arachnids. Body segments are obvious and are not grouped into sections as they are in arachnids and insects. The segments are not as specialised as in arachnids, crustaceans and insects and each retains a pair of walking legs.

## Scorpions (Scorpiones)

The scorpions, with their large pincers (chelate pedipalps) and long tail with its hooked sting, are familiar to most people. Their chelicerae — appendages of the first body segment — are also chelate (pincer-like) and form dissecting mouthparts. Segmentation is obvious in these arachnids though they lack a distinct "waist". Scorpions thrive in dry habitats and, while secretive, can be found in suburban gardens.

Locally, the species can be distinguished by the shape of the sternum, the number of lateral eyes and the presence of tibial spines. The sternum is a plate in the centre of the underside of the body between the bases of legs 3 and 4. The lateral eyes are found at the forward corners of the carapace (head plate); median eyes are in the middle. The tibia is the third segment from the outermost end of the leg; some scorpions have a spine — the tibial spine — on the lower, outermost edge of the tibia.

Queensland Museum

### Large Brown Scorpion
*Liocheles waigiensis*

**Identification:** Length varies from a few millimetres to about 7 cm. Dark brown. Body tapers abruptly to a thin, short tail (tail shorter than body; does not reach head). Robust claws. Sternum pentagonal; three pairs of lateral eyes; two ridges lengthwise on undersurface of tail.

**Habitat and Range:** Under logs and rocks, in shallow burrows in earth banks. Common in gardens and forests throughout Australia.

**Notes:** Nocturnal. Sting delivered by tail, not known to be dangerous.

Bruce Cowell

### Small Mottled Scorpion
*Lychas, Isometrus and Cercophonius* spp.

**Identification:** Mottled brown. Body tapers gradually to long stout tail which can easily reach head. Fine claws. Sternum wide and short (*Cercophonius* 2–4 cm); or triangular (*Lychas, Isometrus*). Tibial spurs on legs 3 and 4 (*Lychas* 3–4 cm); or none (*Isometrus* 3–5 cm).

**Habitat and Range:** Moist forest areas along east coast of Australia. Less common than Large Brown Scorpion.

**Notes**: Sting not known to be dangerous.

# Mites and Ticks (Acari)

The Acari include several suborders of parasites and predators. The chelicerae and pedipalps (appendages of the first and second body segments) together form the capitulum (see diagram below). The only discernible division in the bodies of mites and ticks lies between the capitulum and the rest of the head and body. The mites are a very diverse group extracting nutritive juices from a wide variety of animals, plants and dead material. Both the chelicerae and pedipalps reflect this. Ticks — the suborder Ixodides — are much bigger than mites and are all parasites of vertebrate animals.

## Mites

**Identification:** Minute to small (1 mm), free-living or parasitic arachnids. Chelicerae are pincer-like in predators and scavengers; piercing in parasitic mites.

**Habitat and Range:** In all terrestrial and aquatic environments.

**Notes:** Diverse families and species; some larvae cause itching. Red Velvet Mites (family Trombidiidae) are very big (3 mm) and are found in rainforest. Larvae feed on other arthropods. Adults are free-living.

Red Velvet Mite                    Queensland Museum

## Ticks

**Identification:** Size varies from a few millimetres to 10–15 mm when engorged. Flat with hard, piercing chelicerae; sensory pedipalps with bases formed into barbed prong (hypostome). Adults and nymphs have eight legs; larvae six.

**Habitat and Range:** Many species in various habitats throughout Australia. Scrub Tick, *Ixodes holocyclus*, occurs in eastern Australia in association with bandicoots.

**Notes:** Dangerous paralysing toxin is released by adult female Scrub Ticks after several days feeding. Hypersensitivity to larval or adult tick saliva (Scrub Itch) follows repeated bites. Opinions differ but treatment aims to prevent more of these fluids entering victim. Squeezing body of tick must be avoided. Fine forceps can be used to catch the head and ease it out; or tick can be killed *in situ* with pyrethroid insect repellent (tick will shrivel and drop off).

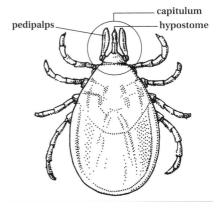

capitulum

pedipalps

hypostome

*Ixodes holocyclus*            Dept of Parasitology, Uni.of Qld

## Pseudoscorpions (Pseudoscorpiones)

Looking for all the world like fat scorpions without tails, these tiny animals can be hard to find. They favour a moist environment among rotting leaves and under bark where their flattened bodies allow easy access.

Queensland Museum

### Pseudoscorpions

**Identification:** Length only a few millimetres. Resemble small scorpions but without the tail and sting. Pincer-like chelicerae and pedipalps.

**Habitat and Range:** Free-living in leaf litter, under stones and bark.

**Notes:** Venom glands on pedipalp claws; silk glands on chelicerae. Some species disperse on Longicorn Beetles. They crawl under the wing covers of beetles emerging from pupation. The beetles then fly to new logs.

## Harvestmen (Opiliones)

Opiliones thrive in moist forests where they rove along mossy logs and stones in search of prey. The chelicerae (appendages of the first body segment) have pincers and are carried high like two great reaping hooks but the pedipalps (appendages of the second body segment) are simple.

Queensland Museum

### Harvestmen

**Identification:** Body length up to about 7 mm. Spider-like but with segmented abdomen and no waist. Very long thin legs.

**Habitat and Range:** Moist forests.

**Notes:** Omnivorous. Not venomous, but acrid secretions used for defence.

# Myriapods (Centipedes and Millipedes)

These two groups share a great many characteristics but are seldom confused. A centipede's first pair of legs have been formed into large poison fangs called forcipules. The last pair of legs are sensory and trail behind the body. The remaining legs are simple walking legs arranged one pair per segment. In the millipedes the body segments are fused in pairs. Thus millipede "segments" seem to have two pairs of legs each. This is a simple way to tell them from the centipedes. Centipedes are venomous hunters while millipedes are grazers of living and dead vegetable matter.

## Centipedes  Chilopoda

**Identification:** Length to 20 cm. Flattened, very flexible body with one pair of legs per body segment. Colour varies from yellow to dark green.

**Habitat and Range:** In logs and leaf litter, under bark and stones. In dry and moist habitats throughout the region.

Queensland Museum

**Notes:** Animal moves rapidly and bites with two powerful jaws under the head. Bite causes severe pain which may last for several days. No deaths recorded.

## Millipedes  Diplopoda

**Identification:** Length to 5 cm. Dark brown. Short fine legs under a cylindrical body. Two pairs of legs per body segment.

**Habitat and Range:** Need a moist environment. Survive dry seasons by sheltering under logs.

**Notes:** Defenses include rolling into tight loops and releasing repellant yellow fluids from glands along sides of body. Fluid may cause blue discolouration and irritation. Favourite food of Funnel-web Spiders.

Bruce Cowell

Queensland Museum

## Pill Millipedes Diplopoda

**Identification:** Stout. About 1–4 cm long. Able to roll into a ball; about 12 segments and 21 pairs of legs.

**Habitat and Range:** Moist forests, in leaf litter and under logs.

**Notes:** Hard plates roll tightly together to protect head and legs. Feed on decomposing vegetable matter.

# Freshwater and Terrestrial Crustaceans

John Short

C rustaceans have often been described as the "Insects of the Sea" for in the oceans of the world they are almost as abundant and diverse as insects are on land. Their enormous diversity is reflected in a great variety of body shapes and sizes ranging from microscopic copepods to the Giant Japanese Spider Crab, *Macrocheira kaempferi*, which can span 4 metres between its outstretched claws.

Although the majority of crustaceans are marine, many families have estuarine and freshwater representatives and a number of groups are confined to freshwater. Much less common are terrestrial crustaceans, and in general these are restricted to moist habitats such as rainforests. Most crustaceans are free-living, but many marine species also live in commensal or parasitic associations with other animals.

Crustaceans can be distinguished from other arthropods (invertebrates with jointed limbs) and other invertebrates by the presence of two pairs of antennae, although the smaller pair can sometimes be difficult to see without the aid of a microscope. They also have double branched (biramous) limbs and in most large forms, well-developed gills. Small crustaceans often lack gills and instead respire directly through the body wall.

In the Greater Brisbane Region, habitat degradation and pollution appear to have had an effect on crustacean diversity and abundance. Most freshwater species are more abundant in upper catchment areas than in lowlands where excessive growth of algae and siltation are major problems. Coastal wetlands are also disappearing at an alarming rate and species restricted to these areas appear to be very sensitive to habitat disturbance.

In the species descriptions that follow, microscopic forms have not been included as they require specialised collection and identification techniques and are rarely seen by naturalists.

# AMPHIPODS

Amphipods are mostly small animals with high, narrow elongated bodies. The highest diversity occurs in the sea but a few are also found in freshwater or on land. Terrestrial forms are often mistaken for insects.

## Land Hoppers

Queensland Museum

### *Arcitalitrus sylvaticus*

**Identification:** Average length 7 mm. Pale.

**Habitat and Range:** Common in drier forests, under logs, leaf litter and in damp areas; abundant in suburban gardens. Widespread in eastern NSW and south-eastern Qld; introduced to Europe and North America.

**Notes:** When disturbed they are capable of leaping considerable distances (relative to small body size) to escape. Sometimes enter houses and swimming pools where they quickly perish.

# ISOPODS

Isopods sometimes resemble amphipods but their bodies tend to be low and flattened rather than high and narrow. As with amphipods, there are many more marine than freshwater and terrestrial species.

## Slaters and Pill Bugs

Queensland Museum

### Garden Slater  *Porcellionides pruniosus*

**Identification:** Length to 10 mm. Bluish-grey.

**Habitat and Range:** Damp locations — under bricks, timber, bark or rocks. Common in suburban gardens.

**Notes:** Probably introduced to Australia from Europe.

Queensland Museum

### Pill Bug  *Sphaerillo grossus*

**Identification:** Length to 15 mm. Body only slightly flattened, robust. Rolls into a ball for defence. Dark grey.

**Habitat and range:** Open forests, under logs. Widespread in south-eastern Qld.

# DECAPODS

This group includes crabs, shrimps, prawns, lobsters and crayfish. It contains all the large, commercially important species of crustaceans. The name Decapoda refers to the presence of 10 walking legs of which the first one to three pairs may be modified as claws.

## Atyid Shrimps

These are generally small, semi-transparent, fast-moving animals with brushes of stiff hairs (setae) on the first pair of legs. They are often sold in aquarium shops as food for native fish.

### Paratya australiensis

**Identification:** Length about 35 mm. Easily distinguished from other species in southern Qld by spine above eye cavity; rostrum moderately short with upper edge more or less straight with serrations along entire length.

**Habitat and Range:** Common in weed beds or among leaf litter in shallow water from lowlands to upper catchment areas. Most widespread species — southern Qld, NSW, Vic., Tas. and SA.

### Caridina indistincta

**Identification:** Length to 30 mm. Rostrum similar to *P. australiensis* but differs slightly in shape and number of serrations.

**Habitat and Range:** Ubiquitous in lowland areas among leaf litter or bottom vegetation. Tolerant of acidic conditions (eg Brown Lake on North Stradbroke Island). Widespread in eastern Qld.

### Caridina nilotica

**Identification:** Length to 30 mm. Rostrum long and upturned but unlike *C. indistincta* has only 1 or 2 serrations on front half.

**Habitat and Range:** Widespread in northern Australia from Kimberley, WA, to southern Qld.

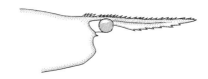

*Caridina indistincta*    John Short

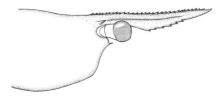

Head and rostrum details of *Paratya australiensis* (top), *Caridina indistincta* (center) and *C. nilotica* (bottom)

Queensland Museum

## Riffle Shrimp  *Australatya striolata*

**Identification:** Unlike other atyid shrimps in southern Qld is robust and well pigmented. Dark green or brown; light stripe down middle of back and 5 longitudinal stripes on each side of carapace.

**Habitat and Range:** Prefers running water; believed to be a filter feeder. In some localities, easily collected by scoop netting through ribbon weed in riffle areas. Cooktown, Qld to Shoalhaven River, NSW.

**Notes:** Protandrous — males change into females within 30–36 mm size range. Mating occurs between old, transformed females and young, untransformed males. Females reach 60 mm and appear to migrate to lowland slow-flowing areas to release their young.

## Long-armed Prawns

Two species are found in the Brisbane region —*Macrobrachium australiense* and *M. tolmerum.* As their common name suggests, the second legs form long slender claws and in the males of many species these may exceed the length of the body.

John Short

## *Macrobrachium australiense*

**Identification:** Length rarely to 80 mm (rostrum excluded); more common at 70 mm or less. Colour varies with age. Old adult males uniformly dark brown or grey. Younger males and females have irregular grey blotches on head/thorax and longitudinal dark bands on palm and wrist of claws. Very young specimens semi-transparent with dark grey, vertical stripes on carapace and alternating grey and orange, transverse bands on claws. Adult males also have conspicuous fine hairs on fingers of claws which form a thick mat.

**Habitat and Range:** Occurs in lowland to upper catchment areas in wide variety of permanent freshwater habitats, excluding offshore sand islands. Most widespread long-armed prawn in Australia and abundant in Brisbane area. Occurs over much of continent.

**Notes:** Known to undergo mass upstream migrations. Juveniles excellent climbers, capable of scaling barriers such as dam walls on humid nights.

## *Macrobrachium tolmerum*

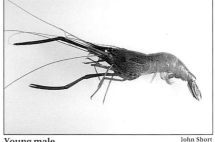

Young male                                    John Short

**Identification:** Length 100 mm. Adults usually reddish-brown with fully grown specimens darker and more uniformly coloured. Young specimens mottled on abdomen with irregular blotches on carapace. Developed males also have distinctive orange patch on base of claws; fingers remain more or less free of hairs. Young specimens similar to *M. australiense* but fingers characteristically white-tipped, shorter and more robust.

**Habitat and Range:** Tolerant of acidic water. Occurs in coastal eastern Australia from Newcastle, NSW to Cape York. Around Brisbane, rare on mainland but common on offshore sand islands. Dominant species in north-eastern Qld where it occupies a variety of habitats.

**Notes:** Long larval cycle and females carry a large number of small eggs. Although adults are found in freshwater, larvae require higher salinity and begin development in estuarine areas. Able to enter isolated fresh-water lagoons along the seashore (eg near Adder Rock on North Stradbroke Island).

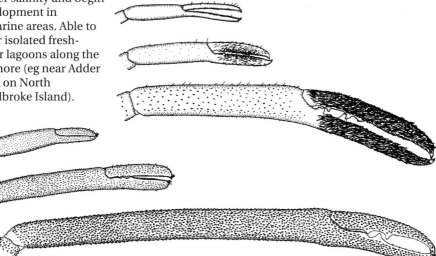

Details of pincers of *Macrobrachium australiense* (top) and *M. tolmerum* (bottom) at different stages of development.

# Freshwater Crayfish

Freshwater crayfish can be recognised by their well-developed claws (modified front legs) and robust bodies. Unlike shrimps and prawns, crayfish are unable to swim upwards and are confined to the bottom of their aquatic environments.

John Short

## Orange-fingered Yabby
*Cherax depressus*

**Identification:** Length 90 mm. Rostrum short and triangular without well-developed spines. Claws broad with underside of palms lacking hairs near base of fixed fingers. Fingertips characteristically orange. Body brown or bluish-green.

**Habitat and Range:** Most common species. Adults typically semi-aquatic in gullies, temporary pools and shallow creeks with limited flow. Burrows near waterline. Also common in farm dams.

**Notes:** Strong burrower; can survive drought periods by burrowing deep down to water table.

John Short

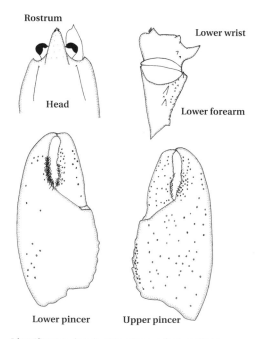

Identification details of the Orange-fingered Yabby

## Slender Yabby
*Cherax dispar*

**Identification:** Length 75 mm. Rostrum long and slender and bears a pair of well-developed spines near tip. Claws more slender and elongated than *C. depressus*. In fully developed adults, underside of claws deep blue, body greenish-grey or brown. Young specimens have orange fingertips on claws as in *C. depressus*.

**Habitat and Range:** Perennial streams and coastal sand lakes. Often occurs with *Macrobrachium tolmerum* and *Caridina indistincta* in acidic waters (see pp 47, 49). Brisbane to Elliott River, south of Bundaberg.

**Notes:** Limited burrower.

John Short

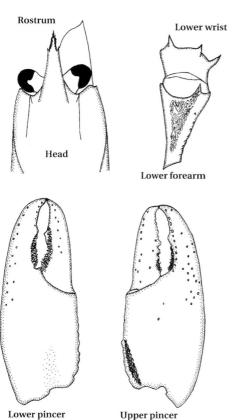

Rostrum

Head

Lower wrist

Lower forearm

Lower pincer          Upper pincer

Identification details of the slender yabby.

John Short

John Short

John Short

## Sand Yabby  *Cherax robustus*

**Identification:** Length 90 mm. Rostrum similar to that of *C. depressus* (see p 50). Deep blue to almost black with underside of claws vivid purple. Claws short and robust with characteristic patch of long hairs on underside of fixed finger which continues slightly onto palm.

**Habitat and Range:** Semi-aquatic; burrows around perimeter of sand lakes or along small creeks. Adapted to living in acidic soft waters in peaty sand areas. In Brisbane area appears to be restricted to offshore sand islands. Recorded as far north as Fraser Island.

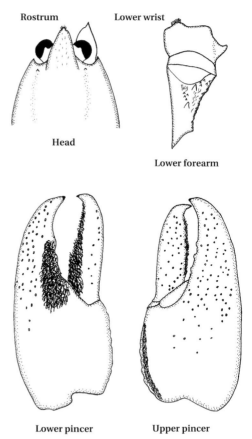

Rostrum          Lower wrist

Head

Lower forearm

Lower pincer          Upper pincer

Identification details of the Sand Yabby.

## Mount Glorious Spiny Crayfish
### *Euastacus setosus*

**Identification:** Length 90 mm. Body dark red or brown above and orange below. Easily distinguished from *Cherax* species (see pp. 50–52) by numerous stiff bristles on body and claws. One of the smaller *Euastacus* species.

**Habitat and Range:** Cool, running creeks; burrows into banks. High rainfall areas on D'Aguilar Range above 500 m altitude.

John Short

## Swamp Crayfish
### *Tenuibranchiurus glypticus*

**Identification:** Reportedly world's smallest crayfish — fully grown at 25 mm. Unlike other crayfish in south-eastern Qld, fingers of claws open and close vertically rather than horizontally or obliquely. Body greyish-brown

John Short

**Habitat and Range:** Paperbark swamps and shallow drainage channels. Prefers to burrow into damp clay but occasionally found in peaty sand. Southern Qld as far north as Woodgate. Originally recorded from Caloundra and Bulimba Creek, Mt Gravatt, but not collected from last locality in past 50 years. May be extinct in Brisbane region due to loss of habitat.

**Notes:** Difficult to collect due to small size, cryptic colouration and well-developed burrowing habits. Occasionally enters baited funnel traps set in shallow water; at end of summer wet season it is also possible to scoop-net specimens from shallow pools.

# Crabs

Only one crab is commonly found in freshwater around the Brisbane region. This is a species of shore crab of the family Grapsidae, of which most members occur in estuarine mangrove swamps.

John Short

## *Varuna litterata*

**Identification:** Maximum body width of 55 mm. Dark brown or black.

**Habitat and Range:** Occasionally found under rocks and debris in shallow freshwater. Wide ranging in the Indo-West Pacific Region.

**Notes:** Breeds in estuaries and migrates to freshwater.

# Dragonflies and Damselflies

Deniss Reeves

Dragonflies and damselflies which together comprise the order Odonata are, with butterflies, cicadas and some of the beetles, among the most noticeable groups of Australian insects. Of approximately 300 species in Australia, about 130 occur in South-East Queensland and many of these can be found in and around the Greater Brisbane Region.

Adult Odonata are predatory flying insects with two pairs of wings and well-developed mouthparts for chewing their prey which they catch while flying or sometimes pick from vegetation.

The Zygoptera or damselflies are generally small to medium-sized insects with fore and hindwings of similar shape. Most Zygoptera hold their wings together along the axis of the body. Their eyes are widely separated. The Anisoptera or dragonflies proper, range in size from small to very large. The eyes in some families are moderately widely separated but in most they either touch or are close together. Anisoptera perch with both pairs of wings spread more or less horizontally.

The following size categories[1] are based on approximate wing span:

**Damselflies**

| | |
|---|---|
| tiny | less than about 25 mm |
| small | about 25–35 mm |
| medium | about 35–50 mm |
| large | about 50–75 mm |
| very large | more than about 70 mm |

**Dragonflies**

| | |
|---|---|
| tiny | less than about 40 mm |
| small | about 40–60 mm |
| medium | about 60–85 mm |
| large | about 85–115 mm |
| very large | more than about 115 mm |

1. Watson, J. A. L., Theischinger, G. and Abbey, H. M., *The Australian Dragonflies*, CSIRO, Canberra and Melbourne, 1991.

## Damselflies

### Ischnura aurora

**Identification:** Tiny. Male — back of thorax dark with green markings, sides pale. Abdomen reddish-yellow, "tail end" black with prominent blue spot.

**Habitat and Range:** Still and slow flowing waters. Widespread.

**Notes:** Flight slow, weak. Perches on reed stems.

Deniss Reeves                    *I. heterosticta*

### Ischnura heterosticta

**Identification:** Small. Male — side of thorax blue, abdomen black with blue "tail light". Female dull greyish.

**Habitat and Range:** See *I. aurora*.

**Notes:** See *I. aurora*.

### Pseudagrion aureofrons

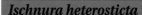

**Identification:** Medium-sized. Male — front of thorax bright golden yellow edged with black, sides bright blue; frons (forehead) golden. Abdomen dark with blue markings, largest at tail.

**Habitat and Range:** Still and flowing waters. Widespread.

**Notes:** Flies close to water surface, also amongst vegetation on banks.

Dr G. May

### Nososticta solida

**Identification:** Medium-sized. Body metallic black, brick red markings on thorax and base of abdomen. Wings of male suffused yellowish.

**Habitat and Range:** Streams and still waters.

**Notes:** Extremely agile, flies expertly in any direction.

Dr G. May

## *Austroargiolestes icteromelas*

**Identification:** Large but slender. Male and female similar. Variable in colour. Zig-zag pattern on side of thorax, pinkish on black to yellow on dark metallic ground colour. Abdomen dull black to metallic with small, pale inter-segmental rings.

**Habitat and Range:** Found on most creeks in area.

**Notes:** Often perches with wings outspread as in dragonflies.

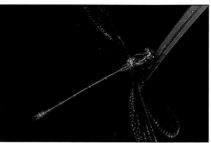
Deniss Reeves

## *Synlestes selysi*

**Identification:** Large; very long abdomen. Yellow, marked with dark bronze-green. Pterostigma (wingmark) small, black. Female abdomen shorter, heavier than male.

**Habitat and Range:** Rainforest streams.

**Notes:** Perches with wings held as in photograph or slightly separated. Abdomen often sways like pendulum immediately on perching.

Dr G. May

## *Synlestes weyersii tillyardi*

**Identification:** Large, similar to *S. selysi*, but yellow marked with bright metallic green. Pterostigma (wingmark) white when immature, becoming yellowish.

**Habitat and Range:** Rainforest streams.

**Notes:** See *S. selysi* above.

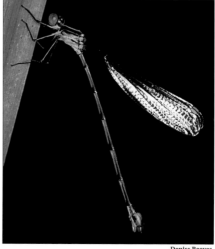
Deniss Reeves

Dr G. May

## *Diphlebia coerulescens*

**Identification:** Large, comparatively heavy. Male — eyes black; thorax bright blue and black; abdomen, first three and 8th and 9th segments largely blue, intervening four black with a narrow blue apical ring; end segment black. Female — dull olive.

**Habitat and Range:** Streams in open forest and rainforest.

**Notes:** Perches on rocks in streams and on streamside vegetation, with wings outspread. Similar species *D. nymphoides* is more copiously marked with blue.

# Dragonflies

Dr G. May

## *Austroaeschna pulchra*

**Identification:** Large. Body dark reddish-brown, pair of bright green dorsal spots at base of each abdominal segment

**Habitat and Range:** Streams.

**Notes:** Flight swift, hovers frequently. *A. unicornis* similar, but paired green spots are placed centrally on abdominal segments.

## *Austrogynacantha heterogena*

**Identification:** Medium-sized. Sides of thorax bright apple green. Eyes blue and green. Abdomen slender, brown with yellow spots.

**Habitat and Range:** Breeds in still waters. Widespread.

**Notes:** Crepuscular — often seen hawking rapidly at dusk. Sometimes enters houses, attracted to light.

Deniss Reeves

## *Austrogomphus amphiclitus*

**Identification:** Medium-sized. Eyes bright green, separated. Thorax largely yellow on sides with black markings. Abdomen black with yellow markings. Last segments black. Anal appendages small, creamy-white.

**Habitat and Range:** Streams, particularly in open forest. Widespread.

**Notes:** Perches on stones and streamside vegetation.

Dr G. May

## *Austrogomphus melaleucae*

**Identification:** Small. Eyes green, separated. Black and yellow. Yellow spot on thorax below each wing. Anal appendages yellow.

**Habitat and Range:** Common on streams near Mt Coot-tha.

**Notes:** Flies slowly.

Dr G. May

## *Hemigomphus gouldii*
## *H. heteroclytus*

**Identification:** Small. Eyes green, separated. Black and yellow (black predominating). Anal appendages of male, comparatively widely separated at base, look like creamy-yellow horns.

**Habitat and Range:** Streams.

**Notes:** Flies slowly but is alert. Perches on rocks in stream beds. Angles abdomen towards sun.

*Hemigomphus* sp.                     Deniss Reeves

## *Ictinogomphus australis*

**Identification:** Large. Eyes green, separated. Black with yellow markings.

**Habitat and Range:** Common. Lakes and slow flowing streams.

**Notes:** Perches on emergent tall reeds or "sticks". Aggressive species, making frequent forays from, and returning to, its perch. Twice size of preceding three species.

Dr G. May

Deniss Reeves

*H. superba*  Dr G. May

## Petalura gigantea

**Identification:** Very large. Thorax brown with creamy-yellow stripes, abdomen brown with poorly defined pale stripes along the sides. Anal appendages large; spoon or leaf-shaped.

**Habitat and Range:** Fraser, Moreton and North Stradbroke Islands. Also NSW.

**Notes:** Larvae live in burrows in peat bogs. One of largest dragonflies. Flies lazily until disturbed, when it will fly fast and high.

## Hemicordulia australiae

**Identification:** Medium-sized. Body metallic blue-black with dullish yellow markings. Eyes brilliant emerald green. Straight, narrow abdomen; brownish tipped wings. Frons (forehead) metallic blue-green.

**Habitat and Range:** Most creeks in area. Widespread.

**Notes:** Hovers over water, darts rapidly. Often seen hovering at treetop height in company with *H. continentalis* but distinguished by straight, narrow abdomen.

## Hemicordulia continentalis

**Identification:** Medium-sized. Similar to *H. australiae* but end of abdomen swollen laterally to club shape. Wings clear.

**Habitat and Range:** Streams and still waters.

**Notes:** Less common than *H. australiae.*

## Hemicordulia superba

**Identification:** Medium-sized. More clearly marked with yellow than preceding two species. Frons (forehead) marked with two yellow spots.

**Habitat and Range:** Streams.

**Notes:** Seen more often over or near flowing streams.

## *Choristhemis flavoterminata*

**Identification:** Medium-sized. Metallic blue-black marked with yellow. Yellow spot on end of abdomen like "tail light".

**Habitat and Range:** Common on and near small creeks.

**Notes:** Slow, gliding, undulating flight.

Dr G. May

## *Brachydiplax denticauda*

**Identification:** Small. Body bright light blue, "tail" black. Eyes dark, forehead brilliant metallic blue.

**Habitat and Range:** Swampy areas with standing water.

**Notes:** Perches on reeds and sedges. Flight rapid and "nervous". Often returns to same perch.

Deniss Reeves

## *Crocothemis nigrifrons*

**Identification:** Medium-sized. Male — head and thorax black; abdomen dark grey-blue, rather broad. Female — orange-brown with a narrow longitudinal black dorsal stripe on abdomen.

**Habitat and Range:** Slow flowing and still waters. Widespread.

**Notes:** Less common than *O. caledonicum* (see p. 62).

Deniss Reeves

## *Diplacodes bipunctata*

**Identification:** Small. Male — red with heart-shaped dorsal markings on abdomen. Female — sandy-yellow.

**Habitat and Range:** Very common. Still and flowing water.

**Notes:** Perches on ground and low vegetation. Often angles abdomen toward hot sun.

Male                                Deniss Reeves

Deniss Reeves

## *Diplacodes haematodes*

**Identification:** Small. Unmarked bright red. Male hindwings with reddish suffusion at base; female wings yellowish-brown on the ends.

**Habitat and Range:** Still and flowing waters.

**Notes:** Perches on stones in creek beds and on the ground.

Deniss Reeves

## *Orthetrum boumiera*

**Identification:** Medium-sized. Male — blue-grey thorax and abdomen; constricted just behind wings, giving appearance of being "waisted". Eyes lilac-grey. Wings clear. Female — black with paired yellow dorsal spots.

**Habitat and Range:** Dune lakes on Fraser, Moreton and North Stradbroke Islands. Also Wooli Lakes in northern NSW.

**Notes:** Flies about a metre or less above ground. Perches often on emergent and shore vegetation and on sticks and leaves on ground.

Deniss Reeves

## *Orthetrum caledonicum*

**Identification:** Medium-sized. Immature male — similar to female; black and yellow, with drab yellowish thorax marked black; maturing to light powder blue thorax and abdomen, which has extensive black tip. Wings extensively suffused yellow-brown. Female — black abdomen with rectangular yellow dorsal spots creating a ladder pattern. Abdomen and thorax of old females become more or less powdery blue-grey.

**Habitat and Range:** Flowing, still and ephemeral waters. Widespread, common.

**Notes:** Perches on low vegetation. Makes short flights to intercept other flying insects or to feed, usually returning to its perch.

## Orthetrum sabina

**Identification:** Medium-sized. Thorax and first two abdominal segments yellowish-green with black stripes. Abdomen black with several pairs of spots along the sides; and anal appendages creamy-yellow.

**Habitat and Range:** Slow flowing, still and ephemeral waters. Widespread.

**Notes:** Voracious and aggressive, will tackle flying insects almost its own size.

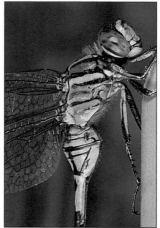

Dr G. May

## Orthetrum villosovittatum

**Identification:** Medium-sized. Male — face red, thorax reddish-brown, abdomen bright crimson-red, waisted. Female — orange-red.

**Habitat and Range:** Slow flowing and still waters, swamps. Widespread, common.

**Notes:** Behaviour similar to other species of *Orthetrum*.

Deniss Reeves

## Rhyothemis graphiptera

**Identification:** Medium-sized. Body length much less than wingspread. Wings tinted golden-yellow, with mottled brown bars and patches. Unmistakable.

**Habitat and Range:** Often flies in suburban gardens near creeks. Widespread.

**Notes:** Flight weak, fluttering and gliding.

Deniss Reeves

## Rhyothemis phyllis chloe

**Identification:** Medium-sized. Slightly larger than *R. graphiptera* (see above). Wings clear, tips black, black patch at midpoint of each wing; base of hindwings with large dark brown patch bisected lengthwise by creamy-yellow band. Unmistakable.

**Habitat and Range:** Widespread.

**Notes:** Slow, gliding flight

Dr G. May

Deniss Reeves

## *Trapezostigma loewii*

**Identification:** Medium-sized. Abdomen dark reddish-brown, tip black, anal appendages long, narrow. Wings clear, base of hindwings with a conspicuous, saddle-like red-brown patch of variable size and shape.

**Habitat and Range:** Still waters. Widespread.

**Notes:** Often seen in small "flocks" flying to and fro, 3 metres or more above ground.

# Termites

Brenton Peters

Termites are a very ancient order of insects whose origins date back more than 100 million years. Although they are commonly called "white ants", the resemblance to ants is superficial and they are more closely related to cockroaches. Australia has more than 350 species of termites and they can be grouped into three categories — dampwood termites, drywood termites and subterranean termites. Dampwood termites generally live in damp rotting logs or rot pockets in dead or living trees. Drywood termites obtain water from the wood in which they feed and have no contact with the soil, nor with any other source of moisture. Subterranean termites are generally ground-dwelling or require contact with the soil or some constant source of moisture. Only a few species can be regarded as "economic" pests, causing problems with timber in homes and other buildings.

All termites are social insects which live together in family groups (colonies). Each colony contains workers, soldiers and reproductives — the king and queen. Soldiers are used as a diagnostic feature to determine the species. Flying kings and queens are called "alates".

# Dampwood Termites

Queensland Museum

## Ringant Termite *Neotermes insularis*

**Identification:** Size is main distinguishing feature — this species has one of largest soldiers (9–15 mm long) of all Australian termites; also strong jaws (mandibles) which turn slightly upwards.

**Habitat and Range:** In forests within 80 km of the coast. Vic. to Torres Strait, across to Darwin, NT.

**Notes:** Colonies founded by alates in branch stubs and dead wood of living trees. Entrance to tree may occur at almost any height and galleries may eventually extend throughout tree. Mature colonies may contain several thousand individuals. Galleries usually clean, sometimes with accumulations of discrete faecal pellets. Concentric gallery system in softer wood of each growth ring is responsible for common name. Pest of some eucalypt species.

# Drywood Termites

Young alate *C. primus*   Queensland Museum

Faecal pellets of *C. primus*   Queensland Museum

## Native Drywood Termite
### *Cryptotermes primus*

**Identification:** Soldier pale cream, 4–6 mm long with short, thick, dark head. Alates pale yellow-brown with iridescent wings.

**Habitat and Range:** Widely distributed throughout coastal and adjacent tableland areas; common in many pre–1940 domestic dwellings in Qld.

**Notes:** Attacks timber in service and dead parts of living trees. Colonies have up to 200 individuals with, generally, less than 10 soldiers. Evidence is usually faecal pellets, holes and other damage in timber in service including house stumps, flooring, skirting boards, beams, furniture and fence posts. Very common in house stumps which may act as a source of infestation in flooring. Related to West Indian drywood termite, *Cryptotermes brevis.*

# Subterranean Termites

## *Coptotermes acinaciformis*

Queensland Museum

**Identification:** Readily recognised by soldiers — up to 6 mm long with rounded, rather pear-shaped, yellowish head; dark, slender, tapering mandibles without visible teeth. When disturbed, exudes a drop of milky fluid from front of head.

**Habitat and Range:** Widely distributed throughout mainland Australia. South of Tropic of Capricorn, *C. acinaciformis* does not construct a mound. Related species *C. lacteus* also occurs in southern Queensland and does build mounds.

**Notes:** Very destructive. Attacks timber structures and damages forest and ornamental trees as well as fruit trees. Infestations in houses often difficult to detect. Colonies may contain more than 500,000 individuals. Soil contact usually maintained, but is not essential provided a source of moisture is available. Colonies have been found on top of multi-storey buildings and in bridge and wharf timbers beyond ground contact.

Nest of *C. lacteus*

## *Schedorhinotermes* spp.

Above, major soldier and below, minor soldier
*Schedorhinotermes* sp. Queensland Museum

**Identification:** Two distinct soldiers which differ in size and shape of heads and mandibles —major soldiers (5–7 mm long), minor soldiers (3–5 mm long).

**Habitat and Range:** *S. intermedius* widely distributed throughout Australia. Related species *S. actuosus* and *S. seclusus* also occur in southern Queensland.

**Notes:** Damages buildings, poles, fences, sawn timber, as well as living and dead trees. Very common for attack to take place under protection of extensive fragile plastering. Little known of nests of *Schedorhinotermes;* thought to be located in root crown area of living, dead and debilitated trees, as well as timber buried in ground. Colonies may consist of many thousands of termites

Queensland Museum

Nest of *M. turneri*

## *Microcerotermes turneri*

**Identification:** Soldiers 4.5–5.5 mm long. Easily recognised by arboreal nest.

**Habitat and Range:** Occupies variety of habitats; has been found in open and moderately dense hardwood forests, grassland, rainforests and vegetated coastal lowlands. Occurs throughout coastal Qld south of Cairns and inland to Carnarvon Range.

**Notes:** Nests usually built on ground or on trunks of living or dead trees or on tops of stumps or fence posts. Arboreal nests commonly found on ironbark trees. Very common in Brisbane region where it attacks hardwood timber in ground contact such as fence posts. Not an important economic species.

*N. walkeri* — soldier   Queensland Museum

Nest of *N. walkeri*

## *Nasutitermes* spp.

**Identification:** Soldiers 5–7 mm. Soldiers have pronounced snout (nasus) on a dark brown head. Body lighter brown.

**Habitat and range:** Common around Brisbane; constructs arboreal nest (*Nasutitermes walkeri*) or large mound (*N. magnus*). *N. exitiosus* also constructs a mound, but is uncommon.

**Notes:** *N. walkeri* maintains soil contact by galleries running down trunk of trees. Nests commonly found on ironbark and stringybark trees. Feeds on dead wood, can attack decayed and weathered timber. Kingfishers and lizards use arboreal nests as temporary residences. *N. magnus* makes low, irregularly shaped mounds often up to 2 m high and is a grass feeder.

Nest of *N. magnus*

# Orthopteroid Insects

Dr G. B. Monteith

Orthopteroids are a group of closely related orders of insects which include grasshoppers, stick insects, cockroaches, mantids, earwigs and others. In general, orthopteroids are plant-eaters and some can even be considered pests. The juvenile phases of these insects resemble the adults in body form and lifestyle.

Most are large and many use camouflage to protect their body size from predators. Because of their camouflaged or secretive way of life, orthopteroids are often not noticed. However many species are common in suburban Brisbane while a few of the more interesting species are restricted to nearby rainforest areas.

# Cockroaches

Cockroaches are generally long-legged nocturnal insects. The head of a cockroach is usually covered from above by an overhanging, shield-like thorax. The few household pest species of cockroaches are introduced to Australia and have given all cockroaches a bad name. In fact, there are hundreds of harmless, often attractive, native cockroaches which live in the bush.

Queensland Museum

## Australian Cockroach
### *Periplaneta australasiae*

**Identification:** Length 40 mm. Large, reddish-brown with distinct yellow and brown pattern on thorax and yellow edges to front of wing covers.

**Notes:** Common large pest in houses. Despite name, not native to Australia. Lays hard egg capsules in crevices and among folds of fabric.

Queensland Museum

## American Cockroach
### *Periplaneta americana*

**Identification:** Length 40 mm. Similar to Australian Cockroach (see above) but with less distinct thorax pattern and without yellow wing edges.

**Notes:** Pest species; also enters houses but more common in compost heaps, sewers and industrial situations.

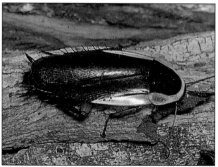
Queensland Museum

## Bush Cockroach  *Methana marginalis*

**Identification:** Length 35 mm. Lustrous reddish-brown with pronounced cream edge to thorax and wing covers.

**Notes:** Lives under loose bark of smooth-barked eucalypts. Sometimes comes into houselights where it may be confused with pest species of *Periplaneta*.

## Barred Cockroach
*Cosmozosteria subzonata*

**Identification:** Length 25 mm. Wingless; reddish-brown with yellow edge to thorax and three yellow bars across rear of thorax segments.

**Notes:** Forages in daytime on ground and shelters beneath logs and debris when disturbed. Copious aromatic secretion when handled. Prefers sandy soils in wallum areas.

Queensland Museum

## German Cockroach
*Blattella germanica*

**Identification:** Length 10 mm. Small, active; pale with two dark bars running lengthwise along thorax.

**Notes:** Introduced household pest, resistant to many chemicals.

Queensland Museum

## *Ellipsidion* spp.

**Identification:** Small. Size range 10–15 mm. Winged, with bold patterns of orange, black and yellow.

**Notes:** Forages on foliage of shrubs during day.

Queensland Museum

## Surinam Cockroach
*Pycnoscelus surinamensis*

**Identification:** Length 18 mm. Dark. Stout, broadly oval with short burrowing legs. Usually wingless but occasional winged males occur.

**Notes:** Introduced species very common in backyard compost heaps where it plays useful role in breaking down organic material. Young born alive. Most individuals are wingless females which can breed without mating. Rarely, a few winged males appear in population.

Queensland Museum

Queensland Museum

## Wood Cockroach *Panesthia cribrata*

**Identification:** Length 35 mm. Black with broad heavy body, stout spiny legs. Thorax dented like shovel.

**Notes:** Powerful burrowing cockroaches living inside rotten logs in open forest. Adults have wings initially but later shed them leaving only stumps on thorax. Nymphs born alive and live in family groups with adults which break down wood for juveniles to eat.

Queensland Museum

## Trilobite Cockroach *Laxta jeanneae*

**Identification:** Length 32 mm. Female — mottled brown, highly flattened, wingless forms with greatly expanded edges to body. Male — rare, long wings and turned up edges to thorax.

**Notes:** Peculiarly shaped cockroaches with ability to slip into very narrow spaces under loose bark and in rock crevices. All legs and antennae concealed beneath body when animal is at rest.

# Praying Mantids

Praying mantids are predatory insects which rely on camouflage to protect them from detection by small prey animals which venture within their reach. Their forelegs are spiny and modified for seizing their prey and holding it while it is eaten. They have large eyes for good vision. Mantids deposit their eggs in a mass surrounded by a foamy secretion which dries to a papery texture.

**Female** Steve Wilson

## Bark Mantis *Paraoxypilus* spp.

**Identification:** Length 20 mm. Small, black with orange patches on inner forelegs. Male —slender and winged; female (pictured) — plump and wingless.

**Notes:** Runs on bark surface of tree trunks, especially when fire-blackened. Exhibits peculiar "boxing" display with forelegs.

## Stick Mantis *Archimantis latistyla*

**Identification:** Length 110 mm. Large, elongated, pale brownish mantis. Resembles dried stick.

**Notes:** Common garden mantis. Khaki-coloured egg masses as big as pullet eggs often seen on topmost twigs of garden shrubs.

Queensland Museum

## Garden Mantis *Orthodera ministralis*

**Identification:** Length 40 mm. Small, green with wide, straight-sided thorax and full length wings.

**Notes:** Cosmopolitan species, probably commonest local mantis. Rests among foliage where it is well concealed.

Queensland Museum

## Burying Mantis *Sphodropoda tristis*

**Identification:** Length 60 mm. Medium-sized, solidly built; grey-brown.

**Notes:** Usually hunts close to ground. Female digs small pit in ground in which to lay eggs, then refills hole.

Steve Wilson

# Earwigs

Earwigs are secretive insects which are easily recognisable because of the strong pincers at the tip of the body. These are used for defence and to capture prey. They have short wing covers under which the hind wings fold. The pincers are also used to assist them in folding their wings.

## Colossus Earwig *Titanolabis colossea*

**Identification:** Length 45 mm. Very large, lustrous reddish-brown, wingless.

**Notes:** One of largest earwigs in world. Occurs in rainforests where it burrows inside soft, rotten logs. Female broods eggs until they hatch. Formidable forceps at rear can draw blood.

Steve Wilson

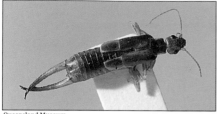

## Common Brown Earwig
*Labidura truncata*

**Identification:** Length 25 mm. Pale coloured with long forceps.

**Notes:** Nocturnal. Frequents margins of streams and dams. During daytime shelters in cracks and under debris.

Queensland Museum

# Stick Insects (Phasmids)

These large, herbivorous insects are masters of camouflage. Some resemble sticks and twigs while others are more leaf-like. They spend much of their time hanging motionless or swaying slightly to resemble wind movement. Stick insects are often confused with praying mantids but differ in not having front legs spined for seizing prey. They drop their eggs to the ground from where the hatchling nymphs walk up tree trunks to the leaves.

## Spiny Leaf Insect *Extatosoma tiaratum*

**Identification:** Length 160 mm. Female (pictured) — fat, spiny, wingless. Hangs upside down with tail curved scorpion-like over back. Male — much more slender, long wings.

**Notes:** Feeds on both wattle and eucalypt foliage, and occasionally rose or grapevine leaves in suburban gardens. Established in overseas pet trade.

Steve Wilson

## Titan Stick Insect *Acrophylla titan*

**Identification:** Length 25 cm. Very large; mottled grey-brown, chequered purplish pattern on hind wings. Thorax has short conical prickles.

**Notes:** Longest insect in Australia. Feeds on leaves of great variety of plants including eucalypts and cypress pine trees.

Bruce Cowell

## Goliath Stick Insect *Eurycnema goliath*

**Identification:** Length 23 cm. Basically green with yellowish rings around abdomen. Hindwings have flash of red when unfolded. Hind legs have prominent curved spines.

**Notes:** Feeds in tops of eucalypts but often comes to notice after being blown down during storms. Has impressive, though harmless, threat display when handled — opens wings and lashes out with its spiny hindlegs. This action also displays two false eyes at base of hind legs.

Queensland Museum

## Grasshoppers, Crickets, Katydids and Allies

These insects almost all have the front wings thickened into leathery wing covers which protect the delicate hindwings that fold up underneath. The hind legs are enlarged so the animal can jump to begin flight or to escape its enemies. Most are herbivorous.

### Hedge Grasshopper
*Valanga irregularis*

**Identification:** Length 85 mm. Large, usually plain khaki but spotted and banded variations also occur. Nymphs may be green or have black and orange patterns.

**Notes:** Common and conspicuous large insect in region. Thrives in well-watered suburban gardens. Feeds mostly on broad-leaved shrubs such as acalypha and hibiscus but also damages palms. Hibernates in adult stage during winter. Mates early summer and lays eggs which hatch with mid-summer rains. During January to March, population is almost entirely nymphs which mature about April.

Queensland Museum

Steve Wilson

## Longheaded Grasshopper
*Acrida conica*

**Identification:** Length 60 mm. Elongated head with bulging eyes and flattened antennae, long spindly legs.

**Notes:** Common after rains in summer, particularly on paspalum grass. Flies with loud clicking noise when disturbed.

Queensland Museum

## Dead Leaf Grasshopper
*Goniaea australasiae*

**Identification:** Length 45 mm. Dark brown with prominent arched crest on thorax. Orange hindwings exposed in flight.

**Notes:** Occurs in dry eucalypt forests where it rests among dead leaves on ground and is strongly camouflaged. Also feeds on dead leaves.

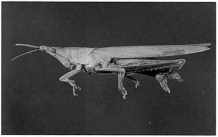

Bruce Cowell

## Vegetable Grasshopper
*Atractomorpha similis*

**Identification:** Length 4 cm. Small, green, body tapers towards both ends.

**Notes:** Inconspicuous — depends on camouflage, reluctant to fly or hop. Common in moist corners of suburban gardens where it feeds on low broad-leaved plants. Minor pest in vegetable gardens.

Queensland Museum

## Spotted Katydid
*Ephippitytha trigintiduoguttata*

**Identification:** Length 65 mm. Wings have 22 brown spots (hence species name) which make it resemble a chewed eucalypt leaf.

**Notes:** Feeds on eucalypt leaves and sometimes comes to house lights. Male has soft call at night which, when recognised, is common from treetops throughout suburbs in summer.

## Mountain Katydid
*Acripeza reticulata*

**Identification:** Length 50 mm. Male and female differ greatly in shape. Female (pictured) — short and broad, forewings convex and shell-like, hindwings missing; male — fore and hindwings normal.

**Notes:** Both sexes generally found on ground in open forests. Female has spectacular defence display — lifts both wing covers to expose brilliant red and purple abdomen and simultaneously inflates orange membrane between head and thorax.

Female                                            Steve Wilson

## Giant King Cricket
*Australostoma australasiae*

**Identification:** Length 70 mm. Very large, wingless, pale brown with long spiny legs. Male (pictured)—enormously enlarged head and mandibles; female—large curved ovipositor with which eggs are inserted into soil.

**Notes:** One of Australia's most impressive insects and closely related to giant wetas of New Zealand. Lives in burrows in soil in rainforests, emerges on wet nights to forage on rainforest floor for live insects and rotten fruit.

Male                                            Queensland Museum

## Common Mole Cricket
*Gryllotalpa pluvialis*

**Identification:** Length 30 mm. Cylindrical with broad, shovel-like forelegs and short, non-jumping hind legs. Thorax is shiny, dark reddish-brown.

**Notes:** Burrows through surface layers of soil, common in compost heaps. Males sing with continuous low trilling from burrows at dusk.

Queensland Museum

Queensland Museum

## Field Cricket  *Teleogryllus commodus*

**Identification:** Length 25 mm. Black with wings drawn out to a long point behind. Female has long needle-like ovipositor at rear.

**Notes:** Common, active; often flies into lights. Lives under debris and in shallow burrows where it feeds on live and dead plant matter. Males chirp repeatedly at dusk. Digs superficial burrows in soil. Can be pest of pastures, lawns and golf courses.

# Cicadas

Tony Ewart

C icadas are familiar insects because of their large empty shells often seen on tree trunks and their ability to "sing". The adult cicadas that we hear in summer represent the final stage of their life history. The young nymphs are subterranean and suck the roots of various trees, shrubs and grasses. When fully grown, the nymphs emerge from under the ground and climb the first vertical object they encounter, usually a tree trunk. Here the nymph grips the bark tightly and its skin splits to allow the winged adult to emerge. The adults use their piercing mouthparts to suck nutrient juices from plants.

Each species (there are more than 200 in Australia) has its own distinctive "song" produced by the males. The sounds originate from the tymbals, located on each side of the abdomen, which work in much the same way as children's tin clicker toys. Each tymbal consists of a fairly rigid, ribbed membrane which is flexed by an internal muscle. The buckling of the tymbal, inward and outward, results in a series of sound pulses. High speed contraction and relaxation of the tymbal muscles often produces such high frequencies that only a continuous sound is heard by our ear. Further complexity is introduced by varying the patterns of song production.

The songs shown in this guide were electronically recorded on tape and then photographed from an oscilloscope image.

## Double Drummer  *Thopha saccata*

**Identification:** Length 39–50 mm; forewing length 50–66 mm. Dominantly pale brown to reddish-brown with black markings on thorax. Head as wide as thorax. Male — very large, swollen brown tymbal covers (opercula) on each side of abdomen. Eyes brown. Wings clear with orange-brown to brown veins.

Deniss Reeves

**Habitat and Range:** Open eucalypt forest.

**Song:** Loud, continuous, chainsaw-like whine.

**Notes:** One of our largest cicadas. December to February.

1.24 seconds

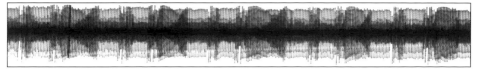

Deniss Reeves

## Razor Grinder *Henicopsaltria eydouxii*

**Identification:** Length 35–42 mm; forewing length 50–55 mm. Dark brown with paler brown marks on thorax, pale stripe along centre of head; dark zig-zag pattern on veins of forewing. Head narrower than thorax and abdomen broader than thorax. Pair of conspicuous pale brown tymbal covers on underside of abdomen in males.

**Habitat and Range:** Open eucalypt forest and margins of rainforest, often on spotted gums.

**Song:** "Metal grinding" sound which rises and after some seconds, abruptly falls in pitch, being repeated many times.

**Notes:** Forms huge aggregations whose combined sound can be painful to the ear. Insects tend to occur at lower to mid-levels of trees. December to February.

4.88 seconds

Deniss Reeves

## Cherry Nose *Macrotristria angularis*

**Identification:** Length 42–47 mm; forewing length 50–60 mm. Dominantly black with prominent orange markings on head and thorax; dark brown on underside of body. Swelling on front of head (postclypeus) bright red (hence common name). Forewings clear with narrow brown colouration bordering veins towards outer part of wing; veins of both wings orange-brown to brown.

**Habitat and Range:** Open eucalypt forest, usually calling from upper parts of taller eucalypts.

**Song:** Continuous tinkling and reverberating song.

**Notes:** Tends to be localised, often showing preference for woodland near rivers or lakes .

1.22 seconds

## Psaltoda claripennis

**Identification:** Length 22–28 mm; forewing length 34–42 mm. Brown to green to dark brown (abdomen), paler brown underneath; eyes red; distinct silvery patch on either side of abdomen. Forewings clear, with vein along leading edge of forewing green.

**Habitat and Range:** Common in open forest and urban areas; dominantly in eucalypts and casuarinas, throughout region.

**Song:** Loud rapid rattling and clanging song.

**Notes:** Typically congregates in a few trees, forming local concentrations of insects. Superficially similar to Yellowbelly (see below). November to late March.

Deniss Reeves

5.40 seconds

## Yellowbelly *Psaltoda harrisii*

**Identification:** Length 21–30 mm; forewing length 30–40 mm. Darkish brown to black, abdomen paler orange-brown beneath; distinct yellowish-silver patch on either side of abdomen. Eyes brown to black. Forewings clear, with vein along leading edge brown.

**Habitat and Range:** Common in open forest; dominantly in eucalypts, and also in coastal wallum environments on banksias and casuarinas.

**Song:** Continuous rising and falling low buzzing song.

**Notes:** Typically occurs in local concentrations of insects, both high and low in trees. November to March, extending to May near coast.

Deniss Reeves

3.35 seconds

Deniss Reeves

## Black Friday *Psaltoda pictibasis*

**Identification:** Length 42–51 mm; forewing 49–60 mm. Black with dark brown patterning on thorax; pale brown underneath. Forewings with small but distinct brown patches (infuscations) towards wing tips; hindwings with narrow, outer faint infuscations; dark brown vein along leading edge of forewing. Distinct yellowish-silver patch on either side of abdomen.

**Habitat and Range:** Open eucalypt forest, normally high in trees.

**Song:** Continuous interspersed low rattling and yodelling song.

**Notes:** One of largest Brisbane cicadas. Common December–February.

6.72 seconds

Deniss Reeves

## Floury Baker *Abricta curvicosta*

**Identification:** Length 25–33 mm; forewing length 30–51 mm. Dominantly deep brown including underside; head lighter brown with paler central line. Wings clear with two distinct spots towards tips of each forewing, and some brown colouration near rear of hindwings. Leading edges of forewings more curved than normal. Fresh adult covered by pale, flour-like dusting, giving common name.

**Habitat and Range:** Open forest, occurs widely throughout suburban Brisbane. Found on many types of trees and shrubs including exotics.

**Song:** Series of staccato, coarse zeep-zeep-zeep phrases, becoming more rapidly emitted, culminating in longer, harsh and coarse "buzzing" phrase. Sequence usually repeated many times.

**Notes:** Unusual cicada habit of sitting on tree branch head downwards. November to March.

7.80 seconds

## Bladder Cicada *Cystosoma saundersii*

**Identification:** Length — male 45–50 mm, female 30–35 mm; forewing length 40–50 mm. Green above and below (although fading to brown in dried specimens); eyes pink-brown (when fresh). Male abdomen greatly inflated and largely hollow. Wings green, opaque, and leaf-like.

**Habitat and Range:** Open forest. Common in suburban gardens, especially in jacarandas and other exotic trees and shrubs. Prefers thick foliage.

**Song:** Distinctive low frequency, deep, frog-like sound, continuing for up to 30 minutes. Sings only at dusk to early nightfall.

**Notes:** Large abdomen acts as resonating chamber for song. Poor flier, does fly actively, but only over short distances, during dusk singing period. September to May.

Deniss Reeves

0.30 seconds

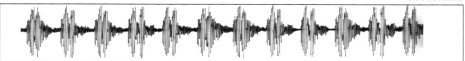

## Bottle Cicada *Glaucopsaltria viridis*

**Identification:** Length — male 28–33 mm, female 18–20 mm; forewing length 28–34 mm. Body green with male having greatly inflated hollow abdomen. Female abdomen much smaller and tapered. Wings clear with greenish tinge, veins green.

**Habitat and Range:** Widespread in suburban gardens, also local closed forest habitats in gullies. Occurs on range of exotic shrubs, including lantana. Common in City Botanic Gardens.

**Song:** Continuous, monotonous whistle, only occurring at dusk.

**Notes:** During day, adults are inactive and well camouflaged in foliage. October to April.

Deniss Reeves

0.30 seconds

Deniss Reeves

## Small Bottle Cicada
### *Chlorocysta vitripennis*

**Identification:** Length — male 20–25 mm, female 15–18 mm; forewing length 20–30 mm. Body green. Male with strongly inflated abdomen, more or less parallel-sided. Female abdomen smaller and tapered. Wings clear with very faint green tinge and green veins.

**Habitat and Range:** Widespread in suburban gardens with foliage-rich shrubs and thick hedges. Also margins around rainforests, and in lantana thickets.

**Song:** Relatively short (up to half a minute), high pitched monotonous "scream" or whistle, repeated at intervals between one to several minutes. Sings during day and also at dusk.

**Notes:** Smallest of three "bladder" cicadas occurring in Brisbane. September to April.

0.31 seconds

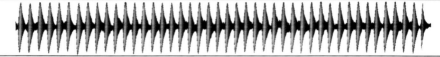

Deniss Reeves

## Mangrove Cicada *Arunta interclusa*

**Identification:** Length 25–31 mm; forewing length 36–43 mm. Head and thorax green with brown markings; abdomen dark brown to black; large white tymbal coverings on either side of male abdomen; underside dark brown. Head narrower than thorax. Wings clear with green to brown veins.

**Habitat and Range:** Characteristic of mangroves, especially Grey Mangrove. Common throughout islands and coastline of Moreton Bay area. Females often found in sand dunes away from mangroves.

**Song:** Continuous, even, loud buzzing call, which can be heard from as much as a kilometre away.

**Notes:** Egg-laying and emergences occur in sand dunes away from mangroves. December to May.

0.34 seconds

## White Drummer *Arunta perulata*

Deniss Reeves

**Identification:** Length 35–43 mm; forewing length 41–54 mm. Dark brown with black markings on head and thorax, and paler stripe along centre of head. Underside of abdomen dark brown. Large white tymbal coverings on either side of male abdomen, and smaller white patches on either side of female abdomen. Pale brown markings towards tips of forewings.

**Habitat and Range:** Frontal dunes and sandy sea fronts, occurring in any available trees, but especially Coastal Sheoak.

**Song:** Continuous, even, loud rattling call, similar to Mangrove Cicada (see p. 84), but slightly higher frequency.

**Notes:** Song especially conspicuous in late afternoon and at dusk.

0.24 seconds

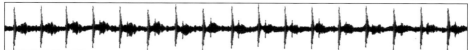

## Brown Bunyip *Tamasa tristigma*

Deniss Reeves

**Identification:** Length 15–20 mm; forewing length 23–31 mm. Pale to medium brown, often with greenish tinge; small black markings on thorax and head; narrow black band across posterior end of abdomen; male abdomen broader than thorax. Wings clear with three brown spots towards tip of each forewing.

**Habitat and Range:** Open forest and also common through suburban Brisbane gardens, especially in casuarinas, acacias, and also jacarandas.

**Song:** Monotonous, even, continuous low pitched buzzing, which may continue for many minutes.

**Notes:** Relatively static cicada, sitting on lower parts of main trunks of trees where it is very well camouflaged. November to April.

0.38 seconds

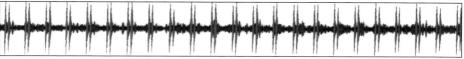

Deniss Reeves

## Black Tree Ticker *Birrima varians*

**Identification:** Length 18–24 mm; forewing length 24–32 mm. Head brown with small fine black markings, and central paler stripe; thorax mostly black. Male abdomen brown with thin, prominent pale orange-brown transverse bands; female abdomen more uniform brown; underside of abdomen brown, with relatively large black tymbal covers in males. Wings clear with brown veins.

**Habitat and Range:** Open forest, extending to parklands and well-treed suburbs.

**Song:** Sings whilst in flight with series of fast, coarse "zits", reminiscent of "quacks" of duck.

**Notes:** Fast, erratic flight while singing is characteristic feature. Late August to February.

6.80 seconds

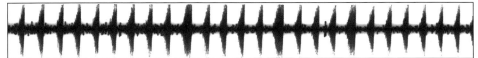

Deniss Reeves

## *Pauropsalta corticinus*

**Identification:** Length 14–18 mm; forewing length 16–21 mm. Body mostly black, with limited brown to dark brown patterning on top of thorax, and thin yellow to yellow-brown bands running transversely across abdomen; dark brown to black on underside of body. Eyes dark brown. Wings clear except for small dark spot on rear edge of hindwings.

**Habitat and Range:** Dry open eucalypt forest; widespread species in suburban Brisbane.

**Song:** Penetrating repetitive song consisting of a series of sharp "zip-zip-zip" phrases (up to about 10), followed by a longer "zeeee—p" phrase.

**Notes:** One of smaller Brisbane cicadas, with conspicuous and loud song. Very wary and mobile insect. Prefers to sit on dark, rough-barked trees where it is well camouflaged when at rest. September to April.

10.8 seconds

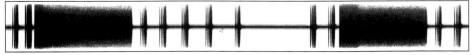

## *Pauropsalta annulata*

**Identification:** Length 11–16 mm; forewing length 14–18 mm. Male — black with minor brown patterning on thorax and head, but conspicuous yellow to yellow-brown bands running across abdomen; female — more brown than black. Eyes normally red, but in rare specimens white. Underside of abdomen yellow-brown with central longitudinal darker brown stripe. Wings clear with faint darker spot on rear margin of hindwings.

Deniss Reeves

**Habitat and Range:** Dry open eucalypt forest, extending as common species throughout suburban Brisbane.

**Song:** Repetitive short sharp and rapidly emitted "zip-zip-zip" song.

**Notes:** Small, inconspicuous, species which inhabits outer foliage of wide variety of trees.

1.63 seconds

## Paperbark Cicada    *Cicadetta hackeri*

**Identification:** Length 15–20 mm; forewing length 18–24 mm. General appearance is of smallish, pale grey to silvery cicada. Head and thorax pale green to brown; abdomen brown with narrow transverse black bands only across central region; orange-brown beneath. Silvery hair on abdomen (pubescence) gives overall pale appearance. Wings clear with pale greenish to brown veins.

Tony Ewart

**Habitat and Range:** Associated most closely with paperbark trees, thus common in coastal swampy areas.

**Song:** Soft repeated "zip" call, initially slow, but then emitted more rapidly.

**Notes:** Small, rather static cicada which relies on excellent camouflage of pale colour against pale bark of melaleucas. Late September to April.

1.65 seconds

Deniss Reeves

## Wattle Cicada *Cicadetta oldfieldi*

**Identification:** Length 15–25 mm; forewing length 20–28 mm. Green to khaki green, with characteristic reddish-brown central stripe extending along whole body. Underside greenish-brown to pale brown. Wings clear with green to greenish-brown veins.

**Habitat and Range:** Generally found in acacias, especially *A. cunninghami*. Open woodland, parkland, and well-treed suburbs.

**Song:** Soft lilting to buzzing song, with two distinct song patterns.

**Notes:** Small, relatively sedentary species hard to locate in branches and trunks of acacias due to camouflage. October to March.

1.50 seconds

Deniss Reeves

## Wallum Cicada *Cicadetta stradbrokensis*

**Identification:** Length 15–18 mm; forewing 17–20 mm. Head and thorax vary from pale brown with black markings to dark brown; abdomen varies from pale brown to dark reddish-brown with transverse narrow black bands across uppermost central part only; underneath pale yellowish-brown. Wings clear with brown veins, distinct bend (angulation) along front edge of forewings.

**Habitat and Range:** Swamp areas near coast, especially within wallum heathland environment. Most commonly associated with sedges and reeds, singing while sitting on long stems of these species.

**Song:** Very melodious and lilting song, with interspersed wing clapping in which "claps" coincide with main song pulses.

**Notes:** Small, very active, wary, and fast flying cicada. October to April.

7.60 seconds

# Beetles and Bugs

Dr G. B. Monteith

B eetles (Order Coleoptera) and bugs (Suborder Heteroptera) are two of the most commonly encountered and easily recognised groups of insects. Though superficially similar in form, these two groups are unrelated and have very different feeding methods and life histories. Beetles are the most abundant and diverse animals on Earth with more than 25,000 species in Australia alone. Beetles have jaws with which they bite and chew their solid food and they have a larval and pupal phase before the adult stage is reached. Bugs feed only by sucking liquid food up through a moveable cylindrical tube (rostrum) beneath the head and the juvenile stages (nymphs) resemble the adult closely in form. There are about 3000 species of bugs in Australia.

## Beetles

### Bombardier Beetle
*Pheropsophus verticalis*

**Identification:** Length 15 mm. Elongated. Dark brown, yellow blotch on each wing cover.

**Notes:** Nocturnal. Shelters under ground debris around damp margins of streams and dams. When disturbed produces audible chemical explosion from rear end accompanied by puff of smoke and acrid smell.

Owen Kelly

### Snail-eating Carabid
*Pamborus alternans*

**Identification:** Length 32 mm. Metallic bronze and green; marked waist, short curved jaws.

**Notes:** Lives under logs in rainforests. Squirts pungent, burning fluid from rear when handled. Feeds on snails and earthworms which it grips with specialised jaws.

Queensland Museum

Owen Kelly

## Tree Trunk Tiger Beetle
### *Distipsidera albicans*

**Identification:** Length 11 mm. Black with white patches on wing covers; long slender legs. Eyes and jaws very large.

**Notes:** Predatory. Runs after prey on trunks of smooth gum trees. Flies actively when disturbed to a new tree. Larvae in vertical burrows in soil.

Owen Kelly

## Diving Water Beetle
### *Cybister tripunctatus*

**Identification:** Length 30 mm. Streamlined. Polished olive-green with yellow border around body.

**Notes:** Predatory. Swims in still waters and bobs to surface regularly to renew air bubble it carries beneath wing covers. Sometimes nibbles swimmers sitting quietly in water.

Queensland Museum

## Whirligig Beetle   *Macrogyrus oblongus*

**Identification:** Length 10 mm. Flattened. Greenish-black, long forelegs and very short mid and hind legs.

**Notes:** Swims in groups on surface of quiet backwaters, often with rapid circular motion. Eyes are divided in two for specialised life-style — one pair for viewing above water while other pair scan under water.

**Male** Steve Wilson

## Rhinoceros Beetle   *Xylotrupes gideon*

**Identification:** Length 40 mm. Large, black. Male (pictured) has forked horns on both head and thorax; female unarmed.

**Notes:** Large, grey, curled larvae common in suburban compost heaps; hatch in summer to adults which often come to lights or aggregate for mating in poinciana trees where they feed on soft bark of young shoots. Adults squeak loudly when handled but are harmless.

**Rhinoceros Beetle larva** Owen Kelly

## Fiddle Beetle  *Eupoecila australasiae*

**Identification:** Length 15 mm. Gains common name from enamelled violin-shaped green pattern on blackish-brown wing covers.

**Notes:** Flies strongly. Feeds on nectar in flowers of eucalypts and other trees. Larvae live in decaying wood and compost and crawl on their backs.

Owen Kelly

## Brown Cockchafer
*Rhopaea magnicornis*

**Identification:** Length 22 mm. Pale brown. Hairy, with soft wing covers and fan-like antennae.

**Notes:** Larvae are white curl-grubs which live in soil of gardens and lawns and feed on plant roots. Adults hatch in large numbers after summer rains and fly backwards and forwards above lawns at dusk.

Queensland Museum

## Washing Beetle  *Phyllotocus* sp.

**Identification:** Length 7 mm. Small. Black thorax and orange wing covers; long legs.

**Notes:** Emerge in thousands in summer to feed on white gum blossoms. Often mistakenly swarm on moving white objects such as washing on the line, tennis players or even brides.

Owen Kelly

## Christmas Beetle
*Anoplognathus porosus*

**Identification:** Length 25 mm. Large. Creamygold with short, dark parallel grooves on wing covers. Grooves more conspicuous in closely related species *A. boisduvali.*

**Notes:** Fly to house lights in midsummer, hence common name. Adults feed on eucalypt foliage while larvae are white curl-grubs which live in soil and feed on plant roots.

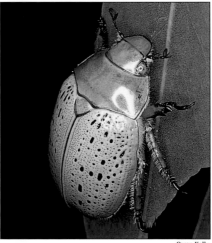
Owen Kelly

Queensland Museum

## Dung Beetle  *Onthophagus dandalu*

**Identification:** Length 9 mm. Small, stout. Black with metallic green thorax and head. Thorax of male bears central horn.

**Notes:** Like most dung beetles it buries animal dung in soil as food for larvae. Common in suburban areas where it buries dog droppings fouling footpaths.

Queensland Museum

## Cypress Jewel Beetle
*Diadoxus erythrurus*

**Identification:** Length 12 mm. Elongated. Dark with three pale stripes on thorax and eight yellow patches on wing covers.

**Notes:** Larvae bore into cypress pine trees and may remain in sawn timber for years to eventually emerge from household timber. They cannot re-infest sawn timber.

Steve Wilson

## Hoop Pine Jewel Beetle
*Prospheres aurantiopictus*

**Identification:** Length 15 mm. Elongated. Dark with 10 pale patches on wing covers.

**Notes:** Larvae bore into hoop pine trees and, as with Cypress Jewel Beetle, may emerge years later from house timber. Cannot re-infest sawn timber.

**Males (foreground), female (upper right)**
Queensland Museum

## Firefly  *Luciola scintillans*

**Identification:** Length 7 mm. Small, soft, with pale thorax and dark brown wing covers. One or two segments on underside of abdomen form white light-emitting organ.

**Notes:** Male beetles (3 pictured foreground) fly in spring, especially in mountains near Brisbane. Flash light as signal to wingless females (upper right) on ground which return weaker flash. Larvae live among damp litter and feed on minute snails.

## Longicorn Beetle  *Agrianome spinicollis*

**Identification:** Length 60 mm. Large. Khaki wing covers; reddish-brown thorax edged with row of pointed teeth. Antennae longer than body.

**Notes:** Breeds as large white grubs in rotten wood, often in dead poinciana trees. Adults sometimes blunder into house lights.

Owen Kelly

## Botany Bay Diamond Weevil
*Chrysolopus spectabilis*

**Identification:** Length 22 mm. Green and black speckled body with elongated rostrum.

**Notes:** Name indicates it was collected by James Cook's party at Botany Bay and was one of first insects named from Australia. Adults and grubs feed on wattles, sometimes becoming a minor garden pest.

Owen Kelly

## Giant Pine Weevil
*Eurhamphus fasciculatus*

**Identification:** Length 60 mm. Very large. Long straight rostrum and tufts of brown and white hairs on thorax and wing covers.

**Notes:** Found in rainforest areas where adults congregate on trunks of dying hoop pine trees. Larvae are white, legless grubs which feed on inner bark of same trees.

Owen Kelly

# Bugs

## Assassin Bug  *Pristhesancus plagipennis*

**Identification:** Length 23 mm. Slow moving. Yellowish-brown with curved rostrum beneath long narrow head. Legs very slender.

**Notes:** Predatory. Lurks among foliage and on flowers and ambushes other insects as food. Prey impaled on bug's rostrum and killed by pumping in digestive enzymes. Liquefied body tissues are then sucked up. These same enzymes cause an extremely intense painful reaction in humans.

Bruce Cowell

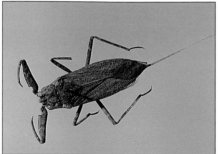

Queensland Museum

## Water Scorpion *Laccotrephes tristis*

**Identification:** Length 55 mm. Long, flattened. Dark brown with hooked forelegs and long slender tail siphon.

**Notes:** Aquatic. Lives in shallow water where it hides among bottom debris with tail siphon up to surface for breathing. Seizes passing small animals with forelegs and sucks their juices. Can fly at night and occasionally enters suburban swimming pools.

Steve Wilson

## Giant Water Bug *Lethocerus insulanus*

**Identification:** Length 70 mm. Very large. Khaki brown with flattened hind legs, very large eyes and short tail siphon.

**Notes:** Aquatic. Captures quite large prey including tadpoles and small fish by seizing them with needle-tipped front legs and impaling them on stout rostrum. Largest sucking bug in Australia.

CSIRO

## Crusader Bug *Mictis profana*

**Identification:** Length 22 mm. Dark grey with a diagonal white cross on back.

**Notes:** Sucks sap from shoots and pods of leguminous plants such as wattles and cassias; minor pest of garden beans.

## Clown Bugs *Amorbus* spp.

**Identification:** Length 22 mm. Several very similar local species of these dark reddish - brown bugs. All have striking nymphs coloured in reds, blues and yellows.

**Notes:** All species suck sap of gum trees. Nymphs often occur in clusters on young shoots projecting from top of small plants. Adults and nymphs produce smelly, defensive fluid when disturbed.

Queensland Museum

## Hibiscus Harlequin Bug
### *Tectocoris diophthalmus*

**Identification:** Rounded, convex bugs with bright metallic colours of greens, blues and reds. Back completely covered with shield-like plate — the scutellum.

**Notes:** Suck sap from hibiscus plants and their relatives. Main native food plant is Beach Hibiscus. Females lay clusters of eggs around twigs and guard them until they hatch.

Steve Wilson

## Mallotus Harlequin Bug
### *Cantao parentum*

**Identification:** Length 20 mm. Long. Orange with two black spots on thorax and eight spots on scutellum (shield-like plate on back).

**Notes:** Sucks sap of *Mallotus* trees. During winter, large numbers of adults form over-wintering clusters which may remain inactive for two to three months.

Steve Wilson

Dept Primary Industries

## Bronze Orange Bug
*Musgraveia sulciventris*

**Identification:** Length 25 mm. Large, broad. Dark bronze with triangular scutellum (shield-like plate) in middle of back. Very flattened nymphs are orange with a central black spot.

**Notes:** Sucks sap from shoots of citrus plants; native food plants are wild limes but bug has become pest of cultivated citrus. Adults and nymphs have corrosive secretion; able to squirt considerable distance.

Queensland Museum

## Gum Tree Shield Bug
*Theseus modestus*

**Identification:** Length 15 mm. Mottled grey and black shield with white tip to scutellum (shield-like plate).

**Notes:** Black and white nymphs occur in clusters under loose bark of living gum trees. Adults more camouflaged and roam more freely on trunk where they suck sap from bark.

# Lacewings

Dr Kevin Lambkin and Shaun Winterton

A dult lacewings (neuropterans) are soft-bodied insects with biting mouth-parts and two pairs of transparent wings of about equal size. They derive their common name, lacewings, from their gauzy, net-like wings which are very richly patterned with veins. Their size range is considerable with wing-spans as little as 5 mm or more than 100 mm. The larger species, with their "lace" wings, are sometimes mistaken for dragonflies, but are distinguished by the tent-like way in which the wings are folded, and by the more conspic-uous and often clubbed antennae. Flight may be a delicate fluttering or strong gliding. Most lacewing larvae are generalist predators of other insects and often have enlarged, sickle-shaped jaws modified for piercing and suck-ing out the contents of their prey. Many are voracious active hunters, while others employ a "sit and wait" ambush strategy. Larvae of most Mantid lacewings are grub-like parasites found inside spider egg sacs. The adults of many species are active during the warmer months of the year, when they are often attracted to the lights of houses. There are more than 600 species of lacewings in Australia, belonging to 14 families. Representatives of 13 of these families occur in the Greater Brisbane Region or nearby.

*Mallada albofacialis* Shaun Winterton

*Plesiochrysa ramburi* Shaun Winterton

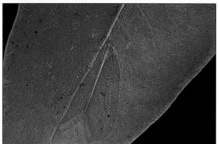
Shaun Winterton

Shaun Winterton

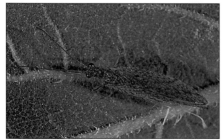
Dept Primary Industries

## Green Lacewings *Mallada* spp., *Chrysoperla* spp., *Plesiochrysa* spp.

**Other Names:** Golden-eyed Lacewings.

**Identification:** Wingspan 20–40 mm. Green bodies with yellow medial stripe and copper eyes.

**Habitat and Range:** Most common lacewings. Seen throughout year in suburban gardens, particularly around lights at night. Some species distributed Australia-wide, others considered rare within limited ranges.

**Notes:** Eggs laid on long, thin stalks either singly or in groups. Larvae of some species cover upper surface of bodies with debris and sucked-out shells of prey.

## *Oligochrysa lutea*

**Identification:** Wingspan 30–40 mm. Broad transparent wings with characteristic wing spots. Body green with yellow stripe and very long, thin antennae.

**Habitat and Range:** Adults seen throughout year, more common in forested areas. Eastern coast of Australia as far south as Sydney.

**Notes:** Eggs stalked. Larvae cover upper surface of body with debris as in *Mallada* spp.

## *Italochrysa insignis*

**Identification:** Robust. Body pale green to light brown. Pair of opposing E-shaped markings just behind head.

**Habitat and Range:** Attracted to lights throughout year. Australia-wide.

**Notes:** Little known of life cycle. Larvae possibly associated with ant colonies.

## *Micromus tasmaniae*

**Identification:** Small, brown body. Wingspan 10 mm.

**Habitat and Range:** Inconspicuous, but frequently encountered throughout year, particularly in early spring. Australia-wide.

**Notes:** Larvae are dark, thin and do not carry debris. They move quickly and during the day hide under bark and on underside of leaves.

## Mantid Lacewing  *Ditaxis biseriata*

**Identification:** Wingspan 35–60 mm. Body pink and cream. Raptorial forelegs like praying mantises but distinguished by transparent wings.

**Habitat and Range:** Open bush, attracted to house lights. Adults occur spring and autumn. Found mainly south-eastern Qld and northern NSW.

**Notes:** Life cycle unknown. Eggs laid in groups of entwined stalks on undersides of leaves. Adult size varies greatly, possibly due to food availability for larvae.

Queensland Museum

## *Nymphes myrmeleonides*

**Identification:** Wingspan 70–90 mm. Large orange body with long wings.

**Habitat and Range:** Common October to March in forested areas and established suburban gardens.

**Notes:** Lays stalked white eggs in characteristic U-shaped groups around houses and buildings. Males may emit pungent, musky odour when disturbed.

Queensland Museum

## *Osmylops armatus*

**Identification:** Broad transparent wings. Green body and short thick antennae.

**Habitat and Range:** Not particularly common, found mainly in forested areas. Eastern Qld and NSW.

Joy Luke

## Owl Flies  *Suhpalacsa* spp.

**Identification:** Long-winged. Wingspan 50–70 mm. Large dragonfly-like eyes. Long thin antennae with large clubbed ends.

**Habitat and Range:** Open forest country. Adults emerge during summer months.

**Notes:** Adults are strong fliers, distinguished from other lacewings by slow, gliding flight similar to dragonflies. Larvae have large, powerful jaws; live in soil and leaf litter; ambush prey.

Dr G. May

J. Clatworthy

## Myrmeleon pictifrons

**Identification:** Fairly large. Wingspan 50 mm. Elongated wings, unpatterned. Body dark.

**Habitat and Range:** Attracted to lights in summer. Australia-wide.

**Notes:** Larvae are the common, pit-forming antlions found in loose soil under suburban houses.

Queensland Museum

## Glenoleon pulchellus

**Identification:** Wingspan 50–60 mm. Body dark. Forewings speckled. Hindwings with two broad black bands towards apex.

**Habitat and Range:** Open forest country throughout eastern Australia.

**Notes:** Life cycle unknown.

Queensland Museum

## Distoleon bistrigatus

**Identification:** Wingspan 60–70 mm. Body light brown. Long transparent wings with brown, narrow longitudinal stripe near apex of hindwings.

**Habitat and Range:** Open forest and grasslands. Australia-wide.

**Notes:** Life cycle unknown.

# Butterflies and Moths

Dr G. B. Monteith

Moths and butterflies are closely related insects which are classified together in the large insect group called the Lepidoptera. This name literally means "scaly wings" and this feature is very characteristic of both moths and butterflies. Their beautiful colours are formed by the patterns of these coloured scales which cover the wings. The scales come off readily when specimens are handled. Another characteristic feature is the long tubular proboscis through which they suck up liquid food. This curls up tightly beneath the head when not being used.

The larval stages of moths and butterflies are caterpillars and almost all feed on plants, usually eating the leaves. The caterpillars of most species are very fussy about which plants they will feed on. Knowing the plants favoured by particular species is a great assistance in finding their caterpillars. All caterpillars can spin threads of strong silk from glands just behind their mouth. They use it in many ways, but particularly to build a shelter, the cocoon, in which the pupa, or chrysalis, is concealed during the transformation from caterpillar to adult. Butterfly caterpillars do not make a cocoon.

There is no hard and fast rule for telling the difference between a moth and a butterfly. Butterflies generally fly in the daytime, they have a swollen end to their antennae and their front and rear wings are not hooked together during flight. Moths, on the other hand, are mostly nocturnal, their antennae are varied in shape but very rarely swollen at the end, and they generally have some bristles which lock the wings together in flight.

# BUTTERFLIES

There are about 180 species of butterflies in five different families recorded from the south-east corner of Queensland. They are all treated in detail and illustrated in colour in Common and Waterhouse's standard book, *Butterflies of Australia.* Just 25 of the more conspicuous species are listed here.

## Swallowtails

Queensland Museum

### Blue Triangle  *Graphium sarpedon*

**Identification:** Wingspan 60 mm. Fast flying. Triangular wings each with central pale blue area bordered with dark brown.

**Notes:** Common because it breeds on introduced camphor laurel trees. Larva pale green; rests inconspicuously along upper midrib of leaves. Pupa has pointed front end and like other swallowtails is supported by a loop of silk.

Queensland Museum

### Dingy Swallowtail  *Eleppone anactus*

**Identification:** Wingspan 60 mm. Secretive. Brown and white patterned wings, row of red patches bordering hindwings.

**Notes:** Speckled larva feeds on citrus trees in suburban gardens. Pupa has camouflaged stick-like form, suspended from stem by thread of silk.

**Male** Queensland Museum

### Orchard Swallowtail  *Papilio aegeus*

**Identification:** Wingspan 110 mm. Male (pictured) — large, black with narrow white band across forewing, large central pale patch on hindwing. Female — much larger, extensive pale areas on both wings, row of red spots around edge of hindwing.

**Notes:** Caterpillar feeds on citrus. Small brown and white larvae resemble bird droppings; when larger, change to "camouflage" green. When disturbed, larva extrudes reddish tentacles from head and emits strong smell.

## Big Greasy *Cressida cressida*

**Identification:** Wingspan 80 mm. Male (pictured) — semi-transparent forewings, each with two black spots. Hindwings red, white and black. Female uniformly pale brown and semi-transparent.

Male                    Queensland Museum

**Notes:** Breeds on *Aristolochia pubera* — small, inconspicuous vine which scrambles among grass in open forest. Chunky reddish larvae often devour all leaves on plant and then walk along ground to find another.

## Richmond Birdwing
*Ornithoptera richmondia*

**Identification:** Wingspan 110 mm. Male (pictured) — brilliant green and gold; female — much larger, drably patterned in brown and white with red patch on each side of thorax.

Male                    Queensland Museum

**Notes:** Mostly restricted to rainforests where its food plants, the Pipe Vines *Aristolochia praevenosa* (lowlands) and *Aristolochia deltantha* (Border Ranges) grow. Once common in Brisbane area, has declined due to habitat loss. Introduced Dutchman's Pipe Vine, *A. elegans*, attracts egg-laying by females but kills larvae which feed on it.

# Whites, Yellows and Jezebels

## Lemon Migrant *Catopsilia pomona*

**Identification:** Wingspan 70 mm. Medium-sized, cream to yellow, sometimes with darker margins above and reddish blotches beneath.

**Notes:** Massive migrations sometimes occur, with butterflies usually flying from south to north. Green larvae usually feed on Golden Rain trees (*Cassia fistula*). They lie along midrib and are difficult to see. Sometimes occur in great numbers.

Queensland Museum

Queensland Museum

## Common Grass Yellow *Eurema hecabe*

**Identification:** Wingspan 40 mm. Small, bright yellow with notched dark margin to forewing.

**Notes:** Flutters weakly close to ground. Green caterpillars feed on wattles and cassias.

Queensland Museum

## Common Jezebel *Delias nigrina*

**Identification:** Wingspan 60 mm. Plain white with dark margins above; underside of wings dark with brilliant markings in red and yellow.

**Notes:** Active through coldest months of winter. Gregarious, hairy, pale brown caterpillars which feed on mistletoes. Pupa yellow with black spines.

Queensland Museum

## Caper White *Anaphaeis java*

**Identification:** Wingspan 60 mm. Basically white with black margins above (much wider in the female). Underside has greater patches of black with yellow spotting on hindwing.

**Notes:** Breeds in vast numbers on trees and shrubs of genus *Capparis* (Wild Caper, Mock Orange) which are more common inland. First stormy, hot weather of summer often coincides with migrations of adults which may persist for several days. At these times, enormous numbers sometimes aggregate on headlands before flying out to sea.

# Skippers

Queensland Museum

## Regent Skipper *Euschemon rafflesia*

**Identification:** Wingspan 55 mm. Black with yellow patches above and below on both wings. Tip of abdomen is bright red.

**Notes:** Uncommon. Found in rainforest where caterpillars feed on stiff prickly leaves of *Wilkeia* shrubs. Larvae feed from within shelter made by sewing adjacent leaves together with silk.

## Brown Awl *Badamia exclamationis*

**Identification:** Wingspan 55 mm. Large, plain brown skipper with long narrow forewings.

**Notes:** Breeds on coastal almond trees (*Terminalia* spp.); undertakes long migratory flights.

Queensland Museum

## Orange Palmdart *Cephrenes augiades*

**Identification:** Large, orange and black skipper. Female often almost without orange markings.

**Notes:** Rests in sun on upper side of leaves, then darts off at great speed. Eggs laid on palms and larvae sew adjacent leaflets together into retreats from which they feed. Larvae pale green with striking banded heads. Can cause disfigurement of garden palms. Pupate inside same shelter and produce whitish floury deposit at time of pupation.

Queensland Museum

# Blues and Coppers

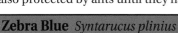

## Common Imperial Blue
### *Jalmenus evagoras*

**Identification:** Wingspan 40 mm. Elegant blue and brown butterfly with long curled tail to each hindwing. Underside pale yellowish-brown with dark lines and spots.

**Notes:** Female lays eggs on wattles. When eggs hatch, ants protect larvae while they feed in groups on foliage. In return, caterpillars provide secretion which ants devour. Eventually larvae pupate on twigs where pupae are also protected by ants until they hatch.

Queensland Museum

## Zebra Blue *Syntarucus plinius*

**Identification:** Wingspan 25 mm. Small, blue-grey with boldly striped underside to wings.

**Notes:** Rarely found far from *Plumbago* plants, including common garden ornamentals. Flattened green larva feeds on buds and flowers.

Queensland Museum

Male Queensland Museum

## Small Green-banded Blue
*Danis hymetus*

**Identification:** Wingspan 25 mm. Small. Male (pictured) — bright blue above; female — large, central white area edged with dark. Underside of hindwing of both sexes has row of bright metallic squares along hind edge, each with central black spot.

**Notes:** Breeds on foliage of Red Ash (Soap Leaf) tree. Flattened, whitish caterpillars feed on underside of leaf and make distinctive marks which show on top of leaf.

# Nymphs, Browns and Crows

Queensland Museum

## Wanderer   *Danaus plexippus*

**Identification:** Wingspan 100 mm. Strongflying. Dark orange with pattern of black veins on both wings.

**Notes:** Also known as Monarch in North America from where it migrated to Australia in 1871. Familiar striped caterpillars feed on introduced milkweed bushes. Green pupae hang upside down beneath leaves.

Queensland Museum

## Lesser Wanderer   *Danaus chrysippus*

**Identification:** Wingspan 60 mm. Native — species similar to introduced Wanderer, but smaller and has prominent whitish areas on forewings.

**Notes:** Also has striped larva which feeds on milkweed, but stripes are more interrupted and three pairs of tentacles on back instead of two like Wanderer larva.

Queensland Museum

## Blue Tiger   *Tirumala hamata*

**Identification:** Wingspan 75 mm. Large, dark with numerous pale blue windows on both wings.

**Notes:** Normally rare in Brisbane area, but every year or two enormous migrations of adults pass through, often eventually flying out to sea. Striped caterpillars have two pairs of tentacles and feed on vines of genera *Secamone* and *Ischnostemma*.

## Common Crow *Euploea core*

**Identification:** Wingspan 65 mm. Black with scattered white marks on upper side and underside. Male — narrow opaque mark (sex brand) on the forewing.

**Notes:** Adults go into quiescent aggregations in protected, shady sites during winter. Boldly striped caterpillars feed mostly on oleanders and figs in Brisbane. Pupa brilliant metallic silver, suspended upside down beneath leaf.

Queensland Museum

Queensland Museum

## Evening Brown *Melanitis leda*

**Identification:** Wingspan 70 mm. Large, orange-brown above, mottled camouflage pattern on underside.

**Notes:** Rests during day on ground where folded wings make it difficult to detect. At dusk, rapid period of swirling flight often takes place. Does not visit flowers but sucks juice from fermenting fruit. Larva green with horned head, feeds on coarse grasses such as blady grass

Queensland Museum

Queensland Museum

## Tailed Emperor *Polyura sempronius*

**Identification:** Wingspan 75 mm. Large, cream and black above with two sharp tails on rear edge of each hindwing. Underside of both wings has dark, ornamented pattern of bands and spots.

**Notes:** Strong and high flying. Adults feed only on fermenting plant juices — favourite being injured pods of Golden Rain tree (*Cassia fistula*) which is also one of food plants for larvae. Larva striking green with enlarged, four-horned head and two bands of yellow. Rests on silken pad in centre of "home" leaf from which it makes short journeys to feed on other leaves. May also be found on poincianas, Chinese elms, wattles and bottle trees.

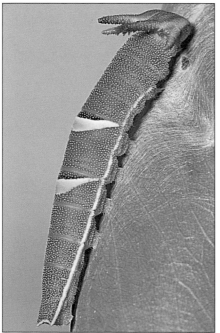

Queensland Museum

Queensland Museum

## Common Aeroplane
*Phaedyma shepherdi*

**Identification:** Wingspan 65 mm. Black and white. Characteristic gliding flight with wings held out flat.

**Notes:** Caterpillars feed on stiff leaves of introduced Chinese elm as well as native *Aphananthe philippensis* and some *Brachychiton* species. Highly camouflaged, rest amid leaf fragments which they attach to exposed midrib of a leaf. Pupa has silver enamelling.

## Common Eggfly *Hypolimnas bolina*

**Identification:** Wingspan 70 mm. Male — black with white spot surrounded by iridescent blue in centre of each wing. Female — very different, variable white and orange markings.

**Notes:** Males very aggressive; will defend small territory from sunny vantage point. Larva brown with numerous tubercles, feeds nocturnally on leaves of weed, sida retusa; by day shelters in leaf litter.

Male                                          Queensland Museum

## Glasswing *Acraea andromacha*

**Identification:** Wingspan 45 mm. Small, yellow and brown with semi-transparent patches in wings.

**Notes:** Females lay clusters of eggs on upper side of leaves of wild passion vines. Caterpillars gregarious; numerous branched, black spines; wander away from food plant to pupate. Elongated, black and white patterned pupae may be found attached to sheltered walls and fences.

Queensland Museum

## Australian Admiral *Vanessa itea*

**Identification:** Wingspan 45 mm. Small, orange and black with large yellow patch on each forewing.

**Notes:** Perches close to ground; very camouflaged when wings are folded. Spined caterpillars feed nocturnally on stinging nettles.

Queensland Museum

# MOTHS

Moths are much more diverse than butterflies and comparatively little is known about their food plants and habits. It is believed that there are several thousand different kinds of moths in South-East Queensland and that these belong to more than 50 families. Just 10 larger common species are mentioned here. *Moths of Australia* by I.F.B. Common is a good reference for further reading.

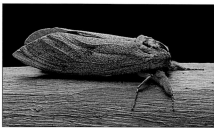
Queensland Museum

## Giant Wood Moth *Endoxyla cinerea*

**Identification:** Wingspan up to 220 mm. Very large, grey with darker hindwings and blotch on middle of thorax.

**Notes:** Larva lives in tunnel in wood of smooth barked gum trees and feeds on inner side of bark. Large hole is cut to exterior of tree when larva is ready to pupate inside. Moth emerges from hole in mid-summer.

Queensland Museum

## Varied Anthelid *Anthela varia*

**Identification:** Wingspan 55–70 mm. Variable colouring — yellow to brown; brush-like antennae.

**Notes:** Adults often come to house lights. Very hairy larva feeds on eucalypt foliage and leaves food plant to make thick cocoon of tough silk in sheltered cavities near ground.

Queensland Museum

## Emperor Gum Moth
*Opodiphthera eucalypti*

**Identification:** Wingspan 95–120 mm. Large, reddish eye-spot on each wing.

**Notes:** Large green larva has many prominent tubercles, each topped by stiff bristles. Feeds on eucalypt foliage and makes hard, oval cocoon, usually under bark of tree.

## Hawk Moth *Gnathothlibus erotus*

**Identification:** Wingspan 90 mm. Large, dark brown, with narrow, swept-back wings. Small hindwings are bright red or orange.

**Notes:** Large, fleshy larva—prominent, curved spine on tail and circular spots along side. Feeds on leaves of cultivated grape vines and related native vines, especially *Cissus antarctica*. Pupates among dead leaves on ground.

Queensland Museum

## Bag-shelter Moth *Ochrogaster lunifer*

Queensland Museum

**Identification:** Wingspan 65 mm. Stout, woolly; brown with bands of yellow on abdomen. Female — large tuft of white scales at tip of abdomen.

**Notes:** Larva covered with long, dense hairs and bristles which irritate human skin on contact. Lives gregariously inside large, pale brown silken bag attached to trunk of wattles or gum trees. Comes out at night to feed on leaves. When larvae leave tree to pupate or to seek new trees they travel in long chain — head to tail — and are then known as processionary caterpillars. Pupate in mass under leaf litter.

## White Cedar Moth *Leptocneria reducta*

Queensland Museum

**Identification:** Wingspan 50 mm. Pale brown, woolly, small eyespot on each forewing.

**Notes:** Hairy caterpillars defoliate white cedar trees in autumn shortly before trees lose their leaves naturally. When no leaves left on feeding tree, large numbers of larvae wander away and may invade houses. Hairs may cause minor itching when caterpillars lodge in clothing.

## Fruit Piercing Moth
*Eudocima salaminia*

Queensland Museum

**Identification:** Wingspan 85 mm. Large, stout; green, camouflaged forewings which part when alarmed to expose yellow and black hindwings.

**Notes:** Uses stout, toothed proboscis to pierce and suck juice from fruit. Larva has black, prominent eyespots on side; rests with loop of body raised. Feeds on heart-shaped leaves of *Stephania* vines.

Queensland Museum

## Granny's Cloak Moth
### *Speiredonia spectans*

**Identification:** Wingspan 75 mm. Large, grey, purplish reflections, wavy dark lines and large eyespots on forewings.

**Notes:** In bush, adults roost in hollow trees and caves in daytime. In houses they favour darkened rooms, cupboards and under floorboards, also in stormwater drains. Sometimes occur in large numbers. Caterpillars and their food plant unknown but they may breed on wattles.

Queensland Museum

## Poinciana Looper    *Pericyma cruegeri*

**Identification:** Wingspan 45 mm. Brownish, lacy pattern on forewing and straight, diagonal dark band across hindwing.

**Notes:** Greenish looper caterpillars often defoliate ornamental poinciana trees.

## Joseph's Coat Moth    *Agarista agricola*

**Identification:** Wingspan 60 mm. Spectacular, dark ground colour blotched with splashes of red, yellow and blue.

**Notes:** Moth flies in daytime and is often mistaken for a butterfly. Larva is brilliantly banded with white, black and orange, rows of hairs with swollen ends along back. Feeds on native vine, *Cayratia*, and occasionally attacks cultivated grape vines.

Queensland Museum

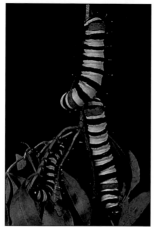
Queensland Museum

# Wasps and Bees

Dr Judith King

Wasps and bees are some of our most useful and interesting insects. Wasps play a significant role in controlling insect pests and their prey includes caterpillars, flies, beetles and crickets. Bees are major pollinators of natural vegetation and farm crops.

Wasps and bees belong to the insect order Hymenoptera and are characterised by having wings with few veins and fore and hindwings that are held together with tiny hooks called hamuli. Like all other insects, they have three parts to their bodies — a head with a pair of antennae; a middle section or mesosoma which bears the legs (and in all but a few species, the wings); and a hind section or metasoma which, in most, is connected to the mesosoma by a distinct "waist". Like many insects their bodies are covered in fine hairs. The differences between bees and wasps are that adult bees feed their larvae protein from a plant source (pollen), while wasps feed their larvae on protein from an animal source (usually other insects or spiders). Adult wasps feed on nectar, insect exudates and fluids from prey insects while adult bees feed mainly on nectar. Adult bees have some plumed (brush-like) hairs on their bodies. Adult wasps have simple hairs.

Wasps and bees are described as either solitary or social according to the way they nest. In solitary species, each female builds her own nest and provides food for her larvae. Wasps and bees are classed as social if there is co-operation and sharing of activities at the nest — the degree of co-operation or sociality depending on the group.

**Paper Wasps** (pp. 114–115) are social wasps living in colonies in nests built of chewed plant tissue or "paper". They prey on caterpillars and are useful garden pest controllers. However they attack and sting when nests are disturbed and nests should be removed from frequently used areas.

**Digger Wasps** (pp. 116) are solitary wasps which make their nests in burrows in the soil. There are many species and the prey depends on the type of wasp.

**Mud-Dauber Wasps** (pp. 116–117) belong to the same family as Digger Wasps — Sphecidae — and again there are many species.

**Spider Wasps** (p. 117) are also solitary insects. The many species include the genera *Cryptocheilus* and *Salius* — some of the largest wasps.

## Wasps

Bruce Cowell

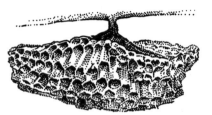

### Paper Wasp *Polistes* spp.

**Identification:** Length several millimetres to more than 20 mm. Mainly black or brown with cream or yellow stripes. Most easily recognised from structure of nest.

**Habitat and Range:** Under branches, in sheltered areas such as under eaves. Several species around Brisbane, including *tepidus, variabilis* and *townsvillensis.*

**Nest:** Disc-shaped and suspended from short stalk (or pedicel) with cells exposed on underside of disc. Cells remain open until larvae pupate, when they are capped. Nest is never enclosed. Size depends on species of wasp and age of nest.

Bruce Cowell

### Paper Wasp *Ropalidia revolutionalis*

**Identification:** Length up to 10–12 mm. Mainly dark brown with narrow yellow band on metasoma, wings brownish.

**Habitat and Range:** Often under eaves of houses and on garden shrubs and creepers. Common in Brisbane.

**Nest:** Combs consist of two joined columns of cells attached to a support by a short stalk. Combs may be several centimetres long and a single colony can include several adjacent combs.

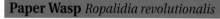

## Paper Wasp *Ropalidia romandi cabeti*

**Identification:** Length 6–8 mm. Mainly yellow with black longitudinal stripes on mesosoma and black bands on metasoma.

**Nest:** Nest consists of many combs usually surrounded by paper envelope; often attached to high tree branch and can be difficult to see. Nests can be very large — some over 60 cm long.

Robert Ashdown

**Notes:** Occasionally nests fall in storms or when a tree sheds its bark — adults then abandon nest and begin to rebuild. Newly fallen nests should be handled with caution as they will contain some developing wasps which will eventually emerge.

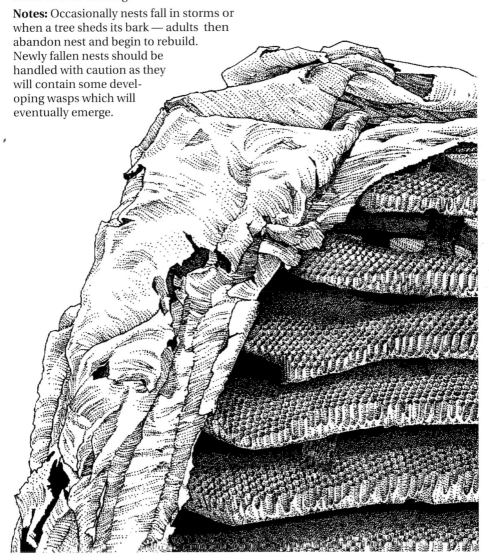

Robert Ashdown

## Cuckoo Wasps

**Identification:** Many species. Length from a few mm to more than 20 mm. Bright metallic blue, green or turquoise.

**Habitat and Range:** Common around Brisbane gardens. Often seen flying slowly up and down walls and around posts and fences where other wasps may be nesting.

**Nest:** None — eggs are laid in nests of other wasps while owner is collecting food for larvae. Cuckoo wasp larva hatches almost immediately and feeds on provisions or hatches much later and feeds on mature larva.

**Notes:** Wasp is heavily armoured and can roll up to protect itself from attack by angry nest owner.

Queensland Museum

## Digger Wasp *Sphex cognatus*

**Identification:** Length about 25 mm. Black, with gold hair on face and mesosoma; thread-like waist.

**Habitat and Range:** Common around Brisbane; prefers sandy soil.

**Nest:** Burrow in ground usually with excavated soil in pile near entrance. Preys on crickets.

Raoul Slater

## Mud-Dauber Wasps
### *Sceliphron laetum, S. formosum*

**Identification:** Length up to 25 mm. Black with yellow patches on mesosoma and yellow banding on metasoma; very slender thread-like waist.

**Habitat and Range:** Common around Brisbane; builds in sheltered locations.

**Nest:** Builds with pellets of mud. Individual cells are flask-shaped and placed in rows. *S. laetum* covers completed cells with extra layers of mud, while *S. formosum* leaves them exposed.

**Notes:** Preys on spiders. Nests very common inside buildings — eg in bookshelves, behind pictures. Wasp emits high-pitched buzz while manipulating mud at nest.

## *Abispa ephippium*

**Identification:** Very large, up to 30 mm. Head, antennae and legs orange, mesosoma black with large orange triangle at "shoulders", metasoma orange at base and apex, wide black band in middle.

**Habitat and Range:** Fairly common in gardens, but one individual uses a large area. Preys only on caterpillars, so forages around infested trees and shrubs.

**Nest:** Sheltered position, on fence behind creeper, corner of carport etc; large mud nest with many cells. Builds entrance chimney which is dispensed with when each group of cells are completed.

**Notes:** When preying on leaf-tying and rolling caterpillars, wasp will cut into the leaf shelter with mandibles to collect prey.

Raoul Slater

## **Spider Wasp** *Salius* sp.

**Identification:** Very large. Length up to 30 mm. Head, antennae and legs orange-yellow, mesosoma black with orange-yellow markings, metasoma black, wings yellow with dark margins.

**Habitat and Range:** Fairly common in Brisbane; hunts in shrubbery and on ground.

**Nest:** Burrow in soil.

**Notes:** Wasps run across vegetation searching for spider prey, which they grasp and sting. Paralysed prey is dragged and carried back to nest.

Peter Slater

D. Ironside

## Orange Caterpillar Parasite
### *Netelia producta*

**Identification:** Orange-brown body and greyish wings; females with long ovipositor. Adults fly backwards and forwards across grass infested with lawn grubs.

**Habitat and Range:** Common around Brisbane gardens; parasitises lawn grubs and other species.

**Nest:** No nest — egg laid onto outside of host and attached by twisted stalk. Wasp larva feeds on caterpillar larva; most of its development takes place after host has pupated.

**Notes:** Related species, *Lissopimpla exelsa*, also parasitises lawn grubs; has orange mesosoma and dark metasoma with cream spots. Very useful pest controllers — lawns with grub problem and attendant caterpillar wasps need not be sprayed.

# Bees

Jeffrey Willmer

## Native Bee *Trigona carbonaria.*

**Other Names:** Stingless Bee, Sugar Bag Bee

**Identification:** Length about 4 mm. Black. Social bees.

**Habitat and Range:** Common around Brisbane. Less active in winter but will forage on warm, sunny days.

**Nests:** Hollow trees and rock crevices. Nest material mixture of wax and resin; combs horizontal. Pollen and honey stored in pots.

**Notes:** Do not sting, but defend nest by biting and swarming. Can be domesticated in hives. Used as pollinators of macadamias.

Queensland Museum

## Blue-banded Bee *Amegilla pulchra*

**Identification:** Length 10–12 mm. Head and mesosoma with golden hairs, metasoma banded with black and blue. Solitary, but will nest in groups.

**Habitat and Range:** Common in Brisbane gardens visiting wide variety of flowers.

**Nest:** Excavates burrows in sheltered

situations such as creek banks, soil banks under houses and planter boxes.

**Notes:** Will nest in wall cavities — gaining access through weak mortar, will replace mortar with mud and saliva. Large colonies can build up over several years. Clusters of sleeping males cling to twigs or grass stems overnight. Related species with similar habits, *A. bombiformis* — up to 15 mm long with light brown hair and brown hair bands on the metasoma.

## Carpenter Bee *Xylocopa aruana*

Pawel Zborowski, CSIRO

**Identification:** Length 20–25 mm. Stout black body, yellow hair on face and mesosoma, grey-black wings. Solitary.

**Habitat and Range:** Common around Brisbane. Seen at leguminous flowering trees such as *Cassia*, *Tipuana* and *Albizia*.

**Nest:** Females tunnel in decaying wood and pithy stems; cells are separated by partitions of chewed wood fibres.

**Notes:** Bees do not damage sound timber. Females buzz loudly and the pitch changes as they hover over flowers, vibrating anthers to release pollen.

## Leafcutter Bee *Megachile* sp.

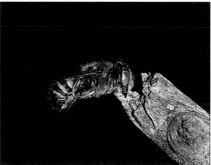

Greg Daniels

**Identification:** Length 6–14 mm depending on species. Mainly black, white hair bands on metasoma; some species have white hair spots on mesosoma. Damage is easiest method of identification — oval and circular pieces cut from leaves, with very smooth edged scars.

**Habitat and Range:** Around Brisbane gardens; collect nectar and pollen from leguminous flowers and daisies.

**Nest:** In existing crevices such as window frames, in hollow twigs and stems. Some species burrow in soil. Cells made of overlapping oval pieces and capped with circular pieces. Cells placed one in front of other till cavity is filled.

**Notes:** Garden plants commonly cut include *Bauhinia galpinii*, wisteria, roses (leaves and petals) and honeysuckle.

Robert Ashdown

## Mason Bee *Chalicodoma mystaceana*

**Identification:** Length 9–15 mm; males are smaller than females. Black head and mesosoma; metasoma covered with bright orange hairs, wing and legs dark.

**Habitat and Range:** Brisbane gardens.

**Nest:** In cracks and crevices, hollow twigs, old borer holes and metal pipes, even between the folds of curtains. Cells are constructed from plant resin, masticated plant material and mud which female carries and moulds with her mandibles. Cells dark brown and slightly shiny.

# Freshwater Fish

Ray Leggett

There are 32 species of fish from 18 families found in freshwater within the Greater Brisbane Region. However, some of these spend most of their life in estuaries and the intertidal zone while others are rarely encountered, so this listing covers the 20 species most commonly seen.

Temperate regions generally have less variety of freshwater fish species than tropical zones yet there are still some very interesting fish to be found around Brisbane. Some are mouth-brooders which hold their eggs within their mouth until the eggs hatch and the fry become free swimming. Others are substrate spawners which lay patches of eggs on driftwood or rock and guard them for up to 12 days until hatching. There are also some fish which spawn eggs with sticky threads that attach to aquatic plants, a strategy which keeps the eggs hidden from many natural predators for 5–7 days till hatching. And finally, there are fish which distribute large numbers of eggs into the water where they either sink to the bottom or float and hatch in 24 to 36 hours.

Before collecting fish for study or pleasure, contact the Queensland Boating and Fisheries Patrol to check if a permit is required. All freshwater fish benefit if a small amount of salt is added to their aquarium — about 4 grams per litre is recommended.

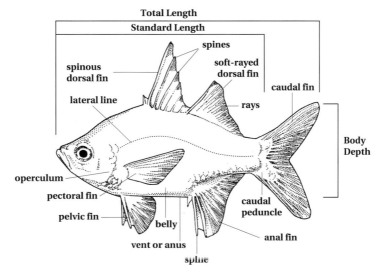

Gunther Schmida

Gunther Schmida

Ray Leggett

## Long-finned Eel  *Anguilla reinhardtii*

**Identification:** Total length up to 1600 mm, commonly seen at 1000 mm. Olive green to brownish-green on back and sides with spots and blotches of a deeper shade; underside paler. Broad head with large mouth extending behind eye and bands of fine teeth. Dorsal fin extends well forward from anal fin.

**Habitat and Range:** Thrives in creeks, rivers and dams; capable of moving considerable distances overland on rainy nights. Eastern Australia from Cape York to Melbourne, northern and eastern coast of Tas.

**Notes:** Carnivorous — preys on fish and crustaceans. Caught by angling or in set traps; good eating after skin has been removed.

## Bony Bream  *Nematalosa erebi*

**Identification:** Total length 270 mm, more often collected at 180 mm. Silvery, often with pale greenish flush to back and sides; small underslung mouth; deeply compressed body and forked tail

**Habitat and Range:** Found in all but shallow, fast flowing waters. Commonly forms large schools which feed over bottom substrate where small aquatic animals and algae are taken. Most areas of northern, eastern and inland Australia.

**Notes:** Small specimens make good bait for most freshwater angling species. Can be successfully kept in aquaria; a small group makes an attractive display.

## Australian Smelt  *Retropinna semoni*

**Identification:** Total length 85 mm, common at 65 mm. Back light olive-grey, sides and belly silver; clear fins. Single dorsal fin is set well back and small adipose fin is located above rear of anal fin. Viewed from above, mature females are broader in belly region.

**Habitat and Range:** Prefers cool, fast flowing streams in Brisbane area but throughout range can be found in large waterholes, dams and lakes. East coast of Australia from the Fitzroy River, south and west to Murray-Darling drainage system.

**Notes:** Make attractive aquarium fish; look best if kept in small schools by themselves in well-filtered tank.

## Salmon Catfish *Arius graeffei*

Neil Armstrong

**Other Names:** Fork-tailed Catfish

**Identification:** Total length 500 mm, common at 400 mm. Dark blue to dusky grey on back with lighter sides and pale silver-white belly. Broad head with 6 barbels on mouth; scaleless body; adipose fin above anal fin and deeply forked tail.

**Habitat and Range:** Adults often caught in brackish water in Brisbane River while juveniles can be collected well into freshwater. Eastern, northern and western coast of Australia from Hunter River, NSW to Ashburton River, WA.

**Notes:** Firm flesh; once skinned they are ideal for sweet and sour or curried fish. Juveniles to 100 mm make good aquarium fish. Mouth-brooders.

## Dewfish *Tandanus tandanus*

Gunther Schmida

**Other Names:** Eel-tailed Catfish

**Identification:** Total length 800 mm, common at 400 mm. Body and fins mottled grey-brown with younger specimens often showing purplish and olive flecks. Four pairs of barbels around mouth; large head; first dorsal and pectoral fins supported by sharp spine. Second dorsal, caudal and anal fins joined. Scaleless body.

**Habitat and Range:** Dewfish favour long deep pools with sandy and gravelly bottoms where they construct circular nests of pebbles in which to place eggs. Juveniles hide in aquatic plants until they reach approximately 120 mm. East coast of Qld and NSW from Cairns to Clarence River and Murray-Darling drainage system.

**Notes:** Juveniles from 30 mm to 100 mm make good scavengers in aquariums. Dewfish are easily caught on lines baited with worms and have good eating qualities.

Gunther Schmida

## Marjorie's Hardyhead
### *Craterocephalus marjoriae*

**Identification:** Total length 80 mm, common at 70 mm. Body yellowish with silver belly, golden mid-lateral stripe nearly always present. Large eye and clear fins.

**Habitat and Range:** Usually found in schools in shallow water over sand. South-eastern Qld to northern NSW from Burnett River to Clarence River.

**Notes:** Seldom kept in aquariums, however will adjust to living in a heavily planted tank. Egg-scatterers.

Neil Armstrong

## Flyspecked Hardyhead
### *Craterocephalus stercusmuscarum fulvus*

**Identification:** Total length 100 mm, common to 75 mm. Grey-green on back with silver sides and belly; body covered with horizontal lines of black dots. Black band runs across snout and through eye. Males in breeding colour have rich orange-yellow throats and bellies.

**Habitat and Range:** Found in a variety of habitats from deep pools to swift flowing streams and large impoundments, generally near and amongst beds of aquatic plants. Eastern Qld and NT.

**Notes:** Hardy, attractive aquarium fish, suitable for community tank. Egg-scatterers.

Gunther Schmida

## Pacific Blue-eye *Pseudomugil signifer*

**Identification:** Total length 40 mm, common at 30 mm. Bright blue eye; olive or silver body often with bluish blush. Second dorsal fin in males can have dark leading edge, with dorsal and anal fins from pale yellow to deep orange. Female has clear fins without the extended rays seen in male.

**Habitat and Range:** Common in mangrove creeks and river estuaries to freshwaters of upper tributaries from Ulladulla in NSW to Cape York, Qld.

**Notes:** Breeds freely in aquariums and outside ponds; excellent destroyer of mosquito larvae; ideal for inclusion in tadpole-rearing containers.

## Soft-spined Sunfish
*Rhadinocentrus ornatus*

Neil Armstrong

**Identification:** Total length 75 mm, common at 60 mm. Grey-green on back and sides, belly silver. Scales edged in black along lateral line and often some iridescent blue-green scales on nape and sides. Several colour varieties can often be found swimming together where males, and to a lesser extent females, show deep red or bright blue fins and back half of body.

**Habitat and Range:** Found in soft, acidic waters of wallum and sandy soils along east coast from northern NSW to Yeppoon, Qld.

**Notes:** Very attractive fish for aquariums and can be bred provided they are kept in soft water with pH below 7.00. Spawn amongst aquatic plants and flood debris.

## Crimson-spotted Rainbow Fish
*Melanotaenia duboulayi*

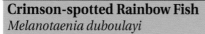

Neil Armstrong

**Identification:** Total length 120 mm, common at 70 mm. Male — green-grey back and sides, silver belly. A series of red lines run longitudinally on sides; fins often with red flecks, edged in black. Crimson spot on gill cover. Female — more rounded fins; shows less colour.

**Habitat and Range:** Adults prefer deep pools with aquatic vegetation; young are found in shallow edges of streams and lakes. Coastal drainages from the Macleay River, NSW to Burnett Basin, Qld.

**Notes:** Rainbows from Australia and New Guinea are very popular as aquarium fish throughout the world. Thirteen species or sub-species are recognised in Australia with a range of colour forms within these species. Eggs hang on threads from aquatic plants.

Neil Armstrong

## Bullrout  *Notesthes robusta*

**Identification:** Total length 300 mm, common at 160 mm. Body and fins mottled brown, tan and creamy-white. Juveniles to 80 mm showing more contrast in colour. Solid, deep-bodied fish. Dorsal, anal and pelvic fin spines have venom glands.

**Habitat and Range:** From brackish water to freshwaters of rivers and creeks where they sit on the bottom among snags and aquatic plants waiting to ambush passing fish. Coastal Qld and NSW from Cape York to Clyde River.

**Notes:** Care should be taken to avoid standing on Bullrouts with bare feet as very painful wounds can result. Interesting aquarium specimens, but should be kept by themselves.

## Agassiz's Glassfish  *Ambassis agassizii*

**Other Names:** Glass Perch

**Identification:** Total length 65 mm, common at 40 mm. Body semi-transparent, with olive hue, scales with dark edges giving a pattern along sides. Dorsal, pelvic and anal fins often have black edging.

**Habitat and Range:** Generally keeps to dense stands of aquatic plants along edges of pools. Coastal to central Qld from Cairns to central NSW including Murray-Darling drainage system.

**Notes:** Hardy aquarium fish but seldom shows good colour unless kept in heavily planted tanks. Spawns amongst fine leafed plants.

Neil Armstrong

## Spangled Perch
### *Leiopotherapon unicolor*

**Other Names:** Spangled Grunter

**Identification:** Total length 300 mm, common at 180 mm. Silver-grey body with numerous orange-brown spots on back, head and sides. Fins dusky in adults. Juveniles to 60 mm often show black stripe on bottom lobe of tail fin.

Neil Armstrong

**Habitat and Range:** Deep pools amongst boulders and aquatic plants. Widespread in drainages across northern half of Australia.

**Notes:** Larger specimens often caught on lines; good eating. Very aggressive fish which should be kept alone in aquaria. Spawn after heavy rain in spring and summer. Egg-scatterers.

## Mouth Almighty *Glossamia aprion gillii*

Neil Armstrong

**Identification:** Total length 160 mm, common at 120 mm. Silvery-cream body with irregular blotches and spots of brown and tan, fins dusky brown. Large mouth and prominent eye.

**Habitat and Range:** Shelters in dense stands of aquatic plants adjacent to pools and areas of deep water. From Fitzroy River, Qld to Clarence River, NSW.

**Notes:** One of the few mouth-brooding fishes found in Australia. Female lays eggs in mass which male takes into his mouth and broods for about 14 days. During this time the male takes no food. A voracious predator of small fish.

## Freshwater Mullet *Myxus petardi*

Gunther Schmida

**Identification:** Total length 800 mm, common at 300 mm. Greenish-black on back, becoming silver on sides and belly; golden eye and dusky fins. Typical mullet shape with first dorsal fin set well back.

**Habitat and Range:** Pools with areas of shallow water over sandy bottom. Feeds in schools on algae and small aquatic animals. Coastal Qld and NSW from Burnett River to Georges River.

**Notes:** Occasionally caught on lines; often has muddy flavour. Can be kept in well aerated aquarium where it takes a variety of foods.

Ray Leggett

## Striped Gudgeon
### *Gobiomorphus australis*

**Identification:** Total length 200 mm, common at 130 mm. Back dark grey to brown, paling to cream-brown sides and belly. Dark brown stripes on side with prominent stripe running from eye to gill plate. Small brown spots form narrow bands on dorsal and tail fins. Young fish often have bluish edge to fins.

**Habitat and Range:** Common in small, clear flowing coastal streams within range. Woodgate, Qld to south-eastern Vic.

**Notes:** Like most gudgeons, is a nocturnal hunter of small fish and crustaceans; has night pattern of irregular brown blotches to blend with surrounds.

Neil Armstrong

## Carp Gudgeon *Hypseleotris compressa*

**Other Names:** Empire Fish

**Identification:** Total length 110 mm, common at 70 mm. Female and juvenile — olive-brown body with clear fins. Male in breeding colours — brown back and sides with deep pink flush on belly; anal and dorsal fins show wide bands of red, black and blue. Adult male has deeper body than female.

**Habitat and Range:** Stays close to and hides within aquatic plants and tangled snags. Feeds mainly on fish and aquatic insects. Eastern and northern coast of Australia from Victorian border to Kimberley region and Murchison River, WA.

**Notes:** Make attractive aquarium specimens which readily spawn in spring. Fry are extremely small and difficult to raise. Substrate spawner.

Neil Armstrong

## Firetail Gudgeon *Hypseleotris galii*

**Identification:** Total length 60 mm, common at 35 mm. Bronze to grey body with margins of dorsal and anal fins pale red. Tail deeper red. Females and young show less colour.

**Habitat and Range:** Common amongst snags and aquatic plants in most rivers, creeks and dams within its range. From central coastal Qld to Eden, NSW.

**Notes:** Substrate spawners; male develops large fatty hump on the top of head before breeding. Have been bred in aquaria.

## Western Carp Gudgeon
*Hypseleotris klunzingeri*

Gunther Schmida

**Identification:** Total length 65 mm, common at 40 mm. Yellow-grey back with lighter sides; dorsal and anal fins have orange-red outer band edged in pale blue. Adult male has brighter colours and in the breeding season develops hump of fat on head.

**Habitat and Range:** Stay amongst aquatic plants and under banks of pools and streams. Coastal Qld and NSW from Fitzroy River to Hunter River; also Murray-Darling drainage system.

**Notes:** Some colour variation within range. Make good aquarium specimens. Spawn on broad leaves of aquatic plants, rocks or cleaned driftwood. Male drives female away from area after spawning and fans eggs while protecting them from predators. Eggs hatch in 6 to 7 days.

## Purple Spotted Gudgeon
*Mogurnda adspersa*

Gunther Schmida

**Identification:** Total length 130 mm, common at 90 mm. Brown on back and upper sides with a wide band of blue from gills to base of tail overlaid with tan, orange and purple spots. Dorsal and anal fins dusky with tan and red spots; yellow to orange edge on dorsal fins; anal fin edged in blue.

**Habitat and Range:** Slow flowing pools where they hide within aquatic plants or under snags and ledges during daylight. Nocturnal feeders preying on fish, crustaceans and aquatic insects. Coastal Qld, NSW and Murray-Darling drainage system.

**Notes:** Female lays a patch of eggs on boulder or driftwood. Male guards eggs until they hatch. Fry are free swimming. Easily bred in aquariums; ideal for studies on parental care of fishes.

# Lungfish

Dr Anne Kemp

The lungfish was first described in 1870 and has long been considered a remarkable animal. As its common name suggests it possesses a lung as well as gills, but it only breathes air frequently when it is particularly active (eg feeding at night or during the breeding season). Under normal circumstances it breathes through its gills like any other fish.

Gunther Schmida

## Queensland Lungfish
*Neoceratodus forsteri*

**Other Names:** Djelleh, Ceratodus, Australian Lungfish

**Identification:** Length up to 1200 mm. Brown on back and sides, salmon pink belly. Individuals often have patches of dark, almost black, pigment. Juveniles less distinctly marked with mottled skin of variable colours — mostly brown, dull green, occasionally yellow on back with muddy pink bellies. Hatchlings speckled red-brown on back with green of yolk contained in gut and showing through ventral skin. Large overlapping scales, skin slimy. Adults have small bluish eyes; in young hatchlings eyes are relatively large and patterned in black and silver. Pectoral and pelvic fins paddle-shaped. Eel-like tail combines dorsal, caudal and anal fin.

**Habitat and Range:** Prefers deep, slow flowing waterholes with dense banks of aquatic plants along edges. Rivers and lakes of south-eastern Qld between Albert and Burnett Rivers.

**Notes:** Spawn in spring and early summer among aquatic plants and fine tree rootlets along river banks. Juveniles seldom seen; believed to spend early years hiding in dense stands of aquatic plants. Totally protected — permit required to take or keep lungfish in an aquarium.

# Exotic Fish

Rolly McKay

Exotic freshwater fish are common in Brisbane's urban waterways. There are only a few streams in pristine areas that do not contain one or more alien species. The most widespread exotic fish is now the Mosquitofish, introduced to much of coastal Queensland by military personnel and State health agencies to control mosquito larvae in standing bodies of water. Unfortunately it is no more efficient at mosquito larvae control than a number of native surface-feeding fishes once common in the Greater Brisbane Region.

For an explanation of terms consult the diagram at the beginning of the **Freshwater Fish** chapter on p. 121.

## Mosquitofish  *Gambusia affinis*

**Identification:** Head flattened above; single dorsal fin; tail finely speckled; male with anal fin modified to form copulatory organ. Mature female with posterior part of abdomen dark. Bears live young.

**Habitat and Range:** Widespread. Very common in urban waterways.

Queensland Museum

## Swordtail  *Xiphophorus helleri*

**Identification:** Head flattened above; single dorsal fin; male with copulatory organ and lower rays of tail produced to form long "sword". Red or green. Bears live young.

**Habitat and Range:** Common. Range expanding.

Queensland Museum

## Platy  *Xiphophorus maculatus*

**Identification:** Head flattened above; single dorsal fin; male with copulatory organ. Red, orange or yellow, frequently with black tail. Bears live young.

**Habitat and Range:** Common in restricted areas only.

Queensland Museum

Queensland Museum

## Guppy  *Poecilia reticulata*

**Identification:** Similar to mosquitofish, but male usually has brightly coloured spots on body and tail. Female has reticulate pattern on scales. Bears live young.

**Habitat and Range:** Widespread from northern coastal Queensland to Brisbane where it is uncommon due to colder winters.

Queensland Museum

## Tilapia  *Oreochromis mossambicus*

**Identification:** Single nostril on each side of snout; 15–16 dorsal spines; teeth in brush-like band; 3–4 dark blotches on sides may be present.

**Habitat and Range:** Freshwater and estuaries in Cairns, Townsville and Brisbane. In local dams near Brisbane. Range expanding. Declared noxious under the Fisheries Act.

Queensland Museum

## Blue Acara  *Aequidens pulcher*

**Identification:** Single nostril on each side of snout; scattered blue flecks on head and body; often with indistinct dark bands or a black spot above pectoral fin tip.

**Habitat and Range:** Popular aquarium fish found in only one Brisbane creek. May not survive winter.

Queensland Museum

## Goldfish  *Carassius auratus*

**Identification:** Large blunt head with small mouth. Long dorsal fin. Wild stocks usually revert from golden-bronze to olive-green and lack the bright colours and fancy fins of aquarium-bred fish.

**Habitat and Range:** Widespread, but not abundant in Brisbane creeks.

# Intertidal Zone Fish

Jeff Johnson

More than 100 species of fish can be found in the intertidal zone — the area between the high and low tide marks of mainland Moreton Bay and the Brisbane River. The area encompasses a rich and diverse variety of habitats including mangroves, seagrass beds, rock pools, mud and sand flats and reefs. The fish found here must be hardy to survive extremes of temperature, salinity and turbidity caused by tidal movement and periodic freshwater run-off from rainfall. They are also among the first to be subjected to the effects of pollutants such as industrial effluent washing through stormwater drains.

Some species utilise the intertidal zone as a nursery for larval and juvenile fish while others such as gobies may occupy them throughout their complete lifecycle. While many of these fish are seldom seen due to their small size, cryptic behaviour or nocturnal habits they are often very common where suitable habitat exists.

It is possible to collect some of the species described here using small mesh nets, scoops or minnow traps but for regulations detailing permitted collecting apparatus, the Queensland Boating and Fisheries Patrol should be consulted.

The fish described here represent only a small selection of those found in the intertidal zone. For more information contact the Ichthyology section of the Queensland Museum.

Two sizes are given in the species descriptions — the maximum length, followed by an average length. For an explanation of terms, consult the diagram at the beginning of the **Freshwater Fish** chapter on p. 121.

Queensland Museum

## Striped Catfish *Plotosus lineatus*

**Identification:** Length 900 mm, 140 mm. Eight barbels around mouth; chocolate-brown body with conspicuous cream stripes, fading in larger specimens.

**Habitat and Range:** Bays, estuaries and reefs, often sheltering among rocks and logs. Large individuals sometimes occupy burrows. Common throughout Moreton Bay and lower reaches of Brisbane River. Northern Australia from Sydney to Esperance, WA.

**Notes:** Aggregations of young fish often form compact spherical pods — about 1 m diameter. These may contain more than 1000 individuals. Dorsal and pectoral fins include three serrated venomous spines which can inflict a very painful wound.

Queensland Museum

## Barred Fortesque *Centropogon australis*

**Identification:** Length 150 mm, 75 mm. Head with strong spines above upper jaw and on opercles; dorsal fin with 16 spines. Body with five dark bands including one on tail base and another across middle of tail.

**Habitat and Range:** Common among rocks and weeds in bays and lower part of estuaries. Often taken at Myora, Peel Island, and rock walls in Brisbane River. Mallacoota, Vic. to Hervey Bay, Qld.

**Notes:** Dorsal spines venomous, may produce painful sting. Adapts readily to aquarium conditions; voracious feeder on live shrimp and small fishes. Capable of rapid colour changes according to mood or background.

Queensland Museum

## Yellow Perchlet *Ambassis marianus*

**Identification:** Length 110 mm, 65 mm. Body silvery-yellow to opaque; dorsal fin between second and third spines blackish; other fins translucent. Several small spines on head near upper margin of eyes.

**Habitat and Range:** Common in mangrove creeks and around jetty piles, found as far upstream as Colleges Crossing in Brisbane River. Narooma, NSW to about Bundaberg.

**Notes:** Marine species commonly penetrating short distances into freshwater. Often moves in over Moreton Bay beaches with high tide. Usually taken by fishermen using bait nets and drop scoops intended for hardyheads and garfish. Worthwhile aquarium species especially if kept in small groups.

## Estuary Cod *Epinephelus coioides*

**Identification:** Length 240 cm, 50 cm. Rusty brown to orange spots slightly smaller than pupil of eye scattered over head and body. Five indistinct dark bands may also be present.

**Habitat and Range:** Throughout Moreton Bay and lower Brisbane River in estuaries, reefs and deep holes, usually where some cover is available. Northern Australia from Seal Rocks, NSW to Rottnest Island, WA.

Queensland Museum

**Notes:** Very large edible species familiar to most fishermen. Juveniles often escape notice in rock pools and tidal flats. Highly predatory, all except small individuals unsuitable for community aquaria.

## Diamond Fish *Monodactylus argenteus*

**Other Names:** Butter bream

**Identification:** Length 270 mm, 150 mm. Distinguished by silvery diamond-shaped body and black-tipped dorsal and anal fins. Narrow vertical bars through eye and rear of gill cover gradually fade in large specimens. Small juveniles can be almost entirely black except for tips of fins.

**Habitat and Range:** Commonly found in shoals around rocky outcrops, harbours, wharves, jetties and fallen mangrove trees in Moreton Bay and lower estuaries. Northern Australia from Jervis Bay, NSW to Dampier, WA.

Queensland Museum

**Notes:** Reputation as bait-stealer — feeds readily on chopped prawns, squid or fish. Juveniles, occasionally entering freshwater, resemble fallen leaves and are prized acquisitions for aquarists.

Queensland Museum

## Tiger Mullet *Liza argentea*

**Identification:** Length 450 mm, 200 mm. Gold spot on rear of operculum; wedge-shaped snout; 10 rather than eight to nine anal rays.

**Habitat and Range:** Common in lower Brisbane River and beaches and tidal flats of Moreton Bay. Southern Australia from Hervey Bay, Qld to Kalbarri, WA.

**Notes:** Often targeted by anglers burleying with bread and castnetters from jetties such as at Woody Point. One of five species of mullet occurring in region.

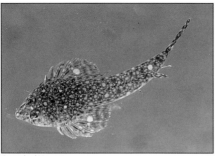

Queensland Museum

## Chalk-spot Stinkfish
*Callionymus macdonaldi*

**Identification:** Length 250 mm, 120 mm. Body scaleless; gill cover with strong preopercular spine armed with an outer forward-directed serration and three or four serrations along inner margin. Very small mouth; chalky white spots on dorsal surface of body. Male has slightly higher first dorsal fin and different colour pattern to first dorsal and anal fins.

**Habitat and Range:** Sometimes found semi-buried in silty or fine sandy bottoms after being stranded by receding tide. Commonly taken near mouth of Brisbane River. Central NSW north to Darwin, NT.

**Notes:** Often mistaken for juvenile Flathead. Regularly caught by cast-netters and trawlers.

Queensland Museum

## Striped Oyster Blenny
*Omobranchus punctatus*

**Identification:** Length 110 mm, 65 mm. Distinct dark patch on upper sides behind head; five or six horizontal stripes from rear of head to about half length of body, sometimes interposed by fainter vertical lines to form a rectangular honeycomb pattern.

**Habitat and Range:** Very common around mangroves and intertidal rocky outcrops from rock walls of Bulwer Island, Brisbane River to foreshore of Redcliffe and Cleveland. Often occupies holes in mangrove logs created by marine molluscs known as shipworms. Northern Australia from Tweed Heads to Shark Bay, WA.

**Notes:** Rare closely related species, Barred Mangrove Blenny, (*Omobranchus verticalis*), distinguished by presence of dark spot between first and second dorsal spines and 10 to 12 vertical bars on body.

## Rotund Oyster Blenny
### *Omobranchus rotundiceps*

Queensland Museum

**Identification:** Length 75 mm, 55 mm. Narrow, oblique, light blue to white lines on body; small dark patch on opercle behind eye; no crest behind head; central dark smudge in rear of dorsal fin. Mature male more distinctly marked and with some caudal rays prolonged as filaments.

**Habitat and Range:** Usually found close to low water mark, often inside dead shells. Fairly common among oyster and mussel encrusted rocks on foreshores such as Bishop Island and Woody Point. Northern Australia from Sydney to Fremantle, WA.

**Notes:** Pairs make active, aquarium subjects. If provided with suitable abandoned shells, they may be observed darting incessantly in and out of adopted homes.

## Spotted Oyster Blenny
### *Omobranchus anolius*

Queensland Museum

**Identification:** Length 80 mm, 60 mm. Head and body to above pectoral fin with several oblique dark bars; black spot on pectoral fin base and numerous small black dots peppered on body; several thin white chevrons and lines often present on sides. Male distinguished from female and juvenile by prominent fleshy crest on top of head and filamentous rays to caudal and rear of dorsal fins.

**Habitat and Range:** Occasionally found on tidal oyster and mussel encrusted rocks in Moreton Bay. Eastern Australia from Spencer Gulf, SA, to Gulf of Carpentaria.

**Notes:** Eggs usually laid in dead oyster shells in groups of about six and reputedly guarded by mated pairs.

Queensland Museum

## Bridled Goby *Arenigobius frenatus*

**Identification:** Length 180 mm, 80 mm. Two dusky bars on head — extending diagonally from eye to pectoral fin base; and from eye to just above pectoral fin base ending in a spot. Row of dark blotches along sides. Dorsal fins with yellow margins. Ventral fins joined at base to form single disc — characteristic of family Gobiidae. Male — more colourful, longer caudal fin with yellow flashes to centre and upper edge.

**Habitat and Range:** Occupies burrows beneath rocks and logs on silty or muddy tidal flats in Moreton Bay and lower Brisbane River estuary. Eastern Australia from Townsville, Qld to north-eastern Tas.

**Notes:** Pairs sometimes observed in shallow pools guarding entrance to their burrows.

Queensland Museum

## Saddle-backed Goby *Drombus* sp.

**Identification:** Length 70 mm, 50 mm. Ventrals joined to form single fin; body generally dark with lighter mottling. Often with four creamish saddles on dorsal surface — first and second at origin of spinous and soft dorsal fins, third at middle of second dorsal and fourth at base of caudal fin. Dorsal and caudal fins with black speckling. Pectoral fin with dark smudge near base.

**Habitat and Range:** Under rocks and logs in lower Brisbane River estuary and rocky foreshore such as at Redcliffe Peninsula. NSW and southern Qld to at least Caloundra.

**Notes:** In Moreton Bay often found in cohabitation with Kreffts Goby, (see p. 139), from which it can be distinguished by lack of silky free rays to upper part of pectoral fin.

Queensland Museum

## Eyed-tail Mangrove Goby
### *Mugilogobius stigmaticus*

**Identification:** Length 50 mm, 35 mm. Ventrals joined to form a single fin; head with bulbous cheeks and four curved stripes radiating from eye. Body with patchwork of alternating dark blotches; two dark eye spots on caudal fin base. First dorsal fin with black basal spot and pale margin.

**Habitat and Range:** Common in mangrove-lined tidal pools in creeks and rivers flowing into Moreton Bay. NSW and southern Qld.

**Notes:** Unsuitable for display due to preference for very muddy substrate. Probably an active destroyer of mosquito larvae.

## Kreffts Goby *Bathygobius kreffti*

**Identification:** Length 80 mm, 55 mm. Ventrals joined to form single fin; some individual rays of upper pectoral fin separated to form silk-like, free filaments. Colour markings on body highly variable — usually mottled greenish-brown on lighter background, sometimes with five or six creamish saddles across dorsal surface. Diffuse blue-green spots or lines of varying intensity may be present on middle of sides.

Queensland Museum

**Habitat and Range:** Common near low tide mark on shelly or rocky coastal reefs such as at Woody Point. Prefers established, encrusted reefs. Eden, NSW to Caloundra, Qld.

**Notes:** This genus makes up one of the most dominant groups of fishes in the rocky littoral zone of Qld.

## Crested Mud Goby
*Cryptocentrus cristatus*

**Identification:** Length 120 mm, 85 mm. Ventrals joined to form single fin; top of head between eyes and origin of dorsal fin has low fleshy crest; first dorsal high, its rays becoming longer and filamentous with age, second dorsal with several rows of dark blue spots. Body dark brown above, grading into rusty reddish-brown below with numerous narrow, wavy and broken blue vertical bars.

Queensland Museum

**Habitat and Range:** Found among mangrove roots and in burrows under rocks and logs on muddy tidal banks in lower part of estuaries. From Sydney north to at least Cairns.

**Notes:** Male has crest, fins and colour more well-developed than female. Can be very attractive aquarium subject, feeding on prawns, mussels and fish. As colours are most brilliant on lower sides of fish, aquaria must be set up appropriately with steeply ascending substrate and partial cover.

Queensland Museum

## Blue-spotted Goby
### *Pseudogobius olorum*

**Identification:** Length 75 mm, 40 mm. Ventrals joined to form single fin; head rounded; eyes close together; mouth slightly underslung. Body freckled with black spots and blotches; dorsal and caudal fins speckled with black spots. Some mid-lateral spots, sometimes bluish.

**Habitat and Range:** Very common in tidal pools and estuaries penetrating into freshwater. Wide variety of habitats from bare muddy bottoms in mangroves to rock pools in coastal reefs and freshwater weed beds near upper limit of tidal influence. Southern WA, SA, Vic., Tas., NSW to central Qld.

**Notes:** East coast population varies from those on south and west coasts and may be separate undescribed species. Adapts readily to aquarium conditions but is unpopular as it is neither colourful nor active.

Queensland Museum

## Large Mouth Goby
### *Redigobius macrostoma*

**Identification:** Length 45 mm, 30 mm. Ventrals joined to form single fin; head and body with small alternating dark blotches; dorsal and caudal fins speckled with black spots. Rear of first dorsal fin with black patch near base. Female with angular snout and small mouth, extending to about anterior margin of eye. Mature male with rounded snout and head deeper; mouth often very large, extending past posterior margin of eye; dorsal and anal fin rays longer than in female. Juvenile darker with two prominent dark spots near caudal base.

**Habitat and Range:** Found in Moreton Bay near mouths of creeks and rivers, penetrating upstream into freshwater. Moreton Bay to Vic. and north-eastern Tas.

**Notes:** The similar Bug-eyed Goby (*Redigobius bikolanus*) also occurs in the area and is reported to sometimes breed in freshwater as evidenced by landlocked populations in Lake Manchester. Small but interesting species suitable for aquaria.

## Flathead Gudgeon  *Butis butis*

Queensland Museum

**Identification:** Length 180 mm, 85 mm. Pair of ventral fins present; eyes widely separated; dorsal surface of head broadly flattened; mouth large, just reaching to level of eye. Head and body greyish-brown to black; often crimson margins to dorsal, anal and upper caudal fins. Pectorals with single or double red-edged black spot at base.

**Habitat and Range:** Fairly common throughout creeks and estuaries, extending into freshwater on occasions. Prefers mangrove creeks with fallen and overhanging logs and branches among which it shelters. Northern Australia south to northern NSW.

**Notes:** Interesting habit of suspending itself vertically or upside down on sunken weeds, rocks and branches. This, and ability to rapidly change colour make it an intriguing aquarium subject.

## Small-eyed Gudgeon
### *Prionobutis microps*

Queensland Museum

**Identification:** Length 230 mm, 120 mm. Eyes very small and widely spaced; mouth and scales relatively large. Pectoral, second dorsal, anal and caudal fins with numerous narrow, wavy dark bands. First dorsal fin is dusky, sometimes with yellowish blotches. Head and body dark brown clouded with lighter blotches.

**Habitat and Range:** Occasionally taken by beam trawlers, anglers and bait-netters in Brisbane River from mouth as far upstream as at least Jindalee, on muddy bottoms. Northern Australia from Moreton Bay to Broome, WA.

**Notes:** A sluggish species feeding voraciously on prawns and small fish. Does not appear to adapt well to aquarium conditions.

Queensland Museum

## Common Toado *Tetractenos hamiltoni*

**Identification:** Length 150 mm, 100 mm. Skin scaleless; single dorsal fin; caudal fin rounded. Upper body dark grey-brown with numerous close-set small black spots and several dark bands across back. Middle of sides and head below eye with about 12 to 14 short black bars. Underside creamish-white.

**Habitat and Range:** Very common throughout tidal flats of Moreton Bay and lower Brisbane River. Merimbula, NSW to at least Townsville.

**Notes:** Very conspicuous. Often found in shallow tidal pools. Flesh poisonous.

Queensland Museum

## Banded Toado *Marilyna pleurosticta*

**Identification:** Length 170 mm, 110 mm. Skin scaleless; single dorsal fin; caudal fin rounded. Upper body light grey to brown; four dark grey or black bands across back — first between eyes and others ending on middle of sides in more distinct black spot. Lower half of body pale.

**Habitat and Range:** Found throughout Moreton Bay and lower estuaries on muddy tidal flats and banks. Northern NSW to at least Cape York.

**Notes:** Poisonous. Prefers mangrove creeks; less frequently encountered than more conspicuous Common Toado, see above.

Queensland Museum

## Scaly-tailed Toado
*Torquigener squammicauda*

**Identification:** Length 150 mm, 85 mm. Skin scaleless; single dorsal fin; caudal fin rounded. Upper body grey to brown; distinctive dark stripe along middle of sides from above pectoral fin base to caudal fin base. No vertical stripes under eye. Body below lateral stripe pale.

**Habitat and Range:** Found on sandy tidal flats of Moreton Bay and Brisbane River mouth. Wattamolla, NSW to Yeppoon, Qld.

**Notes:** Can sometimes be seen nipping off legs of soldier crabs that have failed to burrow into sand quickly enough on rising tide. Flesh poisonous.

# Frogs

Gregory V. Czechura

Thirty-six kinds of native frogs make the Greater Brisbane Region their home. In addition, the now infamous Cane Toad has been deliberately introduced into the region and at least one species native to Queensland's Wet Tropics has been accidently introduced in plant shipments.

Most of the native frogs are common, but a few have declined as their swamps and ponds have been drained and filled. The Salmon-striped Frog and the Green-stripe Frog are two cases in point. Another species, the Southern Dayfrog, may be extinct. The demise of these and related species from further north appears to be part of an ever-expanding web of amphibian declines and extinctions worldwide.

All is not gloom and doom however. The Australian Marsupial Frog has recently been discovered in the same rainforests of the D'Aguilar Range once frequented by the Southern Dayfrog, while the "mysterious" Green-thighed Frog has been making sporadic appearances throughout Brisbane. These discoveries hold in them the hope that the "missing" species may reappear sometime, as well as indicating that other frog species may be admitted to the list of "Brisbane frogs" in the future.

To assist the non-specialist, local frogs in this guide have been grouped according to physical similarities. Frogs are extremely popular among amateur naturalists and are one of the major areas of public inquiry at the Queensland Museum. To this end, the species descriptions here are a comprehensive guide to frogs of the Greater Brisbane Region.

## Identifying Frogs

### Green treefrogs

Medium to large (40–100 mm), blunt-snouted, usually bright green frogs with large expanded discs on tips of fingers and toes.

    **Green Treefrog** *Litoria caerulea* **p. 146**
    **Southern Orange-eyed Treefrog** *Litoria chloris* **p. 146**
    **Graceful Treefrog** *Litoria gracilenta* **p. 147**
    **Cascade Treefrog** *Litoria pearsoniana* **p. 147**

### Sedgefrogs and dayfrogs

Small (25–30 mm) sharp-snouted frogs with expanded discs on tips of fingers and toes.

    **Eastern Sedgefrog** *Litoria fallax* **p. 148**
    **Cooloola Sedgefrog** *Litoria cooloolensis* **p. 148**
    **Wallum Sedgefrog** *Litoria olongburensis* **p. 149**
    **Southern Dayfrog** *Taudactylus diurnus* **p. 149**

### Emerald-spotted treefrogs

Medium-sized (60–65 mm), mottled, rough-skinned frogs with blunt snouts and large expanded discs on tips of fingers and toes.

    **Emerald-spotted Treefrog** *Litoria peronii* **p. 150**
    **Laughing Treefrog** *Litoria tyleri* **p. 150**

### Small brownish treefrogs and nursery-frogs

Small to medium-sized (40–45 mm), brownish to reddish-purple, blunt-snouted frogs with expanded discs on tips of fingers and toes.

    **Bleating Treefrog** *Litoria dentata* **p. 151**
    **Naked Treefrog** *Litoria rubella* **p. 151**
    **Common Nursery-frog** *Cophixalus ornatus* **p. 152**

### Green-thighed Frog

Medium-sized (40 mm) white-lipped frog with pale bordered broad black band from snout to side of body and brilliant blue or green on hind surface of thighs.

    **Green-thighed Frog** *Litoria brevipalmata* **p. 152**

### Rocketfrogs

Small to medium-sized (35–50 mm), sharp-snouted (when viewed from above and in profile) frogs with a dark stripe from nostril through eye to at least level of arm, long powerful legs, tiny discs on tips of fingers and toes.

    **Striped Rocketfrog** *Litoria nasuta* **p. 153**
    **Broad-palmed Rocketfrog** *Litoria latopalmata* **p. 153**
    **Wallum Rocketfrog** *Litoria freycineti* **p. 154**

### Stony-creek Frog

Medium-sized to large (45–70 mm) sharp-snouted frog with dark stripe that runs from nostril through eye and from eye over ear-disc to shoulder, long powerful legs, small discs on tips of fingers and toes. Usually found along permanent watercourses.

    **Stony-creek Frog** *Litoria lesueuri* **p. 154**

### *Green-stripe Frog*

Large (80 mm) slender frog with pointed snout and prominent green stripe down middle of back.

**Green-stripe Frog**  *Litoria alboguttata*  **p. 155**

### *Marshfrogs*

Medium-sized to large (45–70 mm) striped or spotted frogs with snouts that are rounded in profile and pointed or rounded when viewed from above, indistinct ear-discs and fingers and toes lack discs on tips.

**Striped Marshfrog**  *Limnodynastes peronii*  **p. 155**
**Salmon-striped Frog**  *Limnodynastes salmini*  **p. 156**
**Spotted Marshfrog**  *Limnodynastes tasmaniensis*  **p. 156**

### *Tusked Frog*

Medium-sized (40–50 mm), dark, "boof-headed" frog with black and white belly and bright red patches in groin and on lower leg.

**Tusked Frog**  *Adelotus brevis*  **p. 157**

### *Pobblebonks and burrowing frogs*

Medium-sized to large (45–75 mm) snub-nosed, stocky, round frogs. Favour temporary waters or permanent swamps.

**Ornate Burrowing-frog**  *Limnodynastes ornatus*  **p. 157**
**Scarlet-sided Pobblebonk**  *Limnodynastes terraereginae* **p. 158**

### *Barred-frogs*

Large to very large (80–115 mm) flat-headed frogs that have long powerful legs. Favour rivers and creeks.

**Great Barred-frog**  *Mixophyes fasciolatus*  **p. 158**
**Giant Barred-frog**  *Mixophyes iteratus*  **p. 159**

### *Broodfrogs*

Small (35 mm) toad-like frogs with black and white marbling on underside, reddish crowns or backs and unwebbed fingers and toes.

**Copper-backed Broodfrog**  *Pseudophryne raveni*  **p. 159**
**Great Brown Broodfrog**  *Pseudophryne major*  **p. 160**

### *Marsupial frog and froglets*

Very small to small (20–30 mm) greyish to brownish frogs with pointed heads and unwebbed fingers and toes.

**Australian Marsupial Frog**  *Assa darlingtoni*  **p. 160**
**Beeping Froglet**  *Crinia parinsignifera*  **p. 161**
**Clicking Froglet**  *Crinia signifera*  **p. 161**
**Wallum Froglet**  *Crinia tinnula* **p. 162**

### *Gungans*

Small (30 mm) toad-like, short-limbed frogs with red or orange spots in groin and on hind surface of thigh; fingers and toes unwebbed or with only traces of webbing.

**Sandy Gungan**  *Uperoleia fusca*  **p. 162**
**Eastern Gungan**  *Uperoleia laevigata*  **p. 163**
**Chubby Gungan**  *Uperoleia rugosa*  **p. 163**

Queensland Museum

## Green Treefrog *Litoria caerulea*

**Identification:** Length 100 mm. Green or sometimes light brown treefrog with thick fleshy skin between eyes and shoulders; snout short and rounded; slightly "dreamy" facial expression when viewed head-on; irregular white stripe or series of spots from corner of mouth to forearm; white belly. Fingers about one-third webbed, toes about three-quarters webbed.

**Habitat and Range:** Found throughout region; may be locally common in some places. Often found sheltering in toilets, downpipes, brickwork, etc. Northern and eastern Australia.

**Mating Call:** Deep resonant "crow-k".

**Eggs:** Laid in large clumps on surface of water; progressively sink to bottom.

**Tadpoles:** Very large dark green or dark grey-green tadpoles.

Queensland Museum

## Southern Orange-eyed Treefrog
### *Litoria chloris*

**Identification:** Length 65 mm. Green treefrog with large reddish-orange eyes and green lips; forearm mainly green; white to lemon-yellow belly; hind side of thighs purplish or brownish. Fingers almost fully webbed, toes fully webbed.

**Habitat and Range:** Associated with rainforest and tall open forest. Coastal central Qld to Sydney.

**Mating Call:** Rising, rather musical, series of "arc-arc-arcs" followed by softer trills.

**Eggs:** Laid in loose mat, usually among aquatic vegetation.

**Tadpoles:** Dark tadpoles reaching 60 mm.

## Graceful Treefrog *Litoria gracilenta*

**Identification:** Length 45 mm. Bright green and yellow treefrog with orange eyes and yellow lips; green patch on forearm surrounded by yellow; belly yellow; hind surface of thighs rich purplish or purple-brown. Fingers almost fully webbed, toes fully webbed.

Queensland Museum

**Habitat and Range:** Very common throughout lowlands. Often found clinging to leaves with legs tucked tightly to body and eyes closed. Favours ponds, swamps and temporarily flooded situations. Common garden animal. Coastal eastern Australia from Cape York to about Sydney.

**Mating Call:** Long, drawn-out, moaning "aaaare".

**Eggs:** Laid singly or in small clumps.

**Tadpoles:** Dark, fairly uniformly coloured tadpoles.

## Cascade Treefrog *Litoria pearsoniana*

**Identification:** Length 40 mm. Mainly green to brownish treefrog with gold stripe from nostril through eye (if brownish, then has green area between gold stripe and top of head); brown or gold flecks may be present on back; white belly; hind surface of thighs and groin brick red. Fingers webbed only at base, toes about three-quarters webbed.

Queensland Museum

**Habitat and Range:** Largely restricted to mountain streams in rainforest. Seems to have declined in certain parts of its range. Shelters under stones along streams. Calls from low vegetation along water's edge. Coastal southern Qld and coastal NSW.

**Mating Call:** Rising, drawn-out and wavering "eeeeak" followed immediately by clipped "chick-chick".

**Eggs:** Eggs laid in firm clump attached to rocks, debris or aquatic plants in rainforest streams.

**Tadpoles:** Small, dark, high-finned tadpoles.

Queensland Museum

## Eastern Sedgefrog  *Litoria fallax*

**Identification:** Length 25 mm. Green, pale brown or green-sided brown frog with white stripe from jaw to shoulder and dark stripe from nostril through eye; back plain or bronzy patch with scattered dark flecks; underside white; ear disc brown; hind surface of thighs orange. Fingers with rounded toe discs and almost no webbing, toes about three-quarters webbed.

**Habitat and Range:** Smallest and most common treefrog in region. Only frog to be found in many suburban gardens; shelters in plants such as bromeliads and banana trees. Often responds to plant watering by giving short calls. Coastal northern Qld to southern NSW.

**Mating Call:** Series of sharp, high-pitched, "r-e-e-e-ks" often followed by one or more clipped, stacatto "pips".

**Eggs:** Laid singly or in small mats on surface of water.

**Tadpoles:** Dark-tailed tadpoles with pale or highly patterned bodies.

Queensland Museum

## Cooloola Sedgefrog  *Litoria cooloolensis*

**Identification:** Length 30 mm. Dark-spotted, green frog with diffuse dark stripe from nostril to eye and cream stripe below eye; underside cream; ear disc green; hind surface of thigh orange with upper purplish-brown stripe. Fingers with rounded toe discs and about one-third webbed, toes almost fully webbed.

**Habitat and Range:** "Acid frog" — adapted to acidic waters of coastal lowlands (ie wallum). Restricted to coastal south-eastern Qld and islands.

**Mating Call:** Virtually identical to Eastern Sedgefrog (see above) but more highly pitched.

**Eggs:** Laid singly or in small mats floating on water surface.

**Tadpoles:** Dark-tailed tadpoles with pale or highly patterned bodies.

## Wallum Sedgefrog *Litoria olongburensis*

**Identification:** Length 25 mm. Light brown or green frog with dark stripe bordered below by cream streak running from nostril to flank; underside cream with throat peppered with brown; groin orange and purple; hind surface of thighs orange and purple or orange and blue. Fingers with rounded toe discs and webbed at base, toes about half webbed.

**Habitat and Range:** "Acid frog" — adapted to acidic waters of coastal lowlands. Known from Moreton, Bribie and Stradbroke Islands and remnant wallum areas mainly along northern Moreton Bay. Usually found in dense reed beds. Restricted to coastal south-eastern Qld and northern NSW.

**Mating Call:** Drawn-out, rising, wavering "reeeek".

**Eggs:** As for preceding two species.

**Tadpoles:** Highly patterned or uniformly pallid tadpoles.

D. Milledge (Nature Focus)

## Southern Dayfrog *Taudactylus diurnus*

**Identification:** Length 30 mm. Grey or brown ground-dwelling frog with wedge-shaped discs on tips of toes and fingers. Light bar from eye to base of forearm; light-edged dark bar between eyes; back mottled with dark brown to black; H-shaped marking often present across shoulders; throat dark grey with yellow spots rest of underside cream to bluish either with grey spots or plain. Fingers and toes with wedge-shaped discs and unwebbed. Active during day.

**Habitat and Range:** Feared extinct. Mountain rainforest streams at Mt Nebo, Mt Glorious and Blackall and Conondale Ranges. Usually seen basking or hopping around rocks or vegetation along creeks or soaks.

**Mating Call:** Slow, barely audible clucking.

**Eggs:** Large eggs laid in gelatinous clumps under rocks.

**Tadpoles:** Tadpoles with round snouts and tail tips and umbrella shaped lips,

Owen Kelly

Queensland Museum

## Emerald-spotted Treefrog
### *Litoria peronii*

**Identification:** Length 65 mm. Whitish, grey, or brown rather rough-skinned treefrog with darker mottling and small iridescent green spots scattered over back; underside cream or yellowish with dark flecks on throat; groin and sides of thighs boldly mottled in black and bright yellow (often extends to toe webbing); pupil of eye bears a cross-shaped extension when contracted. Fingers about half webbed, toes almost fully webbed.

**Habitat and Range:** Usually found in trees or shrubs or suitable elevated structures. Common, but overlooked frog, better known for its call. Most habitats except extensive rainforest. South-eastern Australia.

**Mating Call:** Loud, penetrating rattle, reminiscent of a jackhammer or machine gun. Call only weakly descends, if at all.

**Eggs:** Laid singly or in small groups on surface of water or amongst aquatic vegetation.

**Tadpoles:** Active, shiny-green tadpoles with prominent, raised tail-fins and large jaws. Tend to hang at 45° in water.

## Laughing Treefrog   *Litoria tyleri*

**Identification:** Length 60 mm. Whitish to brownish rather rough-skinned treefrog with few or no iridescent green spots on back; pupil has no cross-shaped projections when contracted; underside cream or yellowish; groin and hind side of thighs yellow and dark brown to black. Fingers about half webbed, toes nearly fully webbed.

**Habitat and Range:** One of rarer Brisbane frogs, known mainly from Mt Glorious, Mt Nebo and Cleveland. Very patchily distributed; often overlooked because of similarities to preceding species. Coastal south-eastern Qld to southern NSW.

**Mating Call:** Downward series of "acks" that sound like laughter.

**Eggs:** Similar to Emerald-spotted Treefrog.

**Tadpoles:** Similar to Emerald-spotted Treefrog (see above).

Bruce Cowell

## Bleating Treefrog *Litoria dentata*

**Identification:** Length 45 mm. Blunt-snouted, pale brown treefrog with a three-lobed dark stripe down middle of back; dark brown stripe from nostril through eye to groin, darker and narrower towards head; lower sides and hidden parts of thighs may be lemon-yellow; underside yellowish; breeding males may have yellow, brown or black throat. Fingers about one-third webbed, toes about three-quarters webbed.

Eric Vanderduys

**Habitat and Range:** Commonly shelters in crevices of natural and artificial origin. Patchily distributed; usually western and southern suburbs.Coastal south-eastern Qld to southern NSW.

**Mating Call:** Loud, very high-pitched, wavering "creeeeee".

**Eggs:** Single or small groups floating on surface of water.

**Tadpoles:** Uniformly brown tadpoles.

## Naked Treefrog *Litoria rubella*

**Identification:** Length 40 mm. Whitish (almost transparent), grey, fawn, brown or purple-brown treefrog with pair of blackish patches on lower back (approximately in the kidney region). Broad dark band from eye to near groin; hind side of thighs brown dusted with tiny white spots; groin often lemon-yellow; underside white, cream or yellowish; throat may be grey to black in breeding males. Fingers have little webbing, toes about two-thirds webbed.

Eric Vanderduys

**Habitat and Range:** Commonly shelters in natural and artificial crevices. Breeds in permanent and temporary pond situations, including flooded paddocks. Patchily distributed; usually western and southern suburbs. Australia, except for southern coastal margin.

**Mating Call:** Slightly rising, regularly uttered "kreeeeee", similar to Bleating Treefrog but not as high-pitched.

**Eggs:** Laid in thin film on surface of water.

**Tadpoles:** Uniformly brown tadpoles.

Steve Wilson

## Common Nursery-frog
*Cophixalus ornatus*

**Identification:** Length 25 mm. Numerous warts and skin-folds on back; grey to sandy brown with yellow and black bar between eyes and similar W-shaped mark over shoulders; belly smooth and white to heavily mottled. Fingers and toes have large discs and are unwebbed.

**Habitat and Range:** Inhabitant of Queensland's Wet Tropics and occasionally found among live plants, especially epiphytes, transported to Brisbane.

**Mating Call:** Loud, ventriloqual, high-pitched metallic "cheep".

**Eggs:** Large, laid in moist moss or similar.

**Tadpoles:** No free-swimming tadpole, all development occurs within the egg.

Queensland Museum

## Green-thighed Frog
*Litoria brevipalmata*

**Identification:** Length 40 mm. White-lipped frog with weakly pointed snout; back rich brown or chocolate brown, pale-bordered, broad black band that almost encloses ear-disc runs from snout to flank; lower sides yellow with black spots; groin and hind surface of thighs bright blue or green and may have black spots in groin; white to yellow below. Finger and toe discs small; fingers unwebbed, toes about one-third webbed.

**Habitat and Range:** "Mysterious" frog — suddenly erupts in large numbers only to quickly disappear again. Known only from several southern and western suburbs. Patchy distribution through coastal south-eastern Qld to Sydney.

**Mating Call:** Harsh series of short quacks and clucks.

**Eggs:** Loose clumps of small eggs laid among vegetation in shallow water.

**Tadpoles:** Uniformly brown, high-finned tadpoles.

## Striped Rocketfrog *Litoria nasuta*

Queensland Museum

**Identification:** Length — females 50 mm, males 40 mm. Streamlined, sharp-snouted frog; pale grey to dark brown with longitudinal stripes and ridges or skin folds down middle of back; dark stripe from nostril broken by curved pale bar in front of eye; pale-rimmed ear disc enclosed by dark stripe; hind surface of thighs yellow with dark brown stripes; underside white. Fingers unwebbed, toes about half webbed.

**Habitat and Range:** Found in open forests, swamps, pastureland and suburban areas. Coastal northern and eastern Australia.

**Mating Call:** Slow chirps building to high-pitched chattering or quacking and slowly to few chirps at end of call.

**Eggs:** Laid singly or in small groups.

**Tadpoles:** Medium-sized dark brown tadpoles with high tail fins.

## Broad-palmed Rocketfrog
### *Litoria latopalmata*

Queensland Museum

**Identification:** Length — females 45 mm, males 35 mm. Streamlined, sharp-snouted frog; back pale grey to dark brown, sometimes with irregular darker markings; dark stripe from nostril in narrow contact with upper margin of front of eye, but mainly separated from it by pale curved bar; stripe encloses ear disc (not pale-rimmed); hind surface of thighs yellow with darker markings; sometimes thin dark line or spots along hind edge of lower leg and foot; underside white. Fingers and toes long; fingers unwebbed, toes almost fully webbed.

**Habitat and Range:** Open forest, woodland, streams, dams, swamps, temporary ponds and marshes. Central eastern Australia.

**Mating Call:** Series of quacks beginning slowly and accelerating into rapid chattering.

**Eggs:** Loose clumps of small eggs laid among vegetation in shallow water.

**Tadpoles:** Similar to Striped Rocketfrog (see above)

Queensland Museum

## Wallum Rocketfrog *Litoria freycineti*

**Identification:** Length — females 50 mm, males 45 mm. Streamlined, sharp-snouted frog; back grey-brown to dark brown with large dark warts and skin folds arranged more-or-less in "stripes" or lines of blotches; dark stripe from nostril broken by pale bar at front of eye, encloses pale-rimmed ear disc and breaks up near arm; hind surface of thighs light brown with large cream spots. Long fingers and toes; fingers unwebbed, toes about two-thirds webbed.

**Habitat and Range:** "Acid frog" — adapted to acidic waters of coastal lowlands. Known from Bribie, Moreton and Stradbroke Islands. Coastal south-eastern Qld to southern NSW.

**Mating Call:** Raucous, accelerating quacking call.

**Eggs:** Laid singly, in groups or mats on surface of water.

**Tadpoles:** Uniformly dark brown, high-finned tadpoles.

Queensland Museum

## Stony-creek Frog *Litoria lesueuri*

**Identification:** Length — females 70 mm, males 45 mm. Light grey to brown sharp-snouted frogs; back smooth with some irregular blotching; breeding males bright lemon-yellow; narrow black stripe from nostril through eye passes above ear disc to arm (section between nostril and eye may be obscure); groin yellow blotched with black; hind surface of thighs with black and yellow pattern; underside white. Fingers and toes long; fingers unwebbed, toes about three-quarters webbed.

**Habitat and Range:** Usually found in and around streams that have stony or rocky beds; variety of habitats.

**Mating Call:** Low whirring call, nearly inaudible.

**Eggs:** Laid in solid gelatinous mass on bottom of pools or in slow moving water.

**Tadpoles:** Dark tadpole with low tail fin.

## Green-stripeFrog *Litoria alboguttata*

Queensland Museum

**Identification:** Length 80 mm. Olive-brown frog with pointed snout and prominent pale green stripe down middle of back; back warty with longitudinal skin folds; curved blackish stripe from snout through eye, enclosing ear disc, over shoulder to beyond forearm; top lip broadly marbled black to dark grey; area between curved stripe and top lip green; hindside of thighs dark with large white or yellow spots; underside white. Fingers unwebbed, toes about half webbed.

**Habitat and Range:** Lowland alluvial flats. Declining locally. North-eastern and central eastern Australia.

**Notes:** Predator of other frogs. Will utter a penetrating scream if distressed.

**Mating Call:** Short "quack" uttered regularly.

**Eggs:** Loose clump or mat laid on surface amongst vegetation.

**Tadpoles:** Uniformly brown tadpole.

## Striped Marshfrog
### *Limnodynastes peronii*

Robert Ashdown

**Identification:** Length 65 mm. Light brown to grey-brown; pointed snout (from above); broad, dark stripes down back; may also be reddish stripes or thin line along middle of back; broad, curved, dark stripe from snout through nostril, eye and ear disc to base of arm; white or yellowish fold from below eye to arm; upper half of iris golden, lower half dark brown; underside white but males may have yellow throat with brown mottling. Long fingers and toes; fingers with no webbing, toes with only traces of webbing.

**Habitat and Range:** Common and wide-spread. Found near still water where males call while almost totally submerged. Out-door fish ponds favoured as breeding sites. Eastern Australia and Tas.

**Mating Call:** Short, sharp "toc".

**Eggs:** Small brown eggs laid in white foamy mass on surface of water.

**Tadpoles:** Uniformly brown tadpoles.

Queensland Museum

## Salmon-striped Frog
*Limnodynastes salmini*

**Identification:** Length 70 mm. Somewhat round-snouted (from above) brown to grey-brown frog with dark brown blotches and spots on back; three parallel red, pink or salmon stripes on back, outer ones commence near shoulders and central one from snout or behind eyes; curved, broad, dark band from snout through eye to ear disc; dark patch below eye; reddish fold from below eye to arm; iris golden; sides, groin, front and hind surfaces of thighs mottled black and white; underside white and throat spotted with brown. Fingers unwebbed, toes with traces of webbing.

**Habitat and Range:** Lowland alluvial flats and swamps. Declining locally. Central eastern Australia. Males call from edge of water.

**Mating Call:** Resonant "funk".

**Eggs:** White foamy mass on water surface.

**Tadpoles:** Pale, mottled tadpoles.

Robert Ashdown

## Spotted Marshfrog
*Limnodynastes tasmaniensis*

**Identification:** Length 45 mm. Pale grey frog with pointed snout (from above) and scattered darker blotches and spots on back; back has few low warts; curved, broad, dark band runs from snout through nostril, eye and ear disc to arm; white or yellowish fold runs from below eye to base of arm; iris golden; underside white but males have dusky yellow throats. Fingers and toes free of webbing.

**Habitat and Range:** Lowland alluvial flats. Breeds in marshes and temporary waters. Males call while partially submerged among vegetation. Eastern Australia.

**Mating Call:** Rapidly repeated series of harsh "uks".

**Eggs:** Pale, laid in white foamy mass on surface of water.

**Tadpoles:** Uniformly brownish tadpoles.

## Tusked Frog *Adelotus brevis*

Queensland Museum

**Identification:** Length — females 50 mm males 40 mm. Olive-green to blackish frogs with butterfly-shaped mark on top of head; back warty with irregular markings; head of male about half size of body; pair of tusks at front of lower jaw; belly boldly marbled black and white; throat dark grey with light peppering; bright red patches in groin and back of leg.

**Habitat and Range:** Rainforest, tall open forest and pasturelands. Usually found under debris on ground or natural and artificial cavities. Males call throughout year and call while partially submerged. Coastal central Qld to southern NSW.

**Mating Call:** Single clucking "rook" or "r-ook".

**Eggs:** Laid in white foamy mass on surface of water.

**Tadpoles:** Large dark grey tadpoles.

## Ornate Burrowing-frog
### *Limnodynastes ornatus*

Queensland Museum

**Identification:** Length 45 mm. Rotund, snub-nosed frog with protruding eyes and dark vertical bars on lip; colour pattern highly variable and often very complex; pale butterfly-shaped marking may be present between shoulders; pale yellow or pale orange stripe may be present down middle of back; small warts scattered over back, these may have orange tips; underside white. Fingers unwebbed, toes about one-quarter webbed.

**Habitat and Range:** Burrowing frog that emerges to breed after rain. Males call when floating on surface of water. Found in most habitats. Northern and eastern Australia.

**Mating Call:** Resonant, nasal "unkh".

**Eggs:** Laid in whitish, foamy mass on surface of water among floating vegetation.

**Tadpoles:** Small dark tadpoles with mottled tails and striped lips on larger individuals.

Bruce Cowell

Queensland Museum

## Scarlet-sided Pobblebonk
*Limnodynastes terraereginae*

**Identification:** Length 75 mm. Highly distinctive rotund frog with irregular red or reddish-yellow along sides and upper arm; bright red groin and hind surface of thigh; swollen gland on upper surface of lower leg; thick, yellow fold of skin from below eye to arm; underside white or yellow. Fingers unwebbed and toes with traces only.

**Habitat and Range:** Alluvial flats and coastal lowlands where they breed in permanent marshy areas. Males call while almost fully submerged. Eastern Qld and northern NSW.

**Mating Call:** Resonant "bonk".

**Eggs:** Laid in white foamy mass on surface of water.

**Tadpoles:** Dark tadpoles with mottled tails.

## Great Barred-frog  *Mixophyes fasciolatus*

**Identification:** Length 80 mm. Brown frog with broad, flat, rounded head and large dark eyes; T- or Y-shaped dark mark on back; thin black stripe from nostril to eye and continuing backwards over ear disc; legs with thin crossbars that widen at the ends. Fingers unwebbed and toes about three-quarters webbed.

**Habitat and Range:** Found along streams in rainforest or tall open forest. Also found around farm dams near forest. Coastal central eastern Qld to southern NSW.

**Mating Call:** Single resonant harsh "wark".

**Eggs:** Large eggs loosely clumped near water's edge and washed into water after rain or flooded by rising water.

**Tadpoles:** Very large, mottled, brown tadpoles with low-finned tails.

## Giant Barred-frog *Mixophyes iteratus*

**Identification:** Length 115 mm. Brown to olive to black frog with a broad, flat pointed head and eyes that are gold above and dark below; back markings obscure; broad dark stripe of uniform width from nostril to ear disc; legs with dark and pale bands of equal width; hind surface of thigh dark with scattered pale spots. Fingers unwebbed, toes almost fully webbed.

Queensland Museum

**Habitat and Range:** Known in region from single specimen found in rainforest at Burpengary Creek. These frogs may also occur at higher elevations in the D'Aguilar Range. Coastal south-eastern Qld and northern NSW.

**Mating Call:** Soft, low-pitched "aawk".

**Eggs:** As for Great Barred-frog (see p. 158).

**Tadpoles:** Large uniformly brown tadpole.

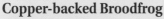

## Copper-backed Broodfrog
*Pseudophryne raveni*

**Identification:** Length 35 mm. Pink or red-backed frog with little or no other back markings; black band along reddish sides; upper arm grey to pink; back smooth or with low warts; underside marbled in black and white.

Robert Ashdown

**Habitat and Range:** Found throughout area in large breeding colonies. Usually found in forested country and low marshy areas. Coastal central and southern Qld.

**Mating Call:** Drawn-out "eaak".

**Eggs:** Large clumps laid in moist earth which are later flooded or washed into shallow water.

**Tadpoles:** Dark brown with mottled tails.

**Notes:** Similar species, Red-backed Broodfrog (*Pseudophryne coriacea*) occurs south from Esk and Nerang. Distinguished by shorter call and completely black sides.

Queensland Museum

## Great Brown Broodfrog
*Pseudophryne major*

**Identification:** Length 35 mm. Brown with rufous crown; back with dark brown to blackish markings, low warts and longitudinal skin folds, and washed or striped with dull red; U- or lyre-shaped black marking may be present; short yellowish stripe on rump; sides greyish; upper arm yellowish; underside marbled black and white. Fingers and toes unwebbed.

**Habitat and Range:** Found throughout area, associated with damp gullies, swamps, runnels and soaks. Males call from grass and leaf litter near water. Often found sheltering under debris and leaf litter. Coastal eastern Qld and northern NSW.

**Mating Call:** Short "eak".

**Eggs:** Relatively large eggs laid on land; guarded by male until they are covered by rising water.

**Tadpoles:** Dark brown with mottled tails.

Queensland Museum

## Australian Marsupial Frog
*Assa darlingtoni*

**Identification:** Length 25 mm. Pale brown to brown to reddish-brown with dark sides and rudimentary first finger and toe; two dark inverted V-shaped markings, one between eyes and one over middle of back; black triangular patch below eye; dark stripe from eye and above shoulder often breaking up into spots from above arm; sides warty, black, dark grey or dark brown; male with two pouches with slit-like openings on hips; underside white, but throat mottled brown; fingers and toes short.

**Habitat and Range:** Known in region only from Mt Glorious area. Inhabits leaf litter of forest floor. Coastal south-eastern Qld and northern NSW.

**Mating Call:** High-pitched series of "chits".

**Eggs:** Few large eggs deposited in moist soil and guarded by the male.

**Tadpole:** Finless white tadpoles are carried in hip-pouches on male after they hatch.

## Beeping Froglet  *Crinia parinsignifera*

**Identification:** Length 25 mm. Brownish or greyish frog with plain or highly patterned smooth, ridged or warty back; pale spot at base of arm;  underside whitish with fine, dark peppering. Fingers and toes long. Froglets of  *Crinia* are similar and highly variable. Identification often relies on call, ventral colouration, habitat and breeding season.

**Habitat and Range:** Occurs throughout area at lower altitudes. Usually found in association with permanent or temporary swamps, marshes and shallow ponds. Males call from cover at edge of water. South-eastern Australia.

**Mating Call:** High-pitched "eeeek", may be repeated with increasing speed.

**Eggs:** Small eggs laid in clumps attached to submerged vegetation.

**Tadpoles:** Short-tailed, fat-bodied tadpoles with low fins.

## Clicking Froglet  *Crinia signifera*

**Identification:** Length 30 mm. Highly variable brownish or greyish frog; back smooth, warty or ridged; pale spot at base of arm and below tail; underside marbled dark grey or blackish and white. Fingers and toes long.

**Habitat and Range:** Found throughout area in association with soaks, swamps, creeks and their backwaters. South-eastern Australia.

**Mating Call:** High-pitched "click-ik" that sounds like a watch being wound.

**Eggs:** Small eggs laid singly or in clumps attached to submerged vegetation.

**Tadpoles:** As for Beeping Froglet (see above).

Queensland Museum

## Wallum Froglet *Crinia tinnula*

**Identification:** Very small. Length 20 mm. Highly variable brownish or greyish frog; back smooth, warty or ridged; underside whitish with fine dark peppering and usually with narrow white line from chin down to belly and transverse line across throat. Fingers and toes long and unwebbed.

**Habitat and Range:** Smallest "acid frog" — adapted to acidic waters of coastal lowlands. Restricted to Bribie, Moreton and Stradbroke Islands and few small pockets on adjacent mainland. Coastal south-eastern Qld and northern NSW.

**Mating Call:** High-pitched, bell-like 'tching-tching', may be repeated with increasing speed.

**Eggs:** As for Beeping Froglet (see p. 161).

**Tadpoles:** As for Beeping Froglet.

Steve Wilson

## Sandy Gungan *Uperoleia fusca*

**Identification:** Length 30 mm. Grey-brown to dark grey with well defined or indistinct darker blotches on back; back warty and large gland present behind eye above shoulder; no stripe on gland; upper surface of forearm often flesh-coloured or yellow; markings in groin and hind surface of thigh orange or yellow; underside completely dark grey. *Uperoleia* species look similar and are often difficult to identify. Furthermore, they resemble recently metamorphosed Cane Toads, but the groin markings are sufficient to separate the three Toadlets.

**Habitat and Range:** Usually encountered only during breeding season or when found sheltering under debris on ground. Open forest, woodland, coastal heath and grassland throughout area. Coastal central Qld to northern NSW.

**Mating Call:** Raspy "e-e-e-e-e-k".

**Eggs:** Small eggs laid singly or in small clumps in shallow water of ponds and temporary pools.

**Tadpoles:** Small dark brown tadpoles with high tail fins.

## Eastern Gungan *Uperoleia laevigata*

**Identification:** Length 30 mm. Grey-brown to greyish with darker blotches on back; back warty with large gland over shoulder and behind eye; a curved dark stripe is present along the upper margin of this gland; upper forearm yellow; markings in groin and hind surface of thighs orange to reddish-orange; underside purplish-brown.

Steve Wilson

**Habitat and Range:** Generally the same as for Sandy Gungan (see p. 162). Favours open forest, woodland and grassland, but rather patchily distributed in region. Mainly found along D'Aguilar Range and in some south-eastern suburbs. Southern Qld to southern NSW.

**Mating Call:** Rasping "e-e-e-k".

**Eggs:** As for Sandy Gungan.

**Tadpoles:** As for Sandy Gungan.

## Chubby Gungan *Uperoleia rugosa*

**Identification:** Length 30 mm. Grey-brown to grey with darker blotches on back; large gland present above shoulder and behind eye and another smaller gland situated immediately behind it; markings in groin and hind surface of thighs yellow, orange or red; underside grey.

H. and J. Beste (Nature Focus)

**Habitat and Range:** As for Sandy Gungan (see p. 162). Eastern Australia.

**Mating Call:** Short, rasping "e-k".

**Eggs:** As for Sandy Gungan.

**Tadpoles:** As for Sandy Gungan.

## Frogs Found Near the Greater Brisbane Region

Steve Wilson

### Whistling Treefrog  *Litoria verreauxii*

**Localities:** Blackall-Conondale Ranges, Mt Tamborine, Great Dividing Ranges.

Queensland Museum

### Whirring Treefrog  *Litoria revelata*

**Localities:** Mt Tamborine, Border Ranges.

Queensland Museum

### Superb Collared-frog
*Cyclorana brevipes*

**Localities**: Brisbane Valley, Darling Downs.

Owen Kelly

### Fleay's Barred-frog *Mixophyes fleayi*

**Localities**: Blackall-Conondale Ranges, Mt Tamborine, Border Ranges.

Robert Ashdown

### Black-soled Frog *Lechriodus fletcheri*

**Localities**: Mt Tamborine, Border Ranges.

Steve Wilson

### Southern Platypus-frog
*Rheobatrachus silus*

**Localities:** Blackall-Conondale Ranges; possibly extinct.

# Cane Toads

Ric Natrass

Cane Toads, *Bufo marinus*, were first released in the cane fields of Far North Queensland in 1935. It was hoped that the toads would control Grey-back and Frenchi Beetles, the larvae of which stunt cane growth. The introduction of the toads, however, had little or no effect on the cane beetles and since that time, the toads have spread south and west to areas where cane has never been grown. It is uncertain how far they will spread beyond the tropical and subtropical areas of Australia.

The Cane Toad, which is also known as the Giant American or Marine Toad, is native to Central and South America. It has one of the widest ranges of any living toad and has also been introduced into the Carribean islands, southern United States and several Pacific islands. The toad is extremely toxic to other animals. It is not uncommon for family pets to die after they have ingested toad venom. In the wild, toads compete for food, shelter and breeding sites with native animals. Scientific evidence suggests that the toad is a nuisance to man and an ecological threat to the environment.

The Cane Toad's success can be attributed to it being a supreme opportunist. Cane Toads do not require specialised diets or conditions to start breeding (unlike many native frogs). Added to their tolerance of a wide range of environments, it is no surprise that they have spread so far and wide.

At home in the Americas, and in its own right, the Cane Toad is a beautiful animal and wanton cruelty to it is to be deplored. Equally however, the capture and humane killing by freezing large numbers has helped to rehabilitate areas once occupied entirely by the species.

## Cane Toad *Bufo marinus*

Bruce Cowell

**Identification:** Very large (20 cm). Head and face unlike any Australian frog. Definite visor or awning over each eye, evident even in juveniles; high bony ridge extending from eyes to meet above nostrils. (These features are not present in any local native frogs.) Grossly enlarged poison glands immediately above and behind exposed eardrums. Skin of back warty, but has texture of fine leather. Brown to mustard coloured; whitish or yellowish underside, sometimes with brown marbling. Toes with leathery webbing.

**Habitat and Distribution:** Very common. Disturbed areas most favoured. Locally, high altitude and correspondingly low temperatures may limit expansion (eg Green Mountains-Lamington National Park; however, while this area is toad-free it is below elevations at which the toad has managed to prosper). Earliest Brisbane toad record is from Cannon Hill in December 1945 — only 10 years after introduction to Australia.

**Mating Call:** Continuous purring trill that sounds like a running motor.

**Eggs:** Toad eggs are unlike those of native frogs. Frog spawn — always a single clump whether floating in foam on water's surface or sunken, resting on vegetation or bottom of a pool. Toad spawn — resembles long strings of egg noodles.

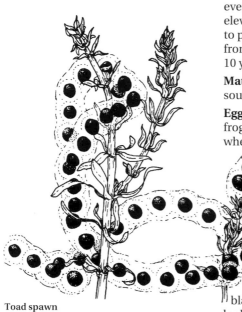

**Toad spawn**

**Tadpoles:** Depending on size, "toadpoles" are very difficult to identify singly — globular bodies, pointy snouts; plain black with slight pruinescence (powdery look); swim and feed in schools. Native frog tadpoles always operate independently. Juveniles distinguished from small native frogs by mottled grey backs with blackish, dark bands on limbs and rusty-tipped warts on back.

**Notes:** If doubt about identification persists, apply the water test. Toads can be handled wet or dry, large or small. Wet native frogs, regardless of size, will slip through fingers. The toad is toxic at all stages of life. Care should be taken when handling because of toxic skin secretions.

**Similar Species:** Striped Marsh Frog, Scarlet-sided Pobblebonks and Tusked Frogs.

**Threats:** Some native animals — such as crows, koels, water rats and keelback snakes — appear to have "learned" how to prey on toads successfully.

# Freshwater Turtles

Dr Colin Limpus and Patrick Couper

There are four species of freshwater turtles in the Greater Brisbane Region. These belong to the family Chelidae which contains 15 species in Australia. Chelid turtles are easily recognised by their webbed, clawed feet and their ability to fold their necks sideways for protection between a bony carapace (top of shell) and plastron (under part of shell). Freshwater turtles in the Brisbane area are divided into two groups — the long-necked turtles (genus *Chelodina*) and the short-necked turtles (genera *Elseya*, *Emydura*).

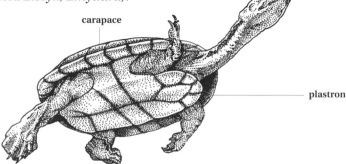

carapace

plastron

## Eastern Long-necked Turtle
*Chelodina longicollis*

**Identification:** Carapace 25 cm; dark brown or black; plastron creamy-yellow; scales edged in black; front of plastron almost as broad as carapace. Head and limbs grey. Head and neck about as long as carapace. Head moderately flattened.

**Habitat and Range:** Prefers standing water and ephemeral wetlands.

**Notes:** Secretes pungent musk odour when disturbed or handled. Frequently seen crossing roads after heavy rain.

John Cann

John Cann

## Broad-shelled River Turtle
*Chelodina expansa*

**Identification:** Carapace 50 cm; brown to blackish-brown; plastron cream; much narrower than carapace. Head and limbs grey. Head and neck about as long as carapace. Head very flat.

**Habitat and Range:** Most frequently found in medium to large rivers and large permanent ponds and lakes.

John Cann

## Saw-shelled Turtle
*Elseya latisternum*

**Identification:** Carapace 20 cm; brown to dark brown; hind edge strongly serrated except in older animals; plastron whitish. Head and limbs olive-brown. Short spiny neck. Juveniles sometimes have yellow stripe on side of face.

**Habitat and Range:** Flowing streams.

**Notes:** One of the few native animals to successfully prey on cane toads.

## Brisbane Short-necked Turtle
*Emydura signata*

**Identification:** Carapace 20 cm; olive to brown; plastron white to yellowish. Short smooth neck. Head and limbs grey. Yellow stripe on side of face.

**Habitat and Range:** Most common turtle in Brisbane catchment area. Permanent slow flowing streams and large standing water bodies.

**Notes:** Inland of Dividing Range this turtle is replaced by similar, but more widely distributed species, *E. macquarii.*

# Marine Turtles

Dr Colin Limpus

The seven existing species of marine turtles in the world are remnants of a once diverse fauna that has survived with little change since the age of the dinosaurs. Unfortunately, most species have suffered marked population declines from human interference during the past few hundred years. Three species have resident populations in Moreton Bay and a fourth is a frequent visitor to our waters. For an explanation of terms, see the diagram at the beginning of **Freshwater Turtles** on p. 167.

## Green Turtle *Chelonia mydas*

**Identification:** Carapace 40 cm to 120 cm; oval and highly domed; greenish-brown with dark mottling. Small bullet-shaped head. Small animals (40 cm) have distinctive "sun ray" pattern on large carapace scales.

**Habitat and Range:** Common — population estimate many thousands; large adults less common in Moreton Bay. All parts of Bay and adjacent reef habitats; most abundant in shallows — Moreton Banks, Pelican Banks and Bribie Passage.

**Notes:** Feeds on seagrass and algae. Migrates to breeding rookeries in southern Great Barrier Reef (Lady Musgrave, Heron, Wreck and North West Islands) and northern Reef (Raine Island) — the last, a swim of 2072 km.

Dept of Environment and Heritage

Dept of Environment and Heritage

## Loggerhead Turtle *Caretta caretta*

**Identification:** Carapace — 70 to 110 cm; heart-shaped and longer than it is wide; red-brown to brown. Head large and triangular.

**Habitat and Range:** Less abundant than Green Turtle — thousands in Moreton Bay — mostly deeper waters.

**Notes:** Feeds on crabs and shellfish. Migrates to breed along Bundaberg coast — Mon Repos to Wreck Rock, southern Barrier Reef cays. Small numbers breed annually in Moreton Bay. Queensland nesting population has declined by about 50 percent during past decade.

Dept of Environment and Heritage

## Hawksbill Turtle
### *Eretmochelys imbricata*

**Identification:** Carapace — 40 to 90 cm; thick and overlapping scales; brown-black. Head small with pronounced beak-like snout.

**Habitat and Range:** Small numbers — reef habitats including artificial reefs of oyster racks.

**Notes:** Feeds mostly on sponges. Breeding rookeries unknown. Nearest known nesting sites are New Caledonia and northern Great Barrier Reef — more than 1500 km away. Species on which tortoiseshell trade was based.

Dept of Environment and Heritage

## Leatherback Turtle
### *Dermochelys coriacea*

**Identification:** Carapace — 2.5 m (total length to 3 m); no scales, 5 distinct longitudinal ridges; shape sometimes likened to upturned dinghy; blackish often with pale marbling on back, neck and flippers.

**Habitat and Range:** Oceanic species — not resident in Moreton Bay. Frequently seen offshore from Moreton and Stradbroke Islands in winter and early summer.

**Notes:** Feeds on jellyfish. Thought to originate in rookeries in northern Papua-New Guinea and Irian Jaya. Second largest reptile in Australia, only surpassed in size by saltwater crocodile. Most widespread reptile on Earth.

# Lizards

Steven K. Wilson and Gregory V. Czechura

It would be unusual to find anyone in the Greater Brisbane Region who has not had some contact with lizards, particularly the small brown skinks that make their homes among the gardenias and roses.The diversity of lizards near Brisbane comes as a surprise to visitors from southern climes. Fifty species representing all five families of lizards found in Australia have so far been recorded. These animals exhibit a remarkable diversity in form and habit. The single most dominant group of local lizards, both in terms of number of species and total number of individuals, is the skinks (family Scincidae). With the exception of some species dependent on rainforest habitats, most Brisbane lizards are maintaining viable populations in spite of human pressures.

Lizards are not easy animals to identify. Expertise in identification is the product of "hands-on" contact with the subjects and a familiarity with the relevant scientific literature. Text books are available, but these usually require some prior understanding of the language and techniques of reptile identification. The following account is not comprehensive, but rather introduces each lizard living here with brief details of its appearance and habitat. Animals are listed in alphabetical order of scientific name.

In the species profiles, size is given in two parts — head and body length (HBL); and total length which includes the tail (TL). Measurements are taken from average rather than maximum-sized individuals.

All reptiles are protected and permits are required if lizards are to be kept in captivity. Permits can be obtained through the Queensland National Parks and Wildlife Service.

## Geckos

Geckos are readily identified by their soft velvety skin and large lidless eyes. Many species have expanded pads beneath their fingers and toes. They prefer dry habitats such as rock faces and eucalyptus woodlands, but some have adapted well to buildings. Geckos hide by day and emerge at night to hunt insects and sometimes feed near outdoor lights. In times of stress, geckos may utter a squeak or a harsh wheezing bark to distract or startle an adversary. Few lizards can vocalise. Geckos and the related Flap-footed Lizards (Pygopodidae) are notable exceptions.

Steve Wilson

### Stone Gecko *Diplodactylus vittatus*

**Identification:** HBL 6 cm. TL 9 cm. Dumpy, with prominent, pale, deeply notched zigzag stripe extending down back from neck to tip of short, plump tail. When tail is regenerated, this stripe stops abruptly at point of breakage. Toes slightly expanded to form pads.

**Habitat and Range:** Shelters in shallow depressions under stones and fallen timber; favours lightly timbered areas. Largely absent from suburbs; common in moderately dry peripheral bushland. Brisbane records include Mt Crosby and Mt Gravatt. Drier parts of eastern Australia.

**Similar Species:** Undescribed Velvet Gecko (*Oedura* sp.) has broader pale stripe, is slender, flatter and arboreal (see p. 174).

Steve Wilson

### Dtella *Gehyra dubia*

**Other Names:** House Gecko

**Identification:** HBL 6 cm. TL 14 cm. Grey-brown with irregular darker mottling; pale, almost patternless when foraging at night. Digits each with very broad, almost circular pad to assist climbing. On all but inner digits (which are clawless), large claw arises from centre of pad, curving forward to protrude beyond it.

**Habitat and Range:** Hides beneath loose bark of dead trees. Readily enters human dwellings, residing in gaps between planks, behind wall hangings, etc. Brisbane records largely restricted to dry south-western regions around Darra, Ipswich and Mt Crosby. Dry forests and woodlands of eastern Australia.

## Asian House Gecko
### *Hemidactylus frenatus*

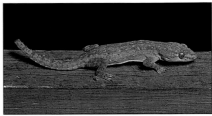

Queensland Museum

**Identification:** HBL 5 cm. TL 9.5 cm. Fawn to pale grey with darker mottling. Distinctive series of small spines along edges of tail. More readily identified by voice rather than appearance — a loud and distinctive "chuck-chuck-chuck".

**Habitat and Range:** Only introduced gecko in Australia. Resident populations largely or entirely restricted to northern towns and cities. Appears to have become established here within past decade. Occurrence still very patchy and largely confined to wharves, residential and business areas as far north as Strathpine.

## Thick-tailed Gecko  *Nephrurus milii*

Steve Wilson

**Identification:** HBL 10 cm. TL 35 cm. Unmistakable; purple-brown body vividly patterned with transverse rows of cream to yellow tubercles. Tail (when original) carrot-shaped and prominently banded with black and white. Regenerated tail blunt without obvious pattern. Only gecko in region to have slender fingers and toes, lacking any expanded pads — an adaption to life on the ground.

**Habitat and Range:** Shelters in burrows and beneath stones or rocks.Uncommon in Brisbane's outskirts. Locality records include Samford, Beaudesert, Pullenvale and Moggill. Dry eastern and southern Australia.

## Robust Velvet Gecko  *Oedura robusta*

Queensland Museum

**Identification:** HBL 8.5 cm. TL 15 cm.  Grey with large, dark-edged, rectangular pale blotches extending from head onto flattened plump tail.

**Habitat and Range:** Perhaps most abundant gecko in Brisbane's outer suburbs and surrounding eucalypt woodlands. Favours hollows in large, smooth-barked eucalypts but will readily take up residence in human dwellings. Central eastern Australia.

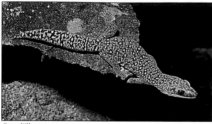
Steve Wilson

## Spotted Velvet Gecko *Oedura tryoni*

**Identification:** HBL 8 cm. TL 15 cm. Boldly patterned with numerous small pale spots, each normally with sharply contrasting dark margin, over a yellowish-brown ground colour. Such colouration cannot be seen on any other lizard in south-eastern Qld.

**Habitat and Range:** Uncommon in suburban Brisbane; abundant in peripheral bushland areas. Largely associated with elevated rocky habitats; Mt Coot-tha and Mt Nebo. Tolerant of cool climates, being only gecko occurring at and above Mt Nebo (540 m altitude in D'Aguilar Range). Occasionally found hiding behind loose bark. Coast and ranges from mid-eastern Qld to north-easten NSW.

Steve Wilson

## *Oedura* sp.

**Identification:** HBL 5.5 cm. TL 11 cm. Poorly known and undescribed. Appears to be closely related to Zig-zag Gecko (*Oedura rhombifera*) being relatively small and slender; dark grey with broad, pale wavy-edged stripe down back. Differs in that pale stripe is broader, edges less deeply notched, and is often broken.

**Habitat and Range:** Recorded at Mt Coot-tha but most localities originate from open forest on coastal lowlands and on islands of Moreton Bay. Arboreal, hiding beneath loose bark.

**Similar Species:** Stone Gecko (see p. 172).

## Dragons

Dragons have rough skin, long limbs and tails, and alert upright postures. Many species are ornamented with spines. Because of the relatively large sizes some species attain and their tendency to perch on elevated sites, dragons are a prominent, easily observed group.

Dragons are swift, keen-eyed, sun-loving lizards, quick to pounce on a passing insect or dash for cover if approached. Small species of dragons feed almost exclusively on arthropods (insects, spiders etc). Large dragons tend to be omnivorous including flowers and fruits in their diets.

## Frilled Lizard *Chlamydosaurus kingii*

**Identification:** HBL 25 cm. TL 75 cm. Australia's most distinctive dragon. Large, thin, scaly ruff almost completely encircles neck. When at rest this lies folded like a cape over neck and shoulders. When threatened, ruff is erected at right angles to body.

**Habitat and Range:** Very uncommon; thought to be locally extinct until rediscovered near Greenbank Army Reserve and Bribie Island in the past five years. Arboreal; usually seen on trunks of rough-barked trees and on roadsides. Brisbane represents southern limit of range.

Queensland Museum

## Tommy Round-head
*Diporiphora australis*

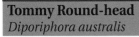

**Identification:** HBL 7 cm. TL 23 cm. Smallest local dragon; no crests or rows of spines. Dorsal scales approximately equal in size. Colour extremely variable; most individuals display two narrow cream to yellow dorsal stripes, and a series of broad dark crossbands.

**Habitat and Range:** Lowland eucalypt forests — particularly Toohey Forest, foothills of D'Aguilar Range, and islands of Moreton Bay. Brisbane approaches southern limit of this essentially tropical species.

**Similar Species:** Nobbi Dragon, especially juveniles (see below).

Steve Wilson

## Nobbi Dragon *Gemmatophora nobbi*

**Identification:** HBL 8 cm. TL 27 cm. Small crests of enlarged scales down spine and down either side of back. Grey with pair of yellow dorsal stripes overlaying (and sometimes broken or notched by) angular dark crossbands. On mature male, yellow stripes become brighter and pinkish-mauve flush develops on sides of tail-base.

**Habitat and Range:** Locally confined to dry eucalypt forests, particularly where rock outcropping is present. Coastal ranges including Brisbane Forest Park, Colleges Crossing, Mt Coot-tha and D'Aguilar Range.

**Similar Species:** Tommy Round-head.

Steve Wilson

Steve Wilson

## Southern Angle-headed Dragon
### *Hypsilurus spinipes*

**Identification:** HBL 13 cm. TL 40 cm. High crest of spines on neck, strongly laterally compressed body and long slender limbs. Top and sides of head meet to form acute angle. Plain or mottled brown to olive-green.

**Habitat and Range:** Subtropical rainforests of D'Aguilar Range, especially at Mt Glorious. Usually seen clinging to tree buttresses and sapling stems. North-eastern NSW and south-eastern Qld.

Queensland Museum

## Eastern Water Dragon
### *Physignathus lesueurii*

**Identification:** HBL 23 cm. TL 80 cm. Crest of spines from neck onto long, tapering, laterally flattened tail. Body yellowish-brown with darker bands; dark stripe from eye to side of neck; chest and belly dull red. Features indistinct on juveniles and females.

**Habitat and Range:** Abundant along Brisbane waterways including semi-polluted creeks, rivers and drains. Rocks, logs or tree branches on water's edge are favoured perches. Large colonies can be seen along Brisbane River adjacent to North Quay. Waterways of eastern Australia.

Bruce Cowell

## Common Bearded Dragon
### *Pogona barbata*

**Other Names:** Frilly.

**Identification:** HBL 23 cm. TL 55 cm. Grey, with low spines scattered over back, tail and limbs. Body flat, edged with long slender spines. Spiny pouch or "beard" beneath throat can be erected to display bright yellow mouth interior.

**Habitat and Range:** Woodlands, dry forests and suburban gardens including inner city. Resident in many backyards, basking on fence posts and letterboxes or foraging for insects and flowers. Eastern Australia.

**Notes:** Incorrectly called "Frilly" (see p. 175).

## Flap-footed Lizards

This family of lizards is restricted to Australia and New Guinea. Its members are superficially very snake-like, being long, slender and apparently limbless. Close examination will reveal a pair of small scaly flaps, one on each side of the body adjacent to the vent. These are all that remain of the hind limbs.

The four species of Flap-footed Lizards occurring in Brisbane can be distinguished from snakes by the following additional characteristics:

1. Ear openings. Snakes do not have these.
2. Belly scales arranged in a paired series. Snakes have single broad plates across the belly or, in the case of worm-like Blind Snakes (Typhlopidae), small scales undifferentiated from those around the body.
3. Thick fleshy tongue. Tongues of snakes are slender and deeply forked.
4. Tail about three to four times longer than the body. Tails of snakes are much shorter than the body, usually significantly less than one-quarter of the total length. Tails of Flap-footed Lizards and snakes begin at the vent. It must be remembered Flap-footed Lizards can lose their tails; care should be taken to distinguish complete snake tails from regenerating lizard tails. An abrupt change in pattern and scalation denotes the point of regeneration.

Despite their serpentine appearance, Flap-footed Lizards are unlikely close cousins of geckos. These outwardly dissimilar lizards share some unique features, the most notable being the use of a voice in times of stress and the employment of a thick fleshy tongue to wipe clean the transparent spectacle covering the eye.

### Common Delma  *Delma plebeia*

**Identification:** HBL 10 cm. TL 35 cm. Slender, snake-like. Uniform brown to olive with little pattern save for dark blotches on sides of head and neck. On juveniles, head is dark in contrast to neck and body. Hind limb flap moderately large.

**Habitat and Range:** Reasonably common throughout region with many records from western and northern suburbs (eg Brookfield, Everton Park). Secretive and nocturnal; usually encountered under leaf litter, logs and rocks or within grass tussocks. Dry areas of north-eastern NSW and south-eastern Qld.

Steve Wilson

Queensland Museum

## Collared Delma  *Delma torquata*

**Identification:** HBL 6 cm. TL 16.5 cm. Smallest of Australia's 17 *Delma* species. Brown, merging to greyish-brown on tail.Vivid broad black and narrow yellow bands extend across head and onto throat.

**Habitat and Range:** Lives under rocks and in soil cracks. Distribution restricted, occurring on heavy, stony, lightly timbered soils near Kenmore, Brookfield and Mt Crosby. Endemic to south-eastern Qld. Conservation status is Vulnerable.

**Similar Species:** Common Delma larger with very weak head markings centred on sides of face (see p. 177).

Bruce Cowell

## Burton's Snake Lizard  *Lialis burtonis*

**Identification:** HBL 27 cm. TL 60 cm. Pointed snout distinctively wedge-shaped, quite unlike any other Australian reptile. Hind limb flaps are minute and difficult to detect. Colour extremely variable; plain pale grey to black, brown-yellow or even orange, with or without prominent stripes or rows of spots.

**Habitat and Range:** Seems equally successful in Brisbane's well-vegetated suburban gardens and peripheral bushland. Shelters in low vegetation such as tussocks, and beneath rocks or logs. Australia, except south-east corner.

Queensland Museum

## Common Scaly-foot
*Pygopus lepidopodus*

**Identification:** HBL 23 cm. TL 73 cm. Extremely variable. Specimens from southeastern Qld normally dull reddish-brown merging to grey on tail, usually with one or more series of pale-edged dark dashes, most conspicuous on tail. Snout rounded. Raised ridges on scales align to form distinctive keels down body and tail. Ear openings and large hind limb flaps quite prominent. .

**Habitat and Range:** Uncommon in Brisbane area; mainly restricted to subcoastal ranges where eucalypts grow above ground cover of tussock grasses. Dry parts of southern and eastern Australia.

# Goannas

Goannas are Australia's largest lizards. They have tough, loose skin protected by an armour of small, bead-like scales. The limbs are powerful and equipped with large curved claws. They have long necks, narrow heads and very sharp recurved teeth. The claws and teeth, along with the muscular tail, combine as formidable defensive weapons.

Goannas are predators and scavengers. They consume carrion and hunt lizards, birds and mammals, raid birds' nests and excavate the eggs of turtles. Goannas walk with a characteristic unhurried swaying gait. Their long, slender, deeply forked tongues are protruded constantly as they explore burrows and hollows. Australia is the stronghold of goannas, the 25 species here represent about three-quarters of the total number worldwide. Two species occur in the Greater Brisbane Region.

## Gould's Goanna
*Varanus gouldii*

Queensland Museum

**Other Names:** Sand Goanna.

**Identification:** HBL 45 cm. TL 110 cm. Large. Colour variable including a row of yellow spots; dark-edged pale line through eye; narrow bands on yellow-tipped tail.

**Habitat and Range:** Patchily distributed through peripheral bushland and islands of Moreton Bay. Localities include Stradbroke Island, Karana Downs and Arana Hills. Normally takes refuge in burrows. Dry areas Australia-wide.

## Lace Monitor  *Varanus varius*

Queensland Museum

**Identification:** HBL 55 cm. TL 140 cm. Largest lizard in Brisbane. Shades of grey to black with narrow pale bands and transverse rows of pale spots on body; broad light and dark bands on tail; and usually dark bands across chin.

**Habitat and Range:** Common in peripheral forests and woodlands; regularly patrolling picnic grounds for scraps. Arboreal, often seen sunning on the trunks of large trees. Eastern Australia, from southern Cape York to Vic.

# Skinks

Variation of form and lifestyle among skinks is so great that few easily visible features can be used to define them. The body scales of skinks are usually smooth and shiny and overlapping like roof tiles. Those on top of the head are arranged symmetrically, side by side. Skinks have thick fleshy tongues and most have moveable eyelids and visible ear openings. Most are small, sun-loving lizards with five fingers or toes on each of their four limbs and long fragile tails. Some skinks have adapted to living in soil and these are limbless or near-limbless, worm-like lizards. Their lives are spent wriggling through humus and loose soil. Skinks are the dominant group of Australian reptiles and comprise nearly half of the total fauna. They are probably the most commonly seen of all reptiles. Most small skinks are insectivorous. Larger species such as Blue-tongues are omnivorous, consuming fruit, flowers, eggs, snails and carrion.

Steve Wilson

## Verreaux's Skink *Anomalopus verreauxii*

**Identification:** HBL 18 cm. TL 33 cm. Long-bodied, weak-limbed (may resemble snake or worm). Forelimbs have three short fingers; hind limbs reduced to minute stubs. Grey above with cream to yellow band across back of head; weakly defined on adults but sharply contrasting on juveniles. Largest of Brisbane's burrowing skinks.

**Habitat and Range:** Common in suburbs, peripheral bushland and rural areas. Often unearthed beneath loose garden soil. Secretive, shade-loving. North-eastern NSW to mid-eastern Qld.

Steve Wilson

## *Calyptotis scutirostrum*

**Identification:** HBL 5 cm. TL 12 cm. Long bodied, weak-limbed species retaining full compliment of five digits on each foot. Copper-brown above with yellow belly and coral pink flush under tail.

**Habitat and Range:** Common in gardens and timbered habitats where damp conditions prevail. Abundant small inhabitant of backyard compost heaps. Secretive, shade-loving. Endemic to north-eastern NSW and south-eastern Qld.

## Carlia munda

Steve Wilson

**Identification:** HBL 4 cm. TL 10 cm. Four fingers and five toes. White mid-lateral stripe "splits" at ear, reaching forward from body to bottom of ear opening and continuing on to head from top of ear opening. Breeding male — top of head coppery green; neck and throat scales white to bluish edged with black; upper flanks black; reddish flush between limbs.

**Habitat and Range:** Inhabits leaf litter in open eucalypt forest in Mt Crosby and Ipswich areas through to drier parts of the Brisbane Valley. Northern Australia. Active, sun-loving.

## Carlia pectoralis

Steve Wilson

**Identification:** HBL 4.7 cm. TL 12 cm. Four fingers and five toes. Dorsal scales each have three longitudinal ridges. White mid-lateral stripe runs through ear opening. Breeding male — top of head coppery-brown; lips neck and throat scales bluish edged with black; two reddish stripes along flanks.

**Habitat and Range:** Inhabits leaf litter in open forests and woodlands throughout region. Active, sun-loving.

**Similar Species:** Lively Skink (see p. 182) has two ridges on each dorsal scale.

## Carlia schmeltzii

Steve Wilson

**Identification:** HBL 5.7 cm. TL 17 cm. Four fingers and five toes. Dorsal scales each with three longitudinal ridges. Narrow yellow-brown stripe runs down either side of back. Breeding male — scales on neck and sides of head greyish-white margined with black; reddish-orange flush on sides.

**Habitat and Range:** Favours leaf litter associated with rocky areas. Locally scarce, known from Mt Coot-tha through to dry habitats within Brisbane Forest Park. Eastern to northern Qld. Active, sun-loving.

Steve Wilson

## Lively Skink  *Carlia vivax*

**Identification:** HBL 4 cm. TL 12 cm. Four fingers and five toes. Dorsal scales each with two longitudinal ridges. Pale stripe often runs down back. White mid-lateral stripe through ear. Breeding male — sides of head and neck bluish; chin and throat scales pale blue speckled brown; flanks reddish-orange to pinkish flush, or stripe from forelimb to hind limb.

**Habitat and Range:** Inhabits leaf litter. Most open bushland peripheral to Brisbane, including islands of Moreton Bay. North-eastern NSW to northern Qld. Active, sun-loving.

**Similar Species:** *Carlia pectoralis* (see p. 181) has three ridges on each dorsal scale.

Steve Wilson

## *Ctenotus arcanus*

**Identification:** HBL 8.2 cm. TL 23 cm. Body with stripes and spots including pale-edged black vertebral stripe (variably developed and sometimes absent on large adults);  brown back, pale stripes along outer back; and black flanks enclosing row of prominent white spots.

**Habitat and Range:** Open forest, woodland and heath on sandy or stony substrates. Locally common on North Stradbroke Island, Mt Coot-tha, D'Aguilar Range and foothills. South-eastern Qld. Swift, sun-loving.

**Similar Species:** Eastern Striped Skink — larger; up to HBL 13 cm. More robust; sides olive and spots diffuse (see p. 183).

Steve Wilson

## *Ctenotus eurydice*

**Identification:** HBL 7.5 cm. TL 22 cm.  Pattern bold; dark and pale stripes, coppery-brown back. Upper flanks black, usually with sparse row of white spots near shoulder.

**Habitat and Range:** Eucalypt forest, often associated with rock outcrops. Scarce in Brisbane area;  known from Mt Coot-tha and Toohey Forest. South-eastern Qld and north-eastern NSW. Swift, sun-loving.

**Similar Species:** Copper-tailed Skink is abundant; smaller (up to HBL 6.5 cm), lacks any spots on upper flanks and snout is sharper in profile (see p.183).

## Eastern Striped Skink
### *Ctenotus robustus*

Steve Wilson

**Identification:** HBL 13 cm. TL 30 cm. Pattern of stripes and spots, including prominent, pale-edged black vertebral stripe; brown back, pale stripes along outer edges of back; dark grey-brown upper flanks enclosing a row of diffuse pale grey spots, and pale stripe.

**Habitat and Range:** Abundant along garden edges throughout suburbs and in open eucalypt forests and woodlands. At high altitudes in D'Aguilar Range it is replaced by *Ctenotus arcanus*. Swift, sun-loving. Widespread over eastern and northern Australia.

**Similar Species:** *Ctenotus arcanus* — black upper flanks enclosing sharp white spots (see p. 182).

## Copper-tailed Skink
### *Ctenotus taeniolatus*

Steve Wilson

**Identification:** HBL 6.5 cm. TL 17 cm. Pattern bold; series of sharply contrasting dark and pale longitudinal lines, including white-edged black vertebral; brown back, copper flush on tail; black upper and lower flanks; and white stripe along middle of side, reaching ear opening and curving forward around upper margin.

**Habitat and Range:** Common in woodland, open forest, heath, parks and gardens throughout area. Eastern Australia. Swift, sun-loving.

**Similar Species:** *Ctenotus eurydice* (see p. 182).

## Wall Skink   *Cryptoblepharus virgatus*

Steve Wilson

**Identification:** HBL 4 cm. TL 8 cm. Flat bodied with long slender limbs. Black above with pair of widely spaced white lines along back. Eye large and permanently open; covered with fixed transparent spectacle.

**Habitat and Range:** Ubiquitous. Favours vertical surfaces such as brick walls and paling fences, tree trunks and rock faces. Appears more common in urban landscapes than in surrounding bushland. Eastern and southern Australia. Swift, extremely agile.

Queensland Museum

## Pink-tongued Skink
### *Cyclodomorphus gerrardii*

**Identification:** HBL 20 cm. TL 40 cm. Long-bodied with narrow neck, slender, prehensile tail; four relatively short limbs. Tongue pink on adults; blue on juveniles. Colour and pattern range between boldly marked (shades of grey with numerous sharp black crossbands) to plain (fawn, little indication of pattern).

**Habitat and Range:** Moist pockets throughout Brisbane and surrounding bushland. Common in well-watered gardens and rockeries. Active by day or night. Excellent climber. Mid-eastern NSW to north-eastern Qld.

**Similar Species:** Blue-tongued Skink (see p. 190).

## Major Skink  *Egernia frerei*

**Identification:** HBL 18 cm. TL 45 cm. Very large, powerfully built. Brown above, usually with fine lines of dark dashes. Sides darker, usually enclosing pale spots.

**Habitat and Range:** Rainforest edges to dry forests and woodlands on Brisbane's periphery. Shy lizard which shelters in hollow logs, large rock crevices and in burrows under thickets and tree roots. Active by day. North-eastern NSW to Cape York.

**Similar Species:** Land Mullet. See below.

Queensland Museum

## Land Mullet  *Egernia major*

**Identification:** HBL 26 cm. TL 57 cm. Very robust and powerful . Uniformly black; juveniles have white spots on sides.

**Habitat and Range:** Common in rainforest and adjacent tall open forest, inhabiting sunny clearings and road verges.Within Brisbane region, probably restricted to D'Aguilar Range, particularly Mt Nebo-Mt Glorious area. Endemic to south-eastern Qld and north-eastern NSW.

**Similar Species:** Major Skink — paler back with dark dashes and usually spotted flanks; tends to be more widespread in drier, more open habitats. See above.

Steve Wilson

## Tree Skink *Egernia striolata*

**Identification:** HBL 11 cm. TL 23 cm. Muscular, dorsally flattened. Each dorsal scale has 2–5 weak ridges. Dark grey above, with longitudinal rows of black blotches. Broad pale grey suffusion extends down each side of back. Flanks black. Lips white.

**Habitat and Range:** One isolated population known from melaleuca and casuarina woodlands of Boondall. Shelters beneath loose bark of standing and fallen casuarinas. Secretive and seldom seen out foraging. Dry parts of eastern Australia, Vic. to mid-eastern Qld.

Steve Wilson

## Narrow-banded Sand-swimmer *Eremiascincus fasciolatus*

**Identification:** HBL 9 cm. TL 20 cm. Glossy orange-brown with numerous very narrow dark bands (10–19 between neck and hips, and 35–40 on original tail).

**Habitat and Range:** Known from Lake Wivenhoe area. Secretive nocturnal inhabitant of burrows and loose soil beneath leaf litter and debris. Extends widely across arid interior

**Similar Species:** Broad-banded Sandswimmer has fewer, broader and generally more prominent bands. See below.

Steve Wilson

## Broad-banded Sand-swimmer *Eremiascincus richardsonii*

**Identification:** HBL 12 cm. TL 24 cm. Glossy orange-brown with numerous evenly spaced dark bands (8–14 between neck and hips and 19–32 on original tail).

**Habitat and Range:** Known from Ipswich-Mt Crosby area. Frequents woodland or grassland on sandy or stony substrates. Nocturnal. Essentially desert species like Narrow-banded Sand-swimmer.

**Similar Species:** Narrow-banded Sandswimmer. See above.

Steve Wilson

Steve Wilson

## Elf Skink *Eroticoscincus graciloides*

**Identification:** HBL 2.8 cm. TL 6 cm. Very small, four fingers and five toes. Reddish-brown with ill-defined, dark-edged, roughly triangular patch behind eye; dull reddish bands on sides of tail. Belly virtually translucent; snout sharply pointed.

**Habitat and Range:** Moist conditions under leaf litter and surface debris in rainforest and low-lying pockets within drier forests. Very secretive, shade-loving. Endemic to south-eastern Qld. Known locally from Mt Nebo, Mt Coot-tha and Pine Mountain.

Steve Wilson

## Martin's Skink *Eulamprus martini*

**Identification:** HBL 5.5 cm. TL 13.5 cm. Pale brown to coppery above with numerous small dark blotches. Ragged black band on sides, sometimes broken to form large dark angular blotches. Tail has narrow dark bands.

**Habitat and Range:** Abundant in rockeries of well-watered gardens, often in houses. Also common among rocks and fallen timber in eucalypt forests, especially where slightly moist conditions prevail. North-eastern NSW and south-eastern Qld. Active in sunny and shady situations.

**Similar species:** Bar-sided Skink (see p. 187)— generally paler with weaker pattern, often including longitudinal dark dash on nape.

Steve Wilson

## Tryon's Skink *Eulamprus murrayi*

**Identification:** HBL 10 cm. TL 22 cm. Robust skink with coppery back heavily flecked with black. Sides blackish-brown dusted with tiny white or bluish spots.

**Habitat and Range:** Restricted to rainforests. Commonly seen on large fallen logs, either basking or resting partly concealed with only head protruding from cavity. Locally confined to D'Aguilar Range. North-eastern NSW and south-eastern Qld.

**Similar Species:** Eastern Water Skink (see p. 187).

## Eastern Water Skink  *Eulamprus quoyii*

**Identification:** HBL 12 cm. TL 25 cm. Sleek, robust with simple but distinctive pattern; rich brown or bronze above with pale yellow line along junction of sides with back, from eye to near base of tail. Upper flanks black with small white spots.

Steve Wilson

**Habitat and Range:** Throughout region where suitable cover exists near permanent water. Waterways of eastern Australia.

**Similar Species:** *Ctenotus* spp. have definite stripes on back and/or sides and favour drier; more open habitats (see pp.182–183). Tryon's Skink (see p.186).

## Bar-sided Skink  *Eulamprus tenuis*

**Identification:** HBL 6.5 cm. TL 15.5 cm. Pale brown, coppery to silvery brown above, with numerous small dark blotches and often dark longitudinal dash on nape. Sides marked with angular black blotches, occasionally joined to form ragged stripe. Tail has narrow dark bands.

Steve Wilson

**Habitat and Range:** Garden rockeries and well-watered areas, sometimes enters houses. Common on fallen and standing timber in moist forest habitats. Eastern NSW to mid-eastern Qld. Active in sunny and shady conditions.

**Similar species:** Martin's Skink (see p.186).

## Secretive Skink  *Lampropholis amicula*

**Identification:** HBL 3 cm. TL 7.5 cm. Tiny, rather short-limbed. Dark coppery-brown to grey-brown above with fine yellowish line along outer back from near eye to base of tail. Upper flanks noticeably darker than back, junction sharply delineated.

Steve Wilson

**Habitat and Range:** Known in Brisbane area from Daisy Hill State Forest, Mt Coot-tha and D'Aguilar Ranges. Open forest, heath and margins of drier rainforest. Extremely shy, sun-loving, leaf litter inhabitant. South-eastern Qld and north-eastern NSW.

**Similar Species:** Grass and Couper's Skinks (see p.188).

Steve Wilson

Steve Wilson

Steve Wilson

## Couper's Skink *Lampropholis couperi*

**Identification:** HBL 4 cm. TL 9.6 cm. Brown with dark flecks above and dark grey on sides, two colours sharply delineated by narrow pale line along outer back from shoulder to hips. Belly scales broadly edged in black.

**Habitat and Range:** Probably locally restricted to D'Aguilar Range. Inhabits rainforests, especially sunny clearings and rocky creek banks. Endemic to south-eastern Qld. An active sun-loving skink.

**Similar Species:** Secretive Skink (see p. 187), and Grass Skink (see below).

## Grass Skink *Lampropholis delicata*

**Identification:** HBL 5 cm. TL 9 cm. Copper brown above, sometimes with pale flecks; sides generally darker than back, often with white mid-lateral stripe. Belly more or less uniform whitish or lightly speckled with black.

**Habitat and Range:** Throughout region, including city centre. Probably most common lizard. All habitats, though most abundant in disturbed areas such as suburban gardens. Eastern Australia. Sun-loving.

**Similar Species:** Secretive Skink (see p. 187). Couper's Skink — scales under body and tail are broadly edged in black, no white stripe on sides (see above). *Carlia* spp. have four fingers and males develop bright breeding colours in summer (see pp. 181–182).

## Burnett's Skink *Lygisaurus foliorum*

**Identification:** HBL 3.2 cm. TL 7 cm. Very small. Four fingers and five toes. Eyelids immovable — lower fused to the upper to form transparent spectacle. Brown with little pattern; dark flecks on back and faint pale spots on flanks. Mature males develop reddish flush on tail and hind limbs.

**Habitat and Range:** Favours tussock grasses, leaf-litter and bark debris in eucalypt forests. Mid-eastern NSW to mid-eastern Qld. Active, secretive, sun-loving.

**Similar Species:** *Carlia* spp. — dorsal scales have obvious keels on all except *Carlia munda*, which has distinctive white mid-lateral stripe (see pp. 181–182).

## Fire-tailed Skink *Morethia taeniopleura*

Queensland Museum

**Identification:** HBL 4 cm. TL 10 cm. Brown with black and white sides and bright red flush on tail and hips. Mature males develop red throats.

**Habitat and Range:** Open forest and woodland on sandy or stony substrates. Swift, sun-loving, dashes for cover under leaf litter, stones and logs when disturbed.Western suburbs and Moreton Bay islands. Eastern Qld.

## *Ophioscincus ophioscincus*

Steve Wilson

**Identification:** HBL 11 cm. TL 19 cm. Completely limbless and worm-like, with minute eyes. Ear opening absent, represented by depression. Silvery-grey above with two to four rows of narrow dark dashes. Sides black. Belly yellow.

**Habitat and Range:** Rainforests and other moist habitats. Secretive; normally encountered in damp wood mulch and loose soil under rocks and logs. Southern to mid-eastern Qld.

## *Ophioscincus truncatus*

Steve Wilson

**Identification:** HBL 7 cm. TL 13 cm. Worm-like, with limbs reduced to barely discernible stubs. Ear opening absent, represented by depression. Grey to brown above, darker on tail, with lines of dark dashes.

**Habitat and Range:** Secretive; sheltering in wood mulch and sand beneath logs and leaf litter. Moist forests and heaths. Restricted to Moreton and North Stradbroke Islands. South-eastern Qld to north-eastern NSW.

Steve Wilson

## *Saproscincus rosei*

**Identification:** HBL 5.5 cm. TL 14 cm. Long-tail; variegated brown (often yellowish-brown), with numerous speckles and flecks on back and sides. Tail with broad reddish or yellowish stripes. Some mature females may have dark sides and/or pale cream or yellowish line from corner of jaw to groin. Formerly referred to as *Lampropholis challengeri*, a species occurring outside the Greater Brisbane Region.

**Habitat and Range:** Inhabits shady and weakly sunlit areas. Rainforest and tall open forest at higher elevations in Brisbane area. North-eastern NSW and south-eastern Qld.

Queensland Museum

## Blue-tongued Skink *Tiliqua scincoides*

**Identification:** HBL 25 cm. TL 40 cm. Robust; with broad triangular head and distinct neck; blue-violet tongue; short legs; short, non-fragile tail. Colour pattern variable, but usually banded to some extent.

**Habitat and Range:** Throughout Brisbane area in most habitats, except rainforest and higher elevations. Common inhabitant of suburban gardens. Active by day. Eastern and northern Australia.

**Similar Species:** Pink-tongued Skink — body slender, tail longer and fragile; tongue pink on adults (see p. 184).

# Land Snakes

Jeanette Covacevich and Steve Wilson

There are 31 species of snakes from the Greater Brisbane Region in the Museum's reference collection. Such a small area can support so many snakes because of the subtropical climate and the diversity of habitats that existed before urbanisation — rainforests, eucalypt forests, a profusion of natural and semi-natural coastal heathlands, and agricultural and pastoral land. Urbanisation, with the clearing of forests, swamps and river banks, the proliferation of roads, and the introduction of pets (cats and dogs) and pests (the poisonous Cane Toad) has changed the original distribution of snakes in the area.

Some snakes are still widespread and encountered frequently in Brisbane. It seems that almost any suburban backyard can support one or more species. Carpet Pythons, Common Tree Snakes, Keelbacks, Yellow-faced Whip Snakes, White-crowned Snakes and Small-eyed Snakes are common here. The White-crowned Snake is even common right in the heart of the city, in parks, and is very well-known in inner suburbs.

Other species are less common, and some, like the Taipan, Red-bellied Black, Death Adder, Australian Coral and Pale-headed Snakes are rarely encountered in or near the Brisbane region.

Because of the potential danger from some species, there is a wide public interest in snakes. Of the thousands of enquiries received at the Queensland Museum Reference Centre, almost a quarter are about snakes — their identification, their potential danger, and how they feed and breed.

## Identification
The colour photographs that follow will often give enough information to identify a snake, but it is not wise to rely on colour alone. Both the Red-bellied Black and Small-eyed Snakes have black upper bodies with red bellies; and Eastern Brown Snakes and Taipans are both brown on the upper body and have cream bellies flecked with orange or salmon pink. Most snakes vary considerably in colour, pattern, and size, and although the colour photographs show typical colour patterns, the additional information in the species accounts should be checked to make an identification. Where two species look alike, the species accounts tell how to distinguish them. If in doubt, or if someone has been bitten, contact the Queensland Museum for advice.

Snakes usually grow quite quickly to an adult size and then growth slows. The sizes given in the species accounts are the most frequently seen for adults of that species, rather than the rare maximum size that is only achieved by a very old specimen. Juveniles are usually secretive and are seldom encountered.

If the snake is dead, or if you have a shed skin, the pattern of scales can be used to confirm an identification. Count the number of rows of scales around the middle of the body (the mid-body scales), starting and finishing at (but not including) the large row of scales on the belly. (Because rows of mid-body scales overlap, they should be counted along a diagonal or in a zig-zag.) Check whether the scale just in front of the cloaca (the anal scale) is single or divided. Check whether the large scales that run from the cloaca to the tip of the tail (the subcaudals) are single, divided, or some of each.

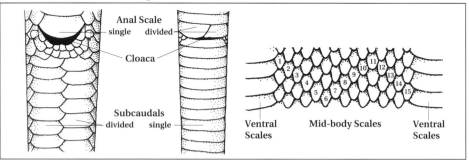

### Potential Danger

The world's most venomous snakes occur in Australia. Two-thirds of the species found in the Greater Brisbane Region are venomous, but only half of these are potentially dangerous. The distinction between being venomous and being potentially dangerous is an easy one.

Snake venom is used primarily to kill prey for food. Defence is a very secondary use of venom. A White-crowned Snake that eats only small lizards does not need to produce large quantities of potent venom. Although venomous, it is unlikely to do much harm to an adult human.

A Death Adder in highly aggressive defence posture. Chris Pollitt

Snakes are not inherently aggressive and they do not seek out human victims. They bite humans only if they are disturbed or provoked.

Some snakes have more potent venom than others. The Western Taipan of far south-western Queensland has the most toxic land snake venom known, and is followed (in descending order) by the Eastern Brown Snake, Coastal Taipan, Tiger Snake and Death Adder — all of which have been recorded in the Greater Brisbane Region.

When we also consider the quantity of venom produced, four snakes from the Greater Brisbane Region rate very highly on Australia's "potentially most lethal" list (Coastal Taipan 2nd, Tiger 3rd, Death Adder 4th, Eastern Brown 7th).

In assessing the likely danger to humans, we could also consider the efficiency of the bite; the temperament and behaviour of the snake; and the frequency of life-threatening bites by particular species. On Australia's "most likely to cause serious harm" list, the Coastal Taipan is rated first, the Death Adder 3rd and the Eastern Brown and Tiger equal 4th.

Such distinctions are interesting only theoretically. A full bite by any one of eight species in the Brisbane region could be fatal if appropriate medical aid were not administered rapidly. These species are the Coastal Taipan, Tiger, Death Adder, Eastern Brown, Rough-scaled, Small-eyed, Red-bellied Black and Spotted Black Snakes. In the species accounts, these are referred to as **dangerous**.

The Black Whip, Pale-headed, Stephen's Banded, and Yellow-faced Whip Snakes are capable of inflicting bites which may have serious local, and occasionally systemic, effects. In the species accounts these are referred to as **potentially dangerous**.

Other venomous snakes, that are too small to give an effective bite, or whose venom is unlikely to cause more than mild local irritation, are referred to as **virtually harmless**.

**Non-venomous** snakes are not listed as harmless because a bite from a large individual (eg a carpet python) can give severe lacerations.

Fortunately, despite the large number of highly venomous species, the frequency of serious cases of snake bite is low, and death from snake bite is extremely rare. (About 3000 cases of snake bite occur in Australia each year and of these, about 10 percent are "serious"). The incidence of deaths from snake bite in Queensland has declined steadily since the late 1940s (3.5 per year) to less than 1 death per year (1988–90). This is no doubt the result of better understanding of the impact of various venoms on the human system and of improved first aid and medical treatment.

Snake venom can contain several toxins, each with a different effect. **Neuro-toxins** affect the peripheral nervous system, causing drowsiness, paralysis, difficulty in breathing; **myotoxins** destroy muscle tissue, causing weakness and kidney malfunction; **haemotoxins** affect the blood by either increasing clotting or bleeding. Snake bites, like bee stings, affect some people more than others, and the severity of the symptoms also depends on the species of snake, its size, and the size of the victim. There may be pain, swelling or bruising around the bite (**local effects**), or more widespread effects on entire body systems (**systemic effects**).

Assess any case of snake bite carefully. Unless the snake is definitely non-venomous, or one of the many species with only mild venom, apply first aid and seek medical help at the nearest casualty section of a public hospital. If a child has been bitten, apply first aid and seek medical help even if the snake is only mildly venomous. A bite from a non-venomous snake may require tetanus protection.

First aid should delay the onset of serious symptoms which may follow snake bite. The following procedure was devised by Dr Straun Sutherland and his colleagues. It is universally recommended for Australia.

1.  Apply a broad firm bandage to cover the bitten area. In the case of a limb as much as possible of the limb should be bound (as tightly as for a sprained ankle).

2.  Immobilise the affected limb with a splint; leave the bandage and splint on until medical care is reached.

3.  Do not permit the victim to move around more than is necessary.

4.  If the snake can be killed safely, bring it with the victim.

5.  Do not wash the bite site.

The best first aid is to avoid being bitten. Most snakes give an "aggressor" every chance to retreat. Several potentially dangerous species adopt characteristic defensive postures to warn off possible "aggressors". Black Snakes flatten their necks and hiss and feint frantically. The Eastern Brown Snake "stands up" in a distinctive "S" position and strikes repeatedly. Some species give little or no warning before biting and the move from defensive posturing to a warning bite or full bite can take place rapidly and with little provocation. For example, just being too close to a Coastal Taipan can result in a bite.

Snakes which are only mildly venomous or which lack venom also use warning behaviour. The Bandy Bandy's bold black and white colour signifies "go away" and it reinforces this message by throwing itself into vertical loops and thrashing and rearranging its posture when provoked. The Brown Tree Snake also "stands up", hisses and feints, sometimes with mouth agape. Blind Snakes are non-venomous, but can emit a repulsive stench from special glands.

The inherent message in any assessment of the potential danger of snakes is clear — always leave them alone.

**Feeding**

Most snakes eat only vertebrates — frogs, lizards, other snakes (even of their own species), birds and mammals. Some species are specialised feeders. Blind Snakes feed solely on ants, termites and their eggs and larvae. The Bandy Bandy feeds on the elusive, burrowing Blind Snakes, and because these are hard to find, the Bandy Bandy has evolved an ability to feed only infrequently.

Snakes can immobilise their prey by constriction (Carpet Python); by the injection of venom (Taipan); or by a combination of both methods (Eastern Brown Snake).

Pythons are masters of constriction. At each gasp for breath made by its victim, a python will tighten its coils. The prey expires, literally, and the snake proceeds to ingest it at what sometimes seems to be an interminably slow pace.

Among snakes from the Greater Brisbane Region, the Coastal Taipan is "top of the class" for efficient capture of prey. This snake (and its close relative the Western Taipan) are the only Australian species to prey solely on mammals, and they have a rapid strike and release bite which is rare among Australian snakes. A taipan of either species will sense its prey (usually a rat or small marsupial); track it; bite it to inject a very potent venom; quickly release the prey; wait for the animal to die; then ingest it (usually head first) and move on.

Another highly venomous species, the Eastern Brown Snake, uses a different strategy, but one which is more common to Australian snakes. When the snake bites and injects its venom, it hangs on, coiling its body round its prey until the animal dies. Only then will the snake release the animal, size it up, and begin the swallowing process — again usually head first. Why a snake which has a

highly potent venom also constricts its prey is not clear. It may be that its short fangs do not easily pierce the protective scales of some of the large skinks it preys on; or that the venom, although potent, may act so slowly that the prey could escape unless the snake holds it; or a combination of both. Both coiling and strike/release are options for minimising prey retaliation.

A Coastal Taipan feeding on a house mouse. Steve Wilson

Snakes can swallow prey much larger than their head and mouth size would suggest possible. The bones of the lower jaws of snakes are not fused, but are joined by ligament. This ligament can stretch, and the bones of the palate and upper jaw are also loosely articulated. A small wallaby or a large hen would pose no problems for a Carpet Python. Similarly, a near fully grown Bandicoot is easily swallowed by a 2 m Coastal Taipan.

## Breeding

Snakes, like some other animals, move into reproductive mode in spring. Mating takes place, and in due course young are born or hatch from their eggs to feed, grow, breed and continue the cycle.

Male combat has been observed during the breeding season in many species found in the Greater Brisbane Region — Carpet Python, Keelback, Marsh Snake, Red-bellied Black, Black Whip Snake, Eastern Brown and Coastal Taipan. These are all species in which the male grows larger than the female.

Combat is a complicated and highly strenuous affair in which two males engage in a ritualised test of strength. It can take from two or three minutes to almost an hour. The snakes inter-twine their bodies, raise their heads, and climb higher and higher until they topple over; then they begin again.

Black Whip Snakes in combat. Jeanette Covacevich

The reasons for this behaviour are unclear. Territoriality, competition between males for mates, testing receptivity in females, driving a rival from a receptive female, gaining access to prey, and defence against homosexual courtship have all been proposed as explanations of the combat phenomenon.

Combat is usually a prelude to mating which, in contrast, is a passive event. Snakes find each other by tracking pheromones — chemical compounds secreted in response to stimulus. They approach cautiously and begin a series of gentle bumps, side brushes and nudges. Mating is slow, prolonged and repeated. The "penis" is a paired organ — two hemipenes — which normally lies inside the body behind the cloaca, the single opening for reproduction and excretion of waste. The size, shape, number and pattern of flounces, whorls and soft spines of the hemipenes vary from species to species, and these variations ensure that the selected mate belongs to the right species. The differences in hemipenes between species are so consistent that they have been one of the most reliable ways to identify species and genera.

When mating occurs, either hemipene can be inserted into the female's cloaca. For this phase, the snakes may lie quietly side by side or slightly intertwined.

Most snakes are solitary — they mate and move on. Promiscuity prevails. Concepts of family and fidelity have no relevance in the world of snakes. Pairing for life is unknown and has not been reliably observed, even for a season.

Some species are, however, communal for some of the time. A large aggregation of hundreds of snakes of three species (Carpet Python, Common Tree Snake, Brown Tree Snake) has been reported from near Cooroy, south of Gympie. The snakes were found in dead, hollow eucalypt trees.

Communal nesting has also been reported for the Yellow-faced Whip Snake. About 600 eggs from this species were found in 1972 in a road cutting near Gympie. As each female Yellow-faced Whip Snake lays 6–9 eggs in a clutch, this represents either a large gathering of snakes or repeated egg deposition by fewer specimens, in an ideal spot for incubation.

**Keelbacks newly emerged from eggs** Queenland Museum

Of the 31 species of snakes occurring in the Brisbane region, most (21 species) are egg-layers. The remainder bear live young. In cool, temperate areas (where developing young need protection from the cold), live bearers are more common.

Parental care is known in other reptiles (eg some crocodiles), but it is rare among snakes. Once female snakes lay their eggs or give birth, they usually leave their offspring to the vagaries of weather, food shortages and predation.

Sometimes (as with Red-bellied Blacks), a female may even devour some of her progeny.

Pythons are an exception. After the female lays her eggs, she coils around them and guards and incubates them for 2–3 months until they hatch. As the sun rises on the carefully chosen nest site and warms the eggs, the female will leave them to bask. When shade envelops the eggs and they cool, the female, now warm, will return and wrap herself around them for the night. She will, when necessary, increase her body heat by producing waves of shivering movements. Female Carpet Pythons, although generally inoffensive, will defend their potential progeny with vigour.

In the species accounts that follow, snakes are listed in family groups. Because the need to identify a snake can sometimes be urgent, species are arranged in decreasing order of danger and the family with the most dangerous species is listed first.

The plus signs after the species name are a measure of the probability of finding the snake in the Greater Brisbane Region: +++ most likely; ++ quite likely; + unlikely; − very unlikely, but possible at the edge of the region.

## Elapid Snakes (Elapidae)

Elapids are the venomous species which dominate the Australian snake fauna. Their fangs (hollow teeth that are connected via ducts to venom glands near the eyes) are immovable, and set at the front of the upper jaw. Although the group includes some of the world's most lethal snakes, the majority of elapids are inoffensive and virtually harmless. (See the essay at the beginning of this section for danger ratings and venom effects).

At least 15 species of elapid snakes live in the Brisbane region (+, ++, +++), and an additional 7 (–) live nearby.

Steve Wilson

### Coastal Taipan *Oxyuranus scutellatus* (–)

**Identification:** Length 2 m (to 3 m). Head long, with distinctive angular brow over each eye. Pale to dark brown; paler brown to cream on snout; belly cream blotched with orange. Midbody scales in 21–23 rows; anal single, subcaudals divided.

**Habitat and Range:** Favours well-drained grassy woodlands, especially with blady grass and lantana; shuns dense moist forests and wetlands. Occurs immediately to the south and west of the Greater Brisbane Region; from Closeburn, Camp Mountain, Canungra, Beaudesert and Ipswich. South-eastern Qld to Cape York Peninsula and patchily across northern Australia.

**Notes:** Active by day. Feeds only on warm-blooded prey, especially rats. Egg-layer (7–11). Normally shy and retiring, but nervous and aggressive if cornered or harassed. **Dangerous**; venom strongly neurotoxic and coagulant; apply first aid and seek urgent medical attention for all suspected bites.

**Similar Species:** Eastern Brown Snake (see p. 200). Taipan has more midbody scale rows (21–23 vs. 17) and longer head with more angular brow. Young Taipans lack black head and neck blotches seen on young Eastern Browns.

## Tiger Snake  *Notechis scutatus* (–)

**Identification:** Length 1.5 m. Shades of brown to olive, usually with numerous ragged-edged crossbands. Midbody scales in 17–19 rows; anal and subcaudals single.

**Habitat and Range:** Elevated moist dense rainforest or swampy coastal wallum. Not recorded from the Brisbane region except for a single specimen in the Museum collection labelled North Stradbroke Island, 1912. Scattered localities in south-eastern Qld (Bunya Mountains, Lamington Plateau, Beerwah, Caloundra).

**Notes:** Active by day. **Dangerous**; venom strongly neurotoxic and coagulant; apply first aid and seek urgent medical attention for all suspected bites.

Steve Wilson

## Death Adder  *Acanthophis antarcticus* (+)

**Identification:** Length to 0.5 m. Body short and thick, with distinct triangular head and abruptly slender tail, segmented at tip and terminating in spur. Shades of grey to reddish-brown with narrow, ragged-edged crossbands. Midbody scales in 21–23 rows; anal single, subcaudals single anteriorly, divided posteriorly.

**Habitat and Range:** Undisturbed eucalypt forest, under leaf litter and overhanging foliage. Rare in the Brisbane region, largely restricted to outer north-western and western suburbs and peripheral bushland, including Mt Nebo and Mt Glorious. Widespread in eastern and southern mainland Australia.

**Notes:** Active by day and night. Prey (frogs, lizards, birds and mammals) lured within striking range by wriggling segmented tail to mimic small twitching animal. Bears live young (1–20). Scarcity throughout the region possibly due to clearing of bushland and undergrowth, and attempted predation on the highly poisonous Cane Toad. Appears sluggish and inactive, but can move quickly and strike with incredible speed. **Dangerous**; venom neurotoxic; seek urgent medical attention for all suspected bites.

Queensland Museum

Steve Wilson

## Eastern Brown Snake
*Pseudonaja textilis* (++)

**Identification:** Length 1.5 m (may exceed 2 m). Shades of brown (rarely dark grey to black) above; belly cream flecked with orange (or dark grey on very dark coloured individuals); juveniles have black blotch on head, broad black band across neck; prominent narrow dark bands may be present or absent, even among siblings; juvenile colours normally disappear at about 50–65 cm. Midbody scales in 17 rows; anal divided, subcaudals divided (occasionally first few single).

**Habitat and Range:** All habitats except rainforest; well adapted to grazed and farmed areas, tends to avoid wetter habitats and swampland. Scarce in well settled suburbs, abundant in bushland and rural areas; present from Kenmore westward, from the north bank of the Brisbane River mouth and from Capalaba, Victoria Point and North Stradbroke Island. Widespread throughout eastern and central Australia.

**Notes:** Mainly active by day; juveniles sometimes nocturnal. Prey (frogs, reptiles, birds, mammals) subdued by combination of envenomation and constriction. Egg-layer (10–35). Pugnacious; rears up in distinctive "S" shape and strikes savagely if provoked; an unmolested snake will go quietly on its way. **Dangerous**; venom strongly neurotoxic and coagulant; apply first aid and seek urgent medical attention for all suspected bites.

**Similar species:** Taipan, (see p. 198). Eastern Brown has fewer midbody scale rows (17 vs. 21–23); a shorter head; and lacks angular brows over eyes.

## Rough-scaled Snake
*Tropidechis carinatus* (++)

Steve Wilson

**Identification:** Length 0.75 m (to 1 m). Each scale on back and sides has raised longitudinal ridge, forming prominent and distinctive keels down length of body and tail. Shades of brown to olive marked with darker cross-bands or transversely elongate blotches. Midbody scales in 23 rows; anal and subcaudals single.

**Habitat and Range:** Favours moist habitats; creek margins, rainforest, wet eucalypt forest and semi-rural areas. Most abundant locally in higher areas near Brisbane, such as the D'Aguilar Range above 400 m; patchy in lowlands, with records from Rochedale, Upper Brookfield and Eight Mile Plains. North-eastern NSW to south-eastern Qld with an isolated population in the wet tropics of north-eastern Qld.

**Notes:** Active by day or night. Eats frogs, lizards and small mammals. Forages on ground, but is one of few elapid snakes which can climb, recorded in vegetation up to 2 m. Bears live young (6–10). Pugnacious if provoked. **Dangerous**; venom neurotoxic, haemotoxic, cytotoxic and strongly coagulant; apply first aid and seek urgent medical attention for all suspected bites.

**Similar Species:** Keelback, (see p. 212). Rough-scaled has more midbody scale rows (23 vs. 15–17), and undivided subcaudals. Keelback has no fangs, only small solid teeth.

Steve Wilson

## Small-eyed Snake
*Rhinoplocephalus nigrescens* (+++)

**Identification:** Length 0.5 m (to nearly 1 m). Eyes minute and black, barely discernible from surrounding scales. Snout slightly squared from above and head slightly flattened in profile. Back and sides shiny immaculate black; belly pink, often with row of dark spots; belly colour does not extend up onto lower flanks, and is not visible unless the animal is turned over. Midbody scales in 15 rows; anal and subcaudals single.

**Habitat and Range:** Normally found under sheets of iron, rocks and logs; favours cavities behind loose bark on fallen logs. Common in most suburbs and bushland. Eastern Australia from Vic. to southern Cape York Peninsula.

**Notes:** Nocturnal. Feeds on small skinks, dragons and occasionally frogs. Bears live young (2–4). Pugnacious if provoked. **Dangerous**; a bite may produce severe symptoms; one fatality known; venom strongly myotoxic; apply first aid and seek urgent medical attention for all suspected bites.

**Similar Species:** Red-bellied Black Snake (see below). Small-eyed Snake lacks conspicuous red on lower flanks, has much smaller eyes and adults are smaller (scarcely larger than juvenile Red-bellied Blacks).

## Red-bellied Black Snake
*Pseudechis porphyriacus* (+)

**Identification:** Length 1.5 m (may exceed 2 m). Shiny immaculate black above and pink to red below; red belly pigment extends outwards onto lower flanks — easily visible on a coiled or moving snake. Midbody scales in 17 rows; anal divided, subcaudals single anteriorly, divided posteriorly (occasionally all divided).

**Habitat and Range:** Usually associated with well-watered environments — river and creek banks, swamp margins, rainforest and wet eucalypt forest; males in search of mates may stray considerable distances over varied terrain during late spring. Once common throughout region, now rare; recorded from Spring Hill in the late 1980s. Eastern Australia, from south-eastern SA to southern Cape York Peninsula.

**Notes:** Active by day. Feeds on frogs, reptiles (including snakes) and small mammals. Scarcity may be due to attempted predation on highly poisonous Cane Toad; now largely confined to cooler high altitudes where toads are scarce. Males in ritualised combat, with bodies intertwined and writhing, are often mistaken for courting pairs. **Dangerous**; venom strongly haemotoxic, cytotoxic; seek urgent medical attention for all suspected bites.

**Similar Species:** Small-eyed Snake, (see p. 202). Red belly colour of Red-bellied Blacks is easily seen as it extends onto flanks (not seen on Small-eyed Snakes unless snake is turned over); adults are much larger.

## Spotted Black Snake
*Pseudechis guttatus* (+)

Steve Wilson

**Other Names:** Blue-bellied Black Snake.

**Identification:** Length 1.5 m. Black or dark grey with scattered to clustered paler scales; belly grey to blue-grey. Midbody scales in 19 rows; anal divided, subcaudals single anteriorly, divided posteriorly.

**Habitat and Range:** Forest, grassland, pasture and cultivation on black soil. Found in dry areas to the near south and west of Brisbane including Lockyer and Brisbane Valleys, Greenbank, Ipswich and Mt Crosby. Interior of north-eastern NSW and south-eastern Qld.

**Notes:** Active by day. Feeds on frogs, lizards, snakes and small mammals. Egg-layer (7–13). **Dangerous**; venom neurotoxic, haemotoxic, cytotoxic, coagulant; bites have rarely (if ever) resulted in death; apply first aid and seek urgent medical attention for all suspected bites.

Steve Wilson

## Black Whip Snake
*Demansia vestigiata* (-)

**Identification:** Length 1.5 m. Eye very large; body and tail long and slender. Rich brown above, spotted with black and flecked with white; small dark blotches on top of head; belly green-grey. Midbody scales in 15 rows; anal and subcaudals divided.

**Habitat and Range:** Open eucalypt forest, pasture. Recorded from Toorbul, Harrisville, North Stradbroke Island and Esk, with old records from Brisbane. Extensive distribution from Sunshine Coast northwards. Northern Australia.

**Notes:** Active by day. **Potentially dangerous**, especially large specimens; a bite may produce local pain, and severe systemic effects; apply first aid and seek medical attention for all suspected bites.

Queensland Museum

## Pale-headed Snake
*Hoplocephalus bitorquatus* (–)

**Identification:** Length 0.8 m. Head broad and distinct from narrow neck. Grey above; paler grey band across rear of head, bordered behind by black band and anteriorly by row of black blotches; lips barred with black; belly grey. Midbody scales in 19–21 rows; anal and subcaudals single.

**Habitat and Range:** Wet and dry eucalypt forest. Single Brisbane record from Mitchelton (1961); common on Darling Downs and near Brisbane (Beaudesert, Brisbane Valley, Caboolture). Central eastern Australia.

**Notes:** Nocturnal. Bears live young (7–10). Arboreal. **Potentially dangerous**; one serious case of envenomation by a large specimen has been reported; first aid and medical attention needed.

## Stephen's Banded Snake
*Hoplocephalus stephensii* (+)

Steve Wilson

**Identification:** Length 0.75 m. Wide head, clearly distinct from narrow neck. Simple pale grey and black bands across body, sharply demarcated on front half and darkening with weaker contrast towards tail; dark and pale vertical bars on lip; belly grey. Midbody scales in 21 rows; anal and subcaudals single.

**Habitat and Range:** Rainforest and wet eucalypt forest; an adept climber, sheltering beneath loose bark, in tree hollows and (rarely) in rafters. Now rare or absent in suburbs (old localities: Enoggera, Mitchelton); moderately common at higher altitudes in D'Aguilar Range (Mt Nebo, Mt Glorious). North-eastern NSW to south-eastern Qld.

**Notes:** Nocturnal. Bears live young (2–3). One of few arboreal elapid snakes. Pugnacious if provoked. **Potentially dangerous**; bite may produce severe local symptoms; first aid and medical attention needed.

## Yellow-faced Whip Snake
*Demansia psammophis* (+++)

Queensland Museum

**Identification:** Length 0.75 m (to 1 m). Very slender with long thin tail and large prominent eyes. Bluish-grey, usually with rusty flush or pair of stripes along front third of back; obvious pale rim around eye and a dark streak curving back beneath it to form a distinct comma; narrow dark line across front of snout, between nostrils; belly usually greenish. Midbody scales in 15 rows; anal and subcaudals divided.

**Habitat and Range:** Open grass and woodland; under rocks, sheets of iron; scarce in rainforest and wetlands. Abundant in all Brisbane suburbs. Widespread through most of Australia.

**Notes:** Active by day. Feeds on small lizards. Egg-layer (6–9). Swift and alert; keen vision. **Potentially dangerous**, especially to children; some bites symptomless, others with fairly severe outcomes; first aid and medical attention needed.

Steve Wilson

## Marsh Snake *Hemiaspis signata* (+++)

**Other Name:** Swamp Snake.

**Identification:** Length 0.5 m. Large eye with round pupil. Shades of olive to grey above; two narrow white lines on each side of face, running through upper lip and from eye onto neck; belly dark grey to black. Midbody scales in 17 rows; anal divided, subcaudals single.

**Habitat and Range:** Wet habitats such as creek banks, edges of swamps, rainforest, heathland, well-watered gardens; may be seen under boards or sheets of iron, or basking or foraging near thick low vegetation. Throughout suburban Brisbane. Eastern Australia, from south-eastern NSW to north-eastern Qld.

**Notes:** Active mainly by day; at night in hot weather. Feeds on small frogs and lizards. Bears live young (4–20). **Virtually harmless** (large individuals may be potentially dangerous).

Steve Wilson

## Golden-crowned Snake
*Cacophis squamulosus* (++)

**Identification:** Length 0.5 m. Greyish-brown with broad, pale yellow-brown streak on each side of neck, sweeping forward onto face (but not forming a cross-band at back of head); belly orange with median line of black spots. Midbody scales in 15 rows; anal and subcaudals divided.

**Habitat and Range:** Rainforest, moist eucalypt forest, heathland, and urban areas. All suburbs, wherever lush vegetation and ground cover of rocks, logs or compost prevails. Mid-eastern NSW to mid-eastern Qld.

**Notes:** Nocturnal. Feeds on small frogs and lizards. Egg-layer (6). When provoked, rears up and "mock-strikes" with mouth closed. **Virtually harmless**; may bite if provoked; large individuals may be potentially dangerous.

## Bandy Bandy *Vermicella annulata* (+)

Steve Wilson

**Identification:** Length 0.5 m (to 0.75 m). Sharply contrasting black and white rings encircling body. Midbody scales in 15 rows; anal and subcaudals divided.

**Habitat and Range:** A burrower, found beneath soil, under stumps, rocks and logs in virtually all habitats, from rainforest to desert. Moderately common in peripheral and urban bushland, uncommon in suburbs. Widespread throughout Australia.

**Notes:** Occasionally forages on surface at night, particularly following rain. Feeds on Blind Snakes. Egg-layer (2–13). When threatened, contorts body into rigid, vertically oriented loops, thrashing and realigning posture when touched. **Virtually harmless**; weakly venomous, small mouth, inoffensive; one case with moderately severe local symptoms reported.

## Dwyer's Snake *Suta dwyeri* (-)

Queensland Museum

**Identification:** Length 0.4 m. Shades of brown; sharply delineated black blotch on top of head. Midbody scales in 15 rows; anal and subcaudals single.

**Habitat and Range:** Dry eucalypt forest, black soil pasture. Mainly found west of Great Dividing Range, extending eastward into Brisbane Valley. Eastern interior of Australia from northern Vic. to south-eastern Qld.

**Notes:** Nocturnal. Feeds on skinks, dragons, snakes. Egg-layer. **Virtually harmless**; weakly venomous.

Steve Wilson

## Australian Coral Snake
### *Simoselaps australis* (+)

**Identification:** Length 0.5 m. Snout slightly upturned with an acute transverse cutting edge. Coral pink above with numerous narrow bands comprising dark-edged pale scales; dark blotch on head and broad dark band across neck; belly cream. Midbody scales in 17 rows; anal and subcaudals divided.

**Habitat and Range:** A burrower, sheltering beneath embedded stumps and rocks or in soil cracks. Brisbane Valley (Gatton, Ipswich) and adjacent parts of Brisbane (Greenbank, Grovely, Goodna, Camira, Mt Crosby). Mainly arid and semi-arid eastern interior of Australia.

**Notes:** Nocturnal. Feeds on skinks, lizard and snake eggs. Egg-layer (4–6). **Virtually harmless**; inoffensive; weakly venomous.

Queensland Museum

## Carpentaria Snake
### *Rhinoplocephalus boschmai* (-)

**Identification:** Length 0.45 m. Brown, darker on scale bases and with darker suffusion along centre of back. Midbody scales in 15 rows; anal and subcaudals single.

**Habitat and Range:** Dry eucalypt forest, pasture. Very common on Darling Downs, extending eastward along Brisbane Valley. Eastern Qld.

**Notes:** Nocturnal. Probably bears live young. **Virtually harmless**; inoffensive; weakly venomous.

## Red-naped Snake   *Furina diadema* (++)

**Identification:** Length 0.25 m. Eye very small, black and barely discernible from surrounding scales. Body reddish-brown with fine, darker, netted pattern; head and neck glossy black, with prominent red to orange blotch on nape; belly white or cream. Midbody scales in 15 rows; anal and subcaudals divided.

**Habitat and Range:** Dry eucalypt forest and pasture. Found hiding under boards, rocks and sheets of iron or in soil cracks. Common

Steve Wilson

in western suburbs (Kenmore, Brookfield, Karana Downs), at Mt Crosby and in the Ipswich area. Eastern Australia.

**Notes:** Nocturnal. Feeds exclusively on small diurnal lizards, especially skinks, presumably captured at night while they sleep. Egg-layer (10). May rear head and forebody if provoked but seldom, if ever, attempts to bite. **Virtually harmless**; inoffensive and weakly venomous.

## Grey Snake *Hemiaspis damelii* (-)

Steve Wilson

**Identification:** Length 0.6 m. Grey above; black blotch on top of head of juveniles, contracting to form dark nape band on adults. Midbody scales in 17 rows; anal divided, subcaudals single.

**Habitat and Range:** Dry eucalypt forest and pasture; sheltering under logs, exfoliated bark, and in soil cracks. Largely restricted to dry areas west of Great Dividing Range (Darling Downs) extending eastward into Brisbane Valley. Interior of south-eastern Qld and north-eastern NSW.

**Notes:** Nocturnal. Bears live young (10). **Virtually harmless**; weakly venomous.

## Dwarf-crowned Snake
*Cacophis krefftii* (++)

Steve Wilson

**Identification:** Length 0.35 m. Dark grey above, with narrow yellow band across neck; belly yellow, with narrow dark edges to ventral scales. Midbody scales in 15 rows; anal and subcaudals divided.

**Habitat and Range:** Rainforest, moist eucalypt forest, and lush well-vegetated gardens; normally found beneath compost, stones and logs where damp conditions prevail. Common but not widespread across Brisbane. Mid-eastern NSW to mid-eastern Qld.

**Notes:** Nocturnal. Feeds on small lizards and frogs. Egg-layer (2–3). When provoked, rears up and "mock-strikes" with mouth closed. **Virtually harmless**; very small and inoffensive; weakly venomous.

## White-crowned Snake
*Cacophis harriettae* (+++)

**Identification:** Length 0.45 m. Dark grey above and below; broad white band across neck, sweeping forward onto face, enclosing a black blotch on top of head; belly light grey. Midbody scales in 15 rows; anal and subcaudals divided.

**Habitat and Range:** Rainforest, moist eucalypt forest, woodland and heathland. Shelters in garden compost heaps, beneath logs or rocks — wherever slightly damp conditions prevail. Abundant in all Brisbane suburbs, including densely populated inner city regions. North-eastern NSW to mid-eastern Qld.

**Notes:** Nocturnal. Feeds on small skinks. Egg-layer (5). When provoked, rears head and forebody and "mock-strikes" with mouth closed. This display of bluff has led to the demise of many snakes at hands of startled gardeners. Possibly Brisbane's most abundant species. **Virtually harmless**; inoffensive and weakly venomous.

Steve Wilson

# Colubrid Snakes (Colubridae)

Outside Australia, colubrids dominate the snake fauna. They may be arboreal, aquatic, burrowing and open foraging snakes. Australia has only 11 species, and colubrids appear to be relatively recent arrivals to a continent already occupied by a plethora of venomous snakes with front fangs (elapids).

Australian colubrids either have no fangs, or fangs at the back of the mouth to kill small animals as they are being swallowed. The three Brisbane species are egg-layers.

## Brown Tree Snake  Boiga irregularis (+++)

**Identification:** Length 1.3 m (to 2 m). Body and tail extremely slender with bulbous head, distinct from narrow neck; eyes large and protruding with vertical cat-like pupils. Brown above with indistinct ragged-edged darker crossbands on back and sides; belly cream to apricot. Midbody scales in 19-21 rows; anal single, subcaudals divided.

Steve Wilson

**Habitat and Range:** Rainforest, wet or dry eucalypt forest, heathland, outer urban areas; found coiled on rafters in buildings, on foliage or rock faces, in tree hollows or caves, or on ground. Common in all suburbs and adjacent bushland. Northern and eastern Australia south to Sydney area.

**Notes:** Nocturnal. Agile climber, able to extend its slender body across gaps between branches. Feeds mainly on mammals and birds. Occasionally enters bird cages (including those suspended from rafters), consumes hapless occupant and, unable to escape through the bars, remains coiled for horrified pet owner to discover in the morning. Pugnacious if provoked, rearing head and neck in "S" posture and striking with mouth agape. **Virtually harmless**; weakly venomous with small fangs set at rear of mouth; large individuals should be treated with caution.

Steve Wilson

## Keelback *Tropidonophis mairii* (+++)

**Other Names:** Freshwater Snake.

**Identification:** Length 0.75 m. Each scale on back and sides has raised longitudinal ridge, forming prominent and distinctive parallel keels down length of body and tail. Shades of brown to olive with indistinct, ragged-edged darker crossbands; dark sutures between scales on upper lip; lower flanks often flushed with orange; belly cream. Midbody scales in 15 (rarely 17) rows; anal and subcaudals divided.

**Habitat and Range:** Wet and dry eucalypt forest, heathland, pasture and urban areas; generally seen foraging close to low vegetation or sheltering beneath logs, old iron or boards. Abundant in well-watered lowland areas of Brisbane region, favouring creek edges and swamp margins. Northern and eastern Australia, south to north-eastern NSW.

**Notes:** Active by day or night. Feeds mainly on frogs, occasionally lizards; one of few Australian animals able to consume young Cane Toads, tadpoles and eggs successfully, though attempts to eat large toads usually prove fatal. Egg-layer (5-12). Preference for moist habitats, coupled with transverse arrangement of dark markings has led to persecution under name of "Swamp Tiger". There is no "Swamp Tiger" species; the true Tiger Snake is largely confined to cool uplands and absent from Brisbane and immediate surrounds. **Non-venomous**.

**Similar Species:** Rough-scaled Snake, (see p. 201). Keelback has fewer midbody scale rows (15-17 vs. 23), divided subcaudals, possesses a loreal scale and has no fangs, only small teeth.

## Common Tree Snake
*Dendrelaphis punctulatus* (+++)

Queensland Museum

**Other Name:** Green Tree Snake.

**Identification:** Length 1.2 m (to 2 m). Extremely slender body, whip-like tail; ridge extends along outer edges of belly. Colour extremely variable, back and sides olive, green, black or, rarely, blue; diffuse to intense yellow often present on throat and belly; pale blue flecks often discernible on anterior flanks. Midbody scales in 13 rows; anal and subcaudals divided.

**Habitat and Range:** Rainforest edges, wet or dry eucalypt forest, heathland, pasture, urban areas; favours lush vegetation, particularly near water courses. Common throughout Brisbane; encountered in gardens, on ground or in trees, in houses, on rafters and verandah railings. Northern and eastern Australia, south to south-eastern NSW.

**Notes:** Active by day. Feeds on frogs and skinks. Egg-layer (6–12). Brisbane's most frequently encountered climbing snake; most sloughed skins presented to Queensland Museum for identification are from this species. Dark specimens with yellow bellies are often erroneously killed as "Yellow-bellied Black Snakes", a name that cannot be applied to any Australian snake species. When harassed, dilates throat and forebody to reveal pale blue between scales. If grasped, stinking secretion may be emitted from anal glands. **Non-venomous.**

# Pythons (Boidae)

Pythons are non-venomous, with large, backwardly curved solid teeth, but no hollow fangs. A python kills its prey by constriction; suffocating it within ever-tightening coils.

Warm-blooded prey is located by means of heat-sensory pits located along the lower jaw. These can detect temperature changes of less than one-thirtieth of one degree. In the Brisbane region, pythons can also be distinguished from all other snakes by the numerous rows of body scales (35 or more vs 24 or less).

Pythons occur in temperate to tropical areas from Australia through Asia to Africa. Australia supports 14 species. Only two occur in Brisbane.

Steve Wilson

## Carpet Python
*Morelia spilota variegata* (+++)

**Identification:** Length 2.5 m (to over 3 m). Series of pits in scales along lower jaw. Olive ground colour with dark-edged fawn cross-bands, blotches and stripes; pattern and colour extremely variable. Midbody scales in 40–60 rows; anal single, subcaudals divided; head scales very small, bead-like and irregularly arranged.

**Habitat and Range:** Rainforest, wet or dry eucalypt forest, heathland, pasture, agricultural and urban areas; may be encountered on ground, draped across boughs of trees or coiled quietly in undergrowth; frequent resident in the roofs of houses, even in well-settled inner suburbs. Common in all Brisbane suburbs, particularly areas retaining good tree cover. Widespread in northern, eastern and southern Australia.

**Notes:** Active by day or night. Feeds mainly on "warm-blooded" prey — possums, rats, flying foxes and birds; occasionally poultry, domestic cats and small dogs. Attempts to prey on Cane Toads invariably prove fatal. Egg-layer (15–47). Unpredictable behaviour, sometimes aggressive (especially female protecting nest). **Non-venomous**; bite may cause lacerations; tetanus protection recommended.

## Spotted Python  *Antaresia maculosa*  (+)

**Identification:** Length 1 m. Series of pits in scales along lower jaw. Fawn with numerous dark purplish-brown, roughly circular blotches, tending to coalesce on nape and tail to form wavy stripe; belly cream. Midbody scales in 35–44 rows; anal single, subcaudals divided; head almost covered with large symmetrical scales

**Habitat and Range:** Favours dry forest and woodlands, especially near rock outcrops, cliffs and caves. Very uncommon in Brisbane area, but occasionally encountered in outer suburbs and urban and peripheral bushland. Common in eastern Qld and north-eastern NSW.

**Notes:** Nocturnal. Feeds on lizards, birds and small mammals. Egg-layer (20–30). Formerly known as "Children's Python", but that species is now considered to be restricted to far northern Australia. **Non-venomous**.

Steve Wilson

## Blind Snakes (Typhlopidae)

Blind Snakes are small (to 0.4 m), smooth, worm-like, burrowing snakes with eyes reduced to diffuse dark spots, probably capable of discerning little more than light and dark. The tail is bluntly rounded, terminating in a short spur. Scales are small, glossy and close-fitting, and belly scales are small and undifferentiated from remaining body scales.

Blind Snakes are egg-layers. They feed on termites and the eggs, larvae and pupae of ants. Blind snakes are often uncovered in the galleries and chambers of their prey or in soil cracks, beneath rocks and stones. At night, particularly following rain, they emerge to forage on the surface. All species are non-venomous. Their sole defences are their cryptic habits and the ability of some species to exude an unpleasant odour if harassed.

At least four species occur within the Brisbane area. They are largely restricted to urban bushland and outer areas.

Identification of Blind Snakes is difficult, requiring microscopic examination to count scales. The following key will identify the Brisbane species.

**KEY:**

1.    (a) Midbody scales (including ventrals) in 20 rows — **2**.
      (b) Midbody scales (including ventrals) in 22 rows — ***Ramphotyphlops nigrescens.***
      (c) Midbody scales (including ventrals) in 24 rows — ***Ramphotyphlops ligatus.***

2.    (a) Body slender and thread-like; colour pink — ***Ramphotyphlops wiedii.***
      (b) Body robust; colour grey — ***Ramphotyphlops proximus.***

*R. nigrescens.*    Steve Wilson

*R. ligatus.*    Steve Wilson

*R. wiedii.*    Steve Wilson

*R. proximus.*    Steve Wilson

# Sea Snakes

Patrick Couper

These snakes, whose affinities lie with the front-fanged land snakes, are superbly adapted to life in a watery domain. A sea snake's most distinctive feature is its paddle-shaped tail, which provides the propulsive thrust necessary for swimming. Sea snakes, like all reptiles, are air-breathers and therefore must surface periodically. The nostrils, positioned on top of the snout, are sealed by valve-like flaps when the snake dives.

Of some 54 known species, 11 have been recorded from Moreton Bay: *Acalyptophis peronii, Aipysurus eydouxii, Aipysurus laevis, Astrotia stokesii, Disteira kingii, Disteira major, Emydocephalus annulatus, Enhydrina schistosa, Hydrophis elegans, Hydrophis mcdowelli,* and *Pelamis platurus.* Of these, only the Elegant Sea Snake (*H. elegans*) is resident in the Bay. The Yellow-bellied Sea Snake (*P. platurus*) occurs outside the Bay but is frequently found beach-washed on Bay islands. Sea snakes are venomous and should be treated with caution.

Queensland Museum

## Elegant Sea Snake *Hydrophis elegans*

**Identification:** Length to 2 m. Body elongated, with hind parts compressed. Head grey, olive or yellowish (darker in juveniles); back greyish with numerous dark crossbands (reduced to mid-back blotches in adults, these may be obscure), dark line often present between the blotches; flanks cream with dark spots.

**Scalation:** Midbody in 37 to 49 rows; ventrals 345 to 432.

**Habitat and Range:** Shallow muddy-bottomed habitats. Coastal waters of northern Australia and southern New Guinea.

**Notes:** Commonly found beach-washed. Familiar to prawners as part of the trawling bycatch.

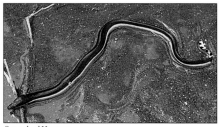

Queensland Museum

## Yellow-bellied Sea Snake
### *Pelamis platurus*

**Identification:** Length to 90 cm. Body moderately robust; bicoloured — black back, yellow belly; tail yellow with black blotches. Elongated head.

**Scalation:** Midbody in 47 to 69 rows; ventrals 264 to 406.

**Habitat and Range:** Oceanic species, commonly found in shallower continental waters around Indian and Pacific Oceans.

**Notes:** Most frequently found beach-washed species — ocean beaches of sand islands.

# Birds

Dr Christine Cannon, Gregory V. Czechura, Dr Darryl Jones, Wayne Longmore, Ric Natrass, Christoph Pavey, Jean Tilly, Ian Venables, Dr Peter Woodall

B risbane people are fortunate that so many varied habitats suitable for bird life exist within 50 km of the city. The Greater Brisbane Region is a sanctuary for more than 370 species of birds, both native and introduced, representing 80 families. The South-East Queensland and northern New South Wales area is one of the richest in Australia for birds and the most species for a capital city have been recorded in Brisbane. There are many comprehensive field guides on birds available and it is not possible to cover all species here. The birds listed represent some of the most commonly encountered in the region and also reflect the most common inquiries to the Queensland Museum. They are grouped according to their taxonomic order. Size is indicated by the use of silhouettes of four familiar birds — pelican (large), crow (medium), Willy Wagtail (small) and wren (very small). Details of nesting behaviour have been excluded because of conservation considerations. Birds of prey (raptors) have been treated separately because of their special appeal.

**SIZE ICONS**

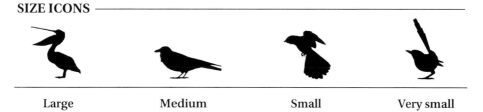

| Large | Medium | Small | Very small |

## Mound-builders

Queensland Museum

### Australian Brush-turkey
*Alectura lathami*

**Other Names:** Scrub Turkey, Brush-turkey, Wild Turkey

**Identification:** Length 64 cm. Head and neck skin crimson; upper body brownish-black, chest skin creamish-yellow; underbody barred dark and pale grey. Breeding male — bright yellow neck wattle.

**Habitat and Range:** Rainforest, dry scrubs and dense vegetation throughout region, including bushy suburbs; from Cape York Peninsula south to Hawkesbury River, NSW; rarely west of Great Dividing Range.

## Ducks and Geese

Ray Viljoen

### Magpie Goose   *Anseranas semipalmata*

**Other Names:** Pied Goose

**Identification:** Length 70–90 cm. Large. Head and long neck black; body white; wings black. Legs yellow.

**Habitat and Range:** Found in open wetland or grassy habitats throughout region including parks and playing fields. Coastal wetlands eastern and northern Australia.

Ray Viljoen

### Australian Wood Duck
*Chenonetta jubata*

**Other Names:** Maned Duck, Maned Goose, Woody.

**Identification:** Length 48 cm. Grey with brownish head and mane and black undertail. In flight, characteristic white "block" on inner lower section of wing. Female — white stripe above and below eye.

**Habitat and Range:** Common throughout area, favours lakes, dams, wetlands and grasslands. Mainland, except for arid centre and Tas.

## Pacific Black Duck  *Anas superciliosa*

Bruce Cowell

**Other Names:** Black Duck, Wild Duck

**Identification:** Length 56 cm. Head brown-black; wing feathers dark brown with lighter edges; off-white banding with brown-black stripes round eyes; iridescent green window (speculum) in upper wing.

**Habitat and Range:** Swamps, dams and reservoirs throughout region. Most of mainland and Tas. except for arid western Australia.

# Grebes

## Australasian Grebe
*Tachybaptus novaehollandiae*

Ray Viljoen

**Other Names:** Dabchick, Australian Little Grebe, Little Grebe, Diver.

**Identification:** Length 25 cm. Small, body brownish-grey; head, back of neck dark grey; chin and throat pale. Bill short and pointed. Breeding plumage — black head with rufous stripe side of head and neck; yellow patch on base of bill. Juvenile resembles non-breeding adult but with black and white net-like pattern over face.

**Habitat and Range:** Widespread on freshwater wetlands. Found throughout Australia.

# Petrels and Albatrosses

## Wedge-tailed Shearwater
*Puffinis pacificus*

Ray Viljoen

**Other Names:** Mutton Bird

**Identification:** Length 46 cm. Dark brown with wedge-shaped tail; beak dark grey; pinkish legs and feet. Pale form also — brown above; underwing and underbody mostly white. Wings held well forward in flight. Identification difficult — very similar to other large shearwaters, distinguished by flight and underwing pattern. Readers should refer to specialist seabird guides.

**Habitat and Range:** Migratory seabird.

# Gannets and Boobies

Queensland Museum

## Australasian Gannet *Morus serrator*

**Other Names:** Booby

**Identification:** Length 85-95 cm. Cigar-shaped body mainly white; head golden yellow; outer wing and central tail black. Wings long and narrow; beak tapered from thick base to sharp point.

**Habitat and Range:** Usually seen offshore. Coastal waters of southern half of Australia.

**Notes:** Often seen plunging into sea with half-folded wings to capture prey.

# Darters

Bruce Cowell

## Darter *Anhinga melanogaster*

**Other Names:** Snakebird, Australian Darter

**Identification:** Length 90 cm. Greyish-brown to blackish with long, thin, kinked neck; large rounded tail and thin, rapier-like beak. Pale streaky pattern on wings. Male — blackish with pale stripe on cheek and neck; chestnut patch on throat and neck. Female — greyish above, whitish throat and dark-edged facial stripe.

**Habitat and Range:** Saltwater and freshwater wetlands, including estuaries, lakes and rivers. Most of mainland Australia except arid centre.

# Cormorants

Ray Viljoen

## Little Pied Cormorant
*Phalacrocorax melanoleucos*

**Other Names:** Yellow-faced or Black and White Shag

**Identification:** Length 50 cm. Head and back black, beak pale yellow, underbody white.

**Habitat and Range:** Along Brisbane and Bremer Rivers, around Moreton Bay, and near large reservoirs, creeks and streams. Coastal Australia and New Zealand.

### Great Cormorant  *Phalacrocorax carbo*

**Other Names:** Black Shag, Black Cormorant

**Identification:** Length 76 cm. Body black, throat pale buff.

**Habitat and Range:** Sheltered saltwater bays and swamps; occurs over whole continent. Also India, South Africa and elsewhere.

Queensland Museum

## Pelicans

### Australian Pelican
*Pelecanus conspicillatus*

**Identification:** Length 1.6 m. White head and body, wings black, bill pinkish-cream.

**Habitat and Range:** Mudflats near City Botanic Gardens or near mouth of Brisbane River. Common around Brisbane region. Australia generally, wherever a suitable habitat of estuaries, rivers and mudflats occur. Also New Guinea and some northern islands.

Bruce Cowell

## Egrets and Herons

### White-faced Heron
*Egretta novaehollandiae*

**Other Names:** Blue Crane

**Identification:** Length 65 cm. Upper body blue-grey with bronze sheen on breast; face white; beak black; legs olive-yellow.

**Habitat and Range:** Very common. Waterholes, swamps, creeks, along Brisbane River, wherever habitat is suitable. Australia-wide; also New Zealand and islands.

Ray Viljoen

Queensland Museum

## Intermediate Egret *Ardea intermedia*

**Other Names:** Plumed Egret

**Identification:** Length 64 cm. Body white; beak yellow; legs dark grey. Breeding adult — green facial skin and orange beak.

**Habitat and Range:** Low-lying areas such as swamps, lakes and streams. Northern, eastern and southern Australia; also Africa, Japan, Malaysia and New Guinea.

Ray Viljoen

## Cattle Egret *Ardea ibis*

**Identification:** Length 53 cm. Body white. Distinguished by shorter, stouter bill — non-breeding adult yellow; breeding adult reddish-orange with yellow tip; juvenile blackish. Breeding plumage — orange-buff plumes on nape, back and breast. Stout grey legs.

**Habitat and Range:** Usually found near livestock. Large aggregations throughout region. Coastal margin of mainland Australia, except Nullarbor region; also much of Africa, Asia and the Americas.

Ray Viljoen

## Striated Heron *Butorides striatus*

**Other Names:** Mangrove Heron, Striated Bittern, Mangrove Bittern

**Identification:** Length 50 cm. Stocky, short-necked, short-tailed with long pointed bill. Body dark grey above and brownish-grey below; black cap and upper part of beak; yellow patch around eye and lower beak. White stripe under throat speckled with black. Legs yellow. Juvenile — similar, but heavily streaked with greyish-brown; white on sides of face and underbody.

**Habitat and Range:** Found in and near mangroves, sandbanks and tidal mudflats. Coastal fringe of northern and eastern Australia.

# Ibises

## Australian White Ibis
### *Threskiornis molucca*

**Other Names:** Sacred Ibis

**Identification:** Length 75 cm. Body white; head and throat black; long curved black beak; black plumes and feathers near tail.

**Habitat and Range:** Common throughout region in grasslands, wetlands, parks. Eastern half and coastal south-west of mainland Australia; also Moluccas and New Guinea.

Queensland Museum

# Storks

## Black-necked Stork
### *Ephippiorhynchus asiaticus*

**Other Names:** Jabiru

**Identification:** Length 1.3 m. Head, bill, neck and throat black; body white; wings black except for white shoulder margin; legs red.

**Habitat and Range:** Uncommon to rare in Brisbane and environs. Swamps, river wetlands, mangrove flats, lagoons and dams. From north-western WA to northern and eastern coastal Australia as far south as Hawkesbury River, NSW; also India, Malaysia and New Guinea.

Ray Viljoen

# Rails and Crakes

## Buff-banded Rail   *Gallirallis philippensis*

**Other Names:** Banded Rail, Banded Land Rail

**Identification:** Length 30 cm. Head brown; nape chestnut; back brown and black with white spots; throat grey; chest rufous; belly fine black and white barring.

**Habitat and Range:** Streams, swamps and moist areas with cover. North-western through to eastern and southern Australia including Tas.; also Philippines, New Guinea and New Zealand.

Ray Viljoen

Ray Viljoen

## Dusky Moorhen *Gallinula tenebrosa*

**Identification:** Length 42 cm. Body very dark brown above, grey below; hard red shield on forehead; red yellow-tipped beak; red legs.

**Habitat and Range:** Freshwater wetlands throughout region and moist areas with thick cover, also ornamental lakes. Eastern and south-western Australia.

# Curlews and Sandpipers

Ray Viljoen

## Bar-tailed Godwit *Limosa lapponica*

**Identification:** Length 45 cm. Adult and juvenile — similar, back mottled grey and dark brown; pale stripe above eye; head and neck cream, finely streaked grey; underbody white. In flight, has white rump and fine dark bars on tail. Long dark legs and dark-tipped pink bill. Breeding plumage — back becomes darker, underbody rich reddish-brown.

**Habitat and Range:** Migratory shore bird, frequents saltwater wetlands and can be seen from September to April. Northern Hemisphere, breeds in Siberia and Alaska.

Ray Viljoen

## Eastern Curlew
### *Numenius madagascariensis*

**Other Names:** Sea Curlew

**Identification:** Length 61 cm. Head, neck and underbody buff marked dark brown; upper body mottled grey and buff. Very long down-curved bill.

**Habitat and Range:** Mud flats and sand flats of Moreton Bay and similar areas. Native of Eastern Siberia migrating to coastal Australia in summer from August to March.

## Red-necked Stint  *Calidris ruficollis*

**Identification:** Length 15 cm. Upper body greyish-brown, white below; white forehead; rump white with black stripe down centre which extends onto grey tail. Short dark beak and dark legs.

**Habitat and Range:** Margins of freshwater and saltwater wetlands throughout region. Especially common on mudflats. Northern Hemisphere migrant.

Ivan Fien

## Sharp-tailed Sandpiper
*Calidris acuminata*

**Identification:** Length 23 cm. Upper body brownish-grey; underbody whitish; crown reddish; white eyebrow. Head, crown, neck and breast streaked; back mottled. Juvenile and breeding adult — more reddish and more heavily marked. Straight medium length bill.

**Habitat and Range:** All wetlands (September to April). Northern Hemisphere migrant.

Ray Viljoen

## Curlew Sandpiper  *Calidris ferruginea*

**Identification:** Length 21 cm. Back grey-brown, underbody whitish; medium length black legs; black, very slightly down-curved beak. In flight, broad white wing bar and white rump. Juvenile — similar, darker mottling on back; faint buff collar. Breeding adult — underbody bright chestnut.

**Habitat and Range:** Freshwater and marine wetlands. Summer migrant from Northern Hemisphere.

Ray Viljoen

## Jacanas

Ivan Fien

### Comb-crested Jacana
*Irediparra gallinacea*

**Other Names:** Lotus Bird, Lily-trotter

**Identification:** Length 23 cm. Red crest; back of head black; neck orange-yellow; wings brown; throat white; toes 8 cm long.

**Habitat and Range:** Often seen running over waterlily leaves in freshwater pools. Sandgate Lagoon, Enoggera Reservoir or Lake Manchester and similar lakes. Coastal areas from north-western WA to Sydney.

## Stone Curlews

Queensland Museum

### Bush Stone-curlew *Burhinus grallarius*

**Other Names:** Southern Stone-curlew, Bush Curlew, Bush Thicknee, Willaroo, Weeloo

**Identification:** Length 53 cm. Upper body mottled brown and grey; underbody buff streaked brown; legs olive.

**Habitat and Range:** Open forest, plains and paddocks. Widespread over continent.

**Notes:** Often heard rather than seen. Call an eerie "kerloo" or "korloo"; usually uttered after dark.

## Oystercatchers

Ray Viljoen

### Pied Oystercatcher
*Haematopus longirostris*

**Other Names:** Eugarie Bird

**Identification:** Length 50 cm. Head and back black; underbody white; beak and legs orange.

**Habitat and Range:** Moreton Bay and islands. Coastal Australia; also New Guinea, New Zealand and other countries.

# Plovers

## Red-capped Plover
*Charadrius ruficapillus*

**Other Names:** Red-capped Dotterel.

**Identification:** Length 15 cm. Upper parts greyish-brown, underbody white. In breeding season rufous cap. Short bill.

**Habitat and Range:** Margins of freshwater and saltwater wetlands throughout region. Often seen on sandy beaches and exposed mudflats and saltmarshes. Australia-wide; also New Zealand.

Ray Viljoen

## Black-fronted Dotterel
*Elseyornis melanops*

**Other Names:** Black-fronted Plover

**Identification:** Length 18 cm. Back light brown; rich reddish-brown patch on shoulder; black band from forehead runs through eye and circles chest; underbody white. Beak red, black tip. Red eye ring. Juvenile — similar, but no shoulder patch; no black band; pink legs; flesh coloured beak with brown tip.

**Habitat and Range:** Usually shallow freshwater wetlands; favours gravel or muddy edges of swamps, creeks and lagoons. Australia-wide.

Ivan Fien

## Masked Lapwing  *Vanellus miles*

**Other Names:** Masked Plover, Spur-winged Plover

**Identification:** Length  35–38 cm. Head black; wings fawnish-brown; black band on sides of neck; yellow wattle around eye; underbody white. Beak yellow, legs dark red.

**Habitat and Range:** Common. Mainly swamps, grasslands and parklands. Often nests in parks and playing fields. Eastern and southern Australia including Tas.; also Moluccas and Christmas Island.

Ray Viljoen

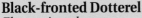

## Gulls and Terns

Queensland Museum

### Silver Gull *Larus novaehollandiae*

**Other Names:** Seagull

**Identification:** Length 40 cm. Body white; wings pale grey; eye-ring, beak and legs red.

**Habitat and Range:** Mostly along coast, sometimes inland shallow stretches of water. Australia; also New Caledonia and New Zealand.

B. Chudleigh (Nature Focus)

### Gull-billed Tern *Sterna nilotica*

**Identification:** Length 43 cm. Body mainly white with pale grey back and wings. Non-breeding adult — white head and black smudge around eye. Breeding adult — black cap that extends to bill. Bill is short, thick and black; tail not deeply forked; legs black. Juvenile — similar to non-breeding adult but more mottled on back.

**Habitat and Range:** Mainly saltwater, occasionally visiting freshwater wetlands and large reservoirs. Mainland Australia; cosmopolitan.

### Crested Tern *Sterna bergii*

**Identification:** Length 47 cm. Head and nape black; upper body pale grey; throat and underbody white; beak pale yellow; legs black.

**Habitat and Range:** Very common around shores of Moreton Bay. Coastal Australia; also Asia and Africa.

Ray Viljoen

## Pigeons and Doves

### Spotted Turtle-dove
*Streptopelia chinensis*

**Other Names:** Indian Dove, Spotted Dove.

**Identification:** Length 30 cm. Head and chest pinkish-grey; neck black spotted white; wings greyish-brown; tail dark brown; belly pale pink to cream.

**Habitat and Range:** Introduced from Asia. Common in cities, towns, parks, gardens and agricultural areas of eastern Australia to Eyre Peninsula. Common throughout region.

Ray Viljoen

### Brown Cuckoo-dove
*Macropygia amboinensis*

**Other Names:** Brown Pigeon.

**Identification:** Length 43 cm. Body rich rusty-brown. Very long tail, short wings.

**Habitat and Range:** Rainforest, scrubs and rainforest regrowth areas. Eastern Australia; also Indonesia, Philippines and New Guinea.

Ray Viljoen

### Crested Pigeon  *Ocyphaps lophotes*

**Other Names:** Crested Bronzewing, Topknot Pigeon (erroneously)

**Identification:** Length 32 cm. Head, neck and underbody pinkish-grey; wings brown barred black with bronze-green; beak black; legs pinkish-red.

**Habitat and Range:** Often seen around parks and outer suburban spaces, occasionally seen in inner city areas, also open forest, grasslands and agricultural areas. Australia except for coastal northern fringe and extreme south-east and south-west.

Ray Viljoen

Bruce Cowell

## Bar-shouldered Dove
*Geopelia humeralis*

**Other Names:** Scrub Dove

**Identification:** Length 29 cm. Back and tail brown with black barring on back; nape and shoulders copper with black barring; face and breast light grey; underbody pinkish-white. Long tail.

**Habitat and Range:** Widespread throughout region where it favours areas with low thick vegetation, usually near water. Evidence of decline in some areas as this dove requires good areas of remnant bushland. Northern and eastern Australia; also New Guinea.

## Wompoo Fruit-dove
*Ptilinopus magnificus*

**Other Names:** Wompoo Pigeon, Magnificent Fruit Pigeon, Bubbly Mary, Purple-breasted Pigeon

**Identification:** Length 40 cm. Upper body green; yellow crescent across shoulder; head arctic white to pale silver-grey; throat and breast deep magenta; belly yellow.

**Habitat and Range:** Locally common in rainforest. Rarely seen outside specific habitat. Eastern Australia; also New Guinea and neighbouring islands.

**Notes:** Deep resonant "woom-poo" call common sound in rainforest, even though the birds can be difficult to locate in forest canopy.

Queensland Museum

## Rose-crowned Fruit-dove
*Ptilinopus regina*

**Other Names:** Rose-crowned Pigeon, Red-crowned Pigeon.

**Identification:** Length 24 cm. Body green; throat and chest greyish; rose forehead; belly pinky-orange fading to yellow. Juvenile — mainly green with yellow belly.

**Habitat and Range:** Rainforest and dense vegetation where fruiting trees are present, especially figs. Also occasionally found in gardens and around stands of camphor laurel trees. These birds often collide with windows. Coastal northern and eastern Australia; also eastern Indonesian island groups.

R. Hill

# Cockatoos and Parrots

## Yellow-tailed Black Cockatoo
*Calyptorhynchus funereus*

**Other Names:** Funereal Cockatoo, Black Cockatoo

**Identification:** Length 60–69 cm. Large black cockatoo with yellow tail panels, yellow ear patch and pale yellow edge to feathers. Male — eye ring pink, beak dark grey. Female — eye ring grey, beak whitish, yellow edges to breast feathers.

**Habitat and Range:** Favours well-timbered areas, ranging from closed forest to open woodland. Seen in small groups which call frequently. Found in south-eastern Australia from central Qld to Eyre Peninsula, SA and Tas.

Ray Viljoen

## Galah  *Cacatua roseicapilla*

**Other Names:** Roseate Cockatoo

**Identification:** Length 36 cm. Pink and grey. Male —brown eyes; female — red eyes.

**Habitat and Range:** Previously uncommon in Brisbane, now seen in pairs and family groups. Open woodlands, tree-scattered grass-lands and agricultural areas throughout most of Australia. Does not occur in Tas., south-western Australia or northern Cape York.

Bruce Cowell

Queensland Museum

## Sulphur-crested Cockatoo
*Cacatua galerita*

**Other Names:** Greater Sulphur-crested Cockatoo, White Cockatoo

**Identification:** Length 49 cm. Large white cockatoo with long yellow crest. Male — dark brown eyes; female — dark reddish-brown eyes.

**Habitat and Range:** Open timbered areas, previously uncommon in Brisbane, now seen in pairs and family groups. Throughout northern, eastern and south-eastern Australia and Tas.

Queensland Museum

## Rainbow Lorikeet
*Trichoglossus haematodus*

**Other Names:** Blue Mountain Lorikeet, Rainbow Lory, Bluey

**Identification:** Length 28 cm. Head purplish-blue; breast yellow-orange; back green; purplish-blue patch on belly; beak red.

**Habitat and Range:** Well-vegetated lowland areas with suitable food trees bearing flowers and fruits. Usually nomadic, moving in search of food. Can occur in large flocks, sometimes in association with Scaly-breasted Lorikeets. Often noticeable at sunset when screeching flocks fly around before roosting. Widespread in timbered areas of coastal eastern Australia from Cape York to Tas. and Eyre Peninsula, SA; also from Lesser Sundas to New Caledonia.

Ray Viljoen

## Scaly-breasted Lorikeet
*Trichoglossus chlorolepidotus*

**Other Names:** Green Lorikeet, Greenie

**Identification:** Length 23 cm. Head and back green; chest barred yellow and green; underwing red; bill red.

**Habitat and Range:** Eucalypt and open forests, urban and parkland. Sometimes seen feeding in mixed flocks with Rainbow Lorikeets, Nomadic, moving in search of flowering trees. North-eastern and eastern Australia from Cooktown, Qld to Sydney.

## Australian King Parrot
*Alisteris scapularis*

**Other Names:** King Parrot, Red Lory (erroneously)

**Identification:** Length about 40 cm. Male — body dark green; head and breast brilliant red; light green on shoulders; tail black. Female — body and head duller green; rump blue; underbelly dull red.

**Habitat and Range:** Higher wooded areas — rainforest and eucalypt forest and outer urban areas where a scrubby environment along creeks provides suitable habitat. In coastal areas, just south of Cooktown, Qld to southern Vic.

Ray Viljoen

## Crimson Rosella   *Platycercus elegans*

**Other Names:** Red and Blue Mountain Parrot, Mountain Lory, Blue-cheeked Rosella.

**Identification:** Length 32–36 cm. Striking long-tailed red parrot; blue wings, cheek patches and tail; black back. Juvenile — green with red flecks.

**Habitat and Range:** Well-wooded suburbs abutting high country of subcoastal ranges. Eastern and south-eastern Australia.

Queensland Museum

## Pale-headed Rosella
*Platycercus adscitus*

**Other Names:** Moreton Bay Rosella, Mealy Rosella

**Identification:** Length 32 cm. Head and upper breast cream-yellow; body blue; shoulder light purple-blue; tail blue-black and green; underbelly red.

**Habitat and Range:** Lowland areas of open forest, cultivated and urban areas. Seen in pairs or family groups, Cape York Peninsula to northern NSW.

Ray Viljoen

## Cuckoos and Coucals

Ray Viljoen

### Fantailed Cuckoo
*Cacomantis flabelliformis*

**Identification:** Length 28 cm. Adult — upper body grey; underbody chestnut; edges of long tail scalloped white; yellow eye-ring. Juvenile — brown, underbody whitish barred grey and edges of long tail scalloped chestnut.

**Habitat and Range:** Forests, mangroves, woodlands, gardens and orchards. Eastern and south-western Australia; also New Guinea and Oceania.

Queensland Museum

### Shining Bronze Cuckoo
*Chrysococcyx lucidus*

**Other names:** Golden Bronze Cuckoo

**Identification:** Length 17 cm. Head coppery brown; upper body iridescent bronze-green; underbody off-white and with complete dark brown bars to chin.

**Habitat and Range:** Open forest and large gardens, especially if they contain native trees; migratory species arriving in Brisbane area for about six months in spring. Australia-wide; also New Zealand, New Guinea, Bismarck Archipelago and Solomon Islands.

Ray Viljoen

### Common Koel
*Eudynamys scolopacea*

**Other Names:** Stormbird, Rainbird, Coo-ee Bird

**Identification:** Length 38 cm. Male — body glossy black, red eye. Female — head and neck black; back and wings brown spotted and streaked white; tail buff and brown barred.

**Habitat and Range:** Summer visitor to rainforest, open forest, parks and gardens of northern and Eastern Australia (south to eastern Vic.). Also New Guinea and some northern islands in winter months.

**Notes:** The distinctive but monotonous "coo-ee, coo-ee" call of these large cuckoos is one of the most conspicuous and commented upon summer bird calls of the region.

## Channel-billed Cuckoo
*Scythrops novaehollandiae*

**Other Names:** Stormbird, Rainbird, Fig Hawk.

**Identification:** Length 67 cm. Large, grey with heavy "toucan-like" beak. Back feathers grey, tipped with black; rest of body grey; underbelly whitish with faint black barring; reddish wattle around base of bill and eye.

**Habitat and Range:** Occurs sporadically throughout region.

Queensland Museum

## Pheasant Coucal *Centropus phasianinus*

**Other Names:** Swamp Pheasant

**Identification:** Length 60 cm. Breeding adult — head and body black; outer wings chestnut, barred black and brown; straw-coloured feather shafts. Non-breeding adult and juvenile — head and back streaked rufous-brown; underbody fawn-brown.

**Habitat and Range:** Common along wooded creeks, swamps, areas of rank blady and other grasses. North-western WA, northern and eastern Australia south to Nowra, NSW.

**Notes:** Responsible for loud, booming "coop-coop-coop", calls heard in morning and evening from thick grass or undergrowth

Ray Viljoen

## Owls

R. J. Borland (Nature Focus)

Ian Gynther and Jack Pettigrew

### Powerful Owl *Ninox strenua*

**Identification:** Length 50–65 cm. Males usually larger than females. Large, solid bird with piercing yellow eyes and massive yellow legs and feet. Upper body darkish brown with white/light brown barring; underbody dull white with brown chevrons from the throat to the vent. In flight, bird is characterised by long broad wings with rounded wing tips.

**Habitat and Range:** In Brisbane hunts in open forest, woodland and suburban gardens, taking mainly arboreal marsupials, fruit bats and roosting birds. Roosts during day in dense vegetation along creeks and gullies where the thick canopy affords protection from harassment by Currawongs, Noisy Miners and Butcherbirds. Endemic. Coastal and sub-coastal areas from Mackay to western Vic.

**Notes:** Distinctive, far carrying "whoo-hoo" call can be heard at any time of night.

### Barn Owl *Tyto alba*

**Other names:** Monkey-faced Owl, Ghost Owl, Ghostbird.

**Identification:** Length 30–40 cm. "White" owl with large facial disc, forward-facing eyes and short tail. Head and back patterned in shades of grey, brown and buff; pure white below with scattered fine spots. Legs fine, long (but do not trail well beyond tail in flight) with white feathers to foot.

**Habitat and Range:** Favours open and lightly timbered areas. Often seen at night in urban areas. Often locally common during rodent "plagues". Cosmopolitan.

### Southern Boobook
*Ninox novaeseelandiae*

**Other Names:** Mopoke, Boobook Owl

**Identification:** Length 30 cm. "Brown" owl with forward-facing eyes and short tail. Upper body rufous brown spotted off-white; underbelly off-white, marked light brown lengthwise.

**Habitat and Range:** Most common owl. Found in almost all timbered habitats, including parks, golf courses and gardens. Australia; eastern Indonesia to New Zealand.

**Notes:** This owl and not the Tawny Frogmouth (see below) is responsible for nocturnal "more-pork" call.

Queensland Museum

## Nightjars and Frogmouths

### Tawny Frogmouth  *Podargus strigoides*

**Other Names:** Mopoke, Frogmouth Owl (both erroneously)

**Identification:** Length 40 cm. Owl-like bird with distinctive beak, long tail and eyes that do not face forward. Upper body mottled fawnish-grey and buff-white, underbody pale grey streaked black. Also red phase where grey is replaced by reddish-brown.

**Habitat and Range:** Open forest and urban areas. Australia-wide.

Bruce Cowell

## Kingfishers

### Laughing Kookaburra
*Dacelo novaeguineae*

**Other Names:** Jackass

**Identification:** Length 46 cm. Head white with dark brown lines through eyes and over crown; wings and shoulders brown, tipped light blue; tail rufous barred dark brown; underbody dull white.

**Habitat and Range:** Common throughout region. Open forest and urban areas. Eastern Australia from Cape York to south-eastern SA, introduced to WA and Tas.

Bruce Cowell

Queensland Museum

## Sacred Kingfisher *Todiramphus sanctus*

**Identification:** Length 20 cm. Head greenish-blue; wings turquoise; throat off-white; underbody buff.

**Habitat and Range:** Common in all suburbs. Australia-wide except rainforest or treeless arid areas; also Philippines to New Guinea, Oceania and New Zealand.

## Bee-eaters

Queensland Museum

## Rainbow Bee-eater *Merops ornatus*

**Other Names:** Rainbowbird

**Identification:** Length 23 cm. Green and blue with orange patch on back of head; yellow throat edged black; and narrow black band through eye. Black, curved beak. Tail has two fine, wire-like projections from middle.

**Habitat and Range:** Occurs throughout area. Australia, except extreme south-east and south-west; also Lesser Sundas to Solomon Islands.

## Rollers

Queensland Museum

## Dollarbird *Eurystomus orientalis*

**Other Names:** Eastern Broad-billed Roller

**Identification:** Length 25 cm. Head dark brown; body brown with turquoise wash; leading edge of wing blue; throat purple blue; tail blue-black; beak orange; pale bluish-white circular mark on underwing.

**Habitat and Range:** Open forest and outer urban areas. Migrant to north-western, northern and eastern Australia and Tas., winters in New Guinea, Solomon Islands and neighbouring island groups.

**Notes:** Conspicuous summer migrant (September to April). Usually seen perched high in trees or hawking insects above the tree canopy. Call is cackling "kak-kak-kak-kak".

## Noisy Pitta  *Pitta versicolor*

Queensland Museum

**Other names:** Dragoon Bird, Anvil Bird

**Identification:** Length 20 cm. Large-headed, ground-feeding bird with short tail. Head rufous with black cap, neck black. Wings, (except for blue shoulder patch), back and tail green. Underbody dull yellow with red and black patch between legs.

**Habitat and Range:** Rainforest areas of region. Eastern Australia from Cape York south to Hawkesbury River, NSW; also New Guinea.

**Notes:** Three-note whistling call which sounds like "walk to work" or "want-a-watch" is usually only indication of presence of these ground-dwelling birds.

# Treecreepers

## White-throated Treecreeper
*Cormobates leucophaea*

W. Labbett (Nature Focus)

**Other Names:** Woodpecker

**Identification:** Length 16 cm. Upper body dark brownish-grey; throat white; underbody buff striped black. Female has orange spot near ear.

**Habitat and Range:** Fairly common. Eucalypt forest, open forest and outer urban areas. From Atherton Tableland south to Vic. and SA.

# Australian Warblers

Ray Viljoen

## Red-backed Fairy-wren
### *Malurus melanocephalus*

**Other Names:** Red-backed Wren

**Identification:** Length 10 cm. Male — head black; body and wings brown, upper back red. Female — brown head; back and tail and buffish below.

**Habitat and Range:** Eucalypt and open forests, where there is tall grass, open areas near water and outer urban areas. Tropical northern and eastern Australia, south to Hunter River, NSW.

# Pardalotes and Flowerpeckers

Rodger Fiddler

## Striated Pardalote   *Pardalotus striatus*

**Other Names:** Black-headed Pardalote, Chip-chip Bird, Yellow-tipped Pardalote.

**Identification:** Length 11 cm. Body grey; wings black with white or buff edges; forehead yellow-orange; white eyebrow; throat yellow; underbody white with yellowish flanks; rump off-white to brown; crown black or black with white streaks.

**Habitat and Range:** Open forest and woodland areas, also in urban areas where trees are present. Australia-wide.

# Honeyeaters

Queensland Museum

## Noisy Friarbird
### *Philemon corniculatus*

**Other Names:** Leatherhead

**Identification:** Length 29 cm. Upper body brownish-grey with dark bare head (takes its name from friars of old with shaven heads); underbody dull white, large knob on top of beak.  Red eyes.

**Habitat and Range:** One of most common honeyeaters. Most habitats but not rainforest. Eastern Australia; also New Guinea.

## Little Friarbird  *Philemon citreogularis*

**Identification:** Length 26 cm. Upper body greyish-brown; underbody paler; patch of naked bluish skin from base of beak past eye. Juvenile — patch of yellowish streaking on throat.

**Habitat and Range:** Locally common. Open forest, woodland, parks and gardens. Northern and eastern Australia; also southern New Guinea.

Rodger Fiddler

## Striped Honeyeater
### *Plectorhyncha lanceolata*

**Identification:** Length 23 cm. Upper body greyish-brown; underbody whitish with black and white striped head and neck. Short beak compared to other honeyeaters.

**Habitat and Range:** Dry scrubs and woodlands in the west, and swamp woodlands, small bush areas in pastures and suburban gardens in the east. West to Charleville and north-west to Winton.

**Notes:** Has become more common in region in recent years and its distinctive sweet, rolling whistle — "cheeridid-cheeree, cheeridid-cheeree, cheeridid-cheeree" — can be heard wherever the birds are active.

Dept of Education

## Blue-faced Honeyeater
### *Entomyzon cyanotis*

**Other Names:** Bananabird

**Identification:** Length 26 cm. Bright olive back with black head and throat; white underbody; bright cobalt blue skin patch around eye of adult.

**Habitat and Range:** Common in open eucalypt forest, trees along watercourses, plantations, clumps of trees around farms, suburban gardens and parks. Northern and eastern Australia; also southern New Guinea.

Queensland Museum

Brisbane Forest Park

## Bell Miner  *Manorina melanophrys*

**Other Names:** Bellbird

**Identification:** Length 18 cm. Upper body olive-green; underbody light olive-green; orange patch behind eye; beak and feet maize yellow.

**Habitat and Range:** Dense eucalypt forests and woodlands. Eastern Australia from the Mary River east of Gympie, south to south-western Vic.

**Notes:** Social and colonial, never seen singly. This is the local "bellbird".

Queensland Museum

## Noisy Miner  *Manorina melanocephala*

**Other names:** Mickey, Soldier Bird

**Identification:** Length 28 cm. Grey with whitish-grey belly; yellow beak and patch behind eye; white forehead; black crown and cheeks.

**Habitat and Range:** Most common honeyeater of suburbs. Natural habitats, dry eucalypt forest, woodland and remnant bushland. Eastern Australia but range broken in the north-east.

**Notes:** Social and highly aggressive. These honeyeaters may chase smaller birds from parks and gardens.

Ray Viljoen

## Lewin's Honeyeater  *Meliphaga lewinii*

**Identification:** Length 21 cm. Dark olive-green with pale yellow gape and pale yellow crescent patch over ear. Beak short and down-curved.

**Habitat and Range:** Rainforest and thick eucalypt forest throughout region. Eastern Australia.

## Mangrove Honeyeater
*Meliphaga fasciogularis*

**Other Names:** Varied Honeyeater

**Identification:** Length 20 cm. Head and back olive-brown with narrow black band through eye; yellow plume behind beak ending in white tuft under ear; scaly yellow barring on throat. Feathers of tail and wings edged with yellow.

**Habitat and Range:** Common. Mangrove areas and tidal streams, bayside suburbs; Boondall Wetlands Reserve, Deception Bay, Hays Inlet, Lota, Lytton, Nudgee Beach, Wellington Point. Townsville, Qld to coastal mid-NSW.

Keith Ireland (Nature Focus)

## White-throated Honeyeater
*Melithreptus albogularis*

**Identification:** Length 13 cm. Head and neck black with thin white band across nape; blue or pale grey patch above eye; wings and back olive-green; underbody white.

**Habitat and Range:** Prefers well-watered districts forests and woodlands. From Kimberley district of north-western Australia south to Nambucca Heads, NSW.

Keith Ireland (Nature Focus)

## Brown Honeyeater *Lichmera indistincta*

**Identification:** Length 14 cm. Back brown; pale lemon patch behind eye; belly buff. Faint yellow wash on wings.

**Habitat and Range:** Particularly common in bayside suburbs. Open forests, mangroves, parks and suburban gardens. Western and northern Australia.

Ray Viljoen

Ray Viljoen

## Eastern Spinebill
*Acanthorhynchus tenuirostris*

**Other Names**: Hummingbird

**Identification:** Length 15 cm. Head black; upper body dark grey; red eye; throat rufous, white collar; brown above with belly rufous, tail black with white edges.

**Habitat and Range:** Forests and woodlands, particularly where there are flowering shrubs Mt Glorious, Mt Nebo, Mt Tamborine. Eastern coastal Australia — Cooktown, Qld to Adelaide.

## Scarlet Honeyeater
*Myzomela sanguinolenta*

**Identification:** Length 10 cm. Male — bright scarlet, black, brown and white plumage. Female — brownish above and buff below with pink wash under chin and throat.

**Habitat and Range:** Wide habitat preference. Favours areas with flowering trees. Eastern Australia

Ray Viljoen

# Australian Flycatchers and Allies

Ray Viljoen

## Eastern Yellow Robin
*Eopsaltria australis*

**Other Names**: Northern Yellow Robin, Southern Yellow Robin.

**Identification:** Length 15 cm. Upper body mid-grey, underbody and rump bright yellow.

**Habitat and Range:** Widespread in well-timbered habitats including forests, woodlands, coastal tea-tree and paperback swamps, parks and gardens. Eastern and south-eastern Australia.

## Varied Sittella
*Daphoenositta chrysoptera*

E.E. Zillman (Nature Focus)

**Other Names:** Sittella

**Identification:** Length 12 cm. Body and breast grey; head and tail tip white; wings and rest of tail black; orange spot on middle of wing. Beak black with yellow base.

**Habitat and Range:** Open forest and woodlands. Usually seen in small groups foraging on branches of tree canopy. Mainland Australia.

## Rufous Whistler
*Pachycephala rufiventris*

Ray Viljoen

**Identification:** Length 17 cm. Male — head and back grey; throat white; black band on chest; underbody rufous. Female — body grey; underbody buff streaked brown

**Habitat and Range:** Wherever eucalypt and open forests or mangroves provide suitable habitat. Australia generally except arid inland; also Moluccas to New Caledonia.

## Grey Shrike-thrush
*Colluricincla harmonica*

Ray Viljoen

**Other Names:** Grey and White Native Thrush, Thrush.

**Identification:** Length 23 cm. Body mid-grey; back and wings with brownish wash; long tail. Male — white patch in front of eye. Female — lightly streaked throat and breast. Juvenile — underbody lighter; heavily streaked breast; reddish eyebrows; reddish edging to wing feathers.

**Habitat and Range:** Widespread in forest and woodland. Australia; also New Guinea.

Ray Viljoen

## Magpie-lark  *Grallina cyanoleuca*

**Other Names:** Peewee, Mud-lark

**Identification:** Length 27 cm. Crown, back and breast black; belly white; adults have white beak. Male — black above and below beak; female — white above and below beak; juvenile — grey beak, black above and white below beak.

**Habitat and Range:** Open and urban areas close to water, often found on lawns. Found throughout Australia; also New Guinea and Timor.

## Grey Fantail  *Rhipidura fuliginosa*

**Other Names:** Cranky Fan

**Identification:** Length 16 cm. Head, upper body and tail dark grey; white eyebrow; tail feathers white-tipped; throat white with black band; underbody buff.

**Habitat and Range:** Rainforest, open forest and well shaded urban areas. Coastal Australia to within a few hundred kilometres; also New Guinea, New Hebridies, New Caledonia and New Zealand.

Ray Viljoen

Ray Viljoen

## Willie Wagtail  *Rhipidura leucophrys*

**Other Names:** Black and White Fantail

**Identification:** Length 20 cm. Upper body and throat black, underbody white.

**Habitat and Range:** Open forest, cultivated lands, parks and gardens. Australia generally, except deserts; also Moluccas to Solomon Islands.

**Notes:** Call distinctive, melodious "sweet pretty creature". Often calls on moonlit nights during breeding season.

# Drongos

## Spangled Drongo *Dicrurus bracteatus*

**Other Names:** Fishtail

**Identification:** Length 32 cm. Body iridescent green-black; eye ruby red; white spots on underwing; fish-tailed.

**Habitat and Range:** Rainforest, forest edge, parks and gardens. Northern and eastern Australia to south-eastern Vic.; also south-eastern Asia to New Guinea.

Ray Viljoen

# Cuckoo Shrikes and Trillers

## Black-faced Cuckoo Shrike
*Coracina novaehollandiae*

**Other Names:** Blue Jay, Shufflewing, Leatherhead (erroneously)

**Identification:** Length 30 cm. Body pale bluish-grey; face and throat black; underbelly white.

**Habitat and Range:** Very common in Brisbane suburbs; open forest and urban areas. Ranges over whole continent and some northern islands.

Queensland Museum

## Cicadabird *Coracina tenuirostris*

**Identification:** Length 26 cm. Male — body uniform slate grey; wings blackish with slate grey edging. Female — back mid-brown; wings edged with sandy tan; underbody sandy tan with grey barring on belly.

**Habitat and Range:** Common summer visitor from northern Australia and New Guinea. More likely to be heard than seen.

J. Purnell (Nature Focus)

## Orioles

Ray Viljoen

### Figbird  *Specotheres viridis*

**Other Names**: Southern Figbird

**Identification:** Length 28 cm. Male — head black; red eye patch; shoulders grey; wings olive-green; tail black; underbody dull green; underbelly white. Female — upper body brown; underbody white striped brown.

**Habitat and Range:** One of the most common birds. Dense brush, rainforest, parks and gardens. Eastern coastal Australia from Cairns to Sydney; also New Guinea, Timor and neighbouring islands.

## Australian Magpies, Butcherbirds and Currawongs

Ray Viljoen

### Grey Butcherbird  *Cracticus torquatus*

**Identification:** Length 26 cm. Head, wings and tail black; back grey; throat and rest of underbody greyish-white.

**Habitat and Range:** Common in open forest, woodland, farms, parks and gardens. Eastern Australia from Cairns to Tas.; also inland through Alice Springs to north-west WA.

Ray Viljoen

### Pied Butcherbird  *Cracticus nigrogularis*

**Other Names:** Black-throated Butcherbird, Organ-bird

**Identification:** Length 32 cm. Head, throat, back and tail black; wings black with some white; underbody and nape, white; beak grey with black tip. Juvenile — brownish head and wings; throat buff; yellowish stripe above eye.

**Habitat and Range:** Common, favours open and lightly timbered habitats, including parks and gardens. Widespread throughout region. Australia, except for southern Vic., Tas. and far south-west corner WA.

## Australian Magpie  *Gymnorhina tibicen*

**Other Names:** Black-backed Magpie

**Identification:** Length 38 cm. Body black except for white nape and white upper wing, rump and top of tail.

**Habitat and Range:** Widespread and common throughout region. Australia; also New Guinea and introduced to New Zealand.

Queensland Museum

## Pied Currawong  *Strepera graculina*

**Identification:** Length 40–50 cm. Body black, under rump white, tip of tail white. Eye yellow.

**Habitat and Range:** Mainly forested country and forest margins, also parks and gardens. Eastern Australia from Cape York to Grampians, western Vic.

Ivan Fien

# Crows and Ravens

## Torresian Crow  *Corvus orru*

**Other Names:** Australian Crow

**Identification:** Length 48 cm. Black plumage — differs from the Raven (*Corvus coronoides*) in having bases of body feathers white not grey; also lacks distinctive stiff throat feathers.

**Habitat and Range:** Very common through-out region in all habitats except dense forest. Most of western and northern Australia; also Moluccas to Bismarck Archipelago.

Queensland Museum

## Bowerbirds and Birds of Paradise

Ray Viljoen

### Regent Bowerbird
*Sericulus chrysocephalus*

**Other names:** Regent Bird

**Identification:** Length 25 cm. Male — body black; head, nape and wings deep golden yellow; orange-red patch on forehead. Female — greyish-brown above with pale grey speckling, crown and throat black; underbody pale grey with fine dark brown barring.

**Habitat and Range:** Rainforest and eucalypt forest; eastern coastal Australia from Eungella Range near Mackay, north-eastern Qld, south to Hawkesbury River, NSW.

**Notes:** Although not common in the region, the brightly plumaged males rarely go unremarked.

## Sparrows and Mannikins

Ray Viljoen

### House Sparrow  *Passer domesticus*

**Identification:** Length 14 cm. Male — head grey merging into chestnut on neck; wings chestnut and black; off-white face patch; throat black; underbody light grey. Female — head light brown and very little chestnut in wings.

**Habitat and Range:** Open grassland, cultivated city and urban land. Qld south to Vic. and west to WA border. Introduced from Europe.

## Chestnut-breasted Mannikin
*Lonchura castaneothorax*

Ray Viljoen

**Other Names**: Chestnut-breasted Finch, Bullfinch.

**Identification:** Length 10 cm. Head grey; face black; back brown; breast chestnut; yellowish rump and tail; under rump black; grey beak. Juvenile — nondescript greyish-brown with yellowish rump and tail; lacks distinctive markings of adult.

**Habitat and Range:** Localised in region where it favours rank grasses, roadside verges, waste ground and similar habitats. Eastern and northern Australia; also New Guinea and Oceania.

## Welcome Swallow *Hirundo neoxena*

Ray Viljoen

**Other Names**: House Swallow

**Identification:** Length 15 cm. Upper body iridescent blue-black; throat rufous; underbody dirty pale grey.

**Habitat and Range:** Most habitats including city and urban areas. Australia-wide except for far north; self-introduced to New Zealand.

## Tree Martin *Hirundo nigricans*

I. R. McCann (Nature Focus)

**Other Names:** Tree Swallow

**Identification:** Length 12 cm. Upper body blue-black; forehead rufous; underbody dirty white. Tail has shallow fork.

**Habitat and Range:** Very common. Open forest, city and urban areas. Australia-wide, except desert areas; also New Guinea and northern islands.

## Old World Warblers

Ray Viljoen

### Golden-headed Cisticola
*Cisticola exilis*

**Other Names:** Golden-headed Fantail
Warbler, Tailor Bird

**Identification:** Length 10 cm. Summer
plumage — head and neck light brownish-
gold; back streaked black; belly golden buff.
Winter plumage — head light brownish-
gold streaked black, tail longer.

**Habitat and Range:** Favours tall grasses and
rank vegetation along drains, creeks, roadsides and pastures. Northern and eastern
Australia; also China and India to Bismarck
Archipelago.

## Silvereyes

Ray Viljoen

### Silvereye  *Zosterops lateralis*

**Other Names:** White-eye, Grey-breasted
Silvereye.

**Identification:** Length 12 cm. Body grey;
white ring around eye; wing olive-green; buff
underwing.

**Habitat and Range:** Open forest, cultivated
lands, orchards and gardens. Eastern
Australia from Cape York to SA.

## Starlings and Mynas

M. F. Soper (Nature Focus)

### European Starling  *Sturnus vulgaris*

**Other Names:** English Starling, Common
Starling

**Identification:** Length 22 cm. Adult
iridescent black; spotted white shoulders;
maize yellow legs and beak. Juvenile — chest
streaked brown and white; wings brown.

**Habitat and Range:**  Urban and agricultural
areas, often in large groups. Native of Europe
and Asia; well established in south-eastern
Australia from Rockhampton to WA border.

# Hawks, Eagles and Falcons

Gregory V. Czechura

R aptors — "birds of prey" such as ospreys, eagles, hawks, harriers, kites and falcons — are difficult birds to identify. They are rarely seen perched at close quarters or at the nest as depicted in many books. Typically, raptors appear briefly or in silhouette high overhead or as a speck somewhere off in the distance.

Successful raptor-watching requires experience built on patient, careful observation and consideration of the prevailing viewing conditions. It must be remembered however that, as with all birds, appearance is dependent on age and condition and what they are doing. They may also appear different under different physical conditions. As well, some non-raptors may look very hawk-like in the distance (eg larger cuckoos, crows, ravens, gulls, the Australian Pelican and Australian Darter). The good raptor-watcher must be prepared to occasionally admit defeat — there are numerous situations where a bird cannot be identified.

This list looks at hawks, eagles and falcons as they are usually seen — that is, in flight with wings outspread as they pass overhead. All 24 species of diurnal raptors occuring on mainland Australia have been recorded from around Brisbane. In the species descriptions that follow, size (compared to a common and familiar bird, the Torresian Crow) and overall shape of the body, tail and extended wings have been used to sort the raptors into five major groupings. References in the text to length and wingspan measurements are based on maximums recorded for the larger sex (ie females).

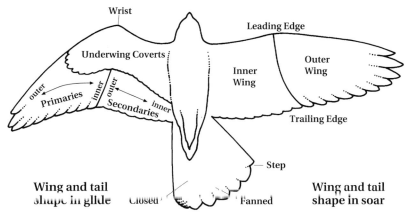

Wrist

Leading Edge

Underwing Coverts

Outer Wing

Inner Wing

outer
Primaries
inner
outer
Secondaries
inner

Trailing Edge

Step

**Wing and tail shape in glide**     Closed     Fanned     **Wing and tail shape in soar**

# Identifying Raptors in Flight

*Group 1.* ───────────────────────────────

Large (ie bigger than a crow) soaring raptors with broad wings, long, deeply spread primaries and short tails (no longer than base of wing).

**Brahminy Kite** *Haliastur indus* **p. 257**
**White-bellied Sea-Eagle** *Haliaeetus leucogaster* **p. 258**
**Black-breasted Buzzard** *Hamirostra melanosternon* **p. 259**
**Osprey** *Pandion haliaetus* **p. 260**

*Group 2.* ───────────────────────────────

Large soaring raptors with broad wings, long, deeply spread primaries and long tails (longer than base of wing).

**Pacific Baza** *Aviceda subcristata* **p. 261**
**Black Kite** *Milvus migrans* **p. 262**
**Whistling Kite** *Haliastur sphenurus* **p. 263**
**Wedge-tailed Eagle** *Aquila audax* **p. 264**
**Little Eagle** *Hieraaetus morphnoides* **p. 265**
**Square-tailed Kite** *Lophoictinia isura* **p. 266**
**Red Goshawk** *Erythrotriorchis radiatus* **p. 267**

*Group 3.* ───────────────────────────────

Large broad-winged raptors with long, deeply spread primaries and long tails, that are usually seen flying slowly close to the ground on strongly upswept wings.

**Spotted Harrier** *Circus assimilis* **p. 268**
**Swamp Harrier** *Circus approximans* **p. 269**

*Group 4.* ───────────────────────────────

Small to medium (ie crow-sized or smaller) secretive raptors with long tails and short, rather rounded wings with primaries that are not deeply separated when spread during soaring.

**Grey Goshawk** *Accipiter novaehollandiae* **p. 270**
**Brown Goshawk** *Accipiter fasciatus* **p. 271**
**Collared Sparrowhawk** *Accipiter cirrhocephalus* **p. 272**

*Group 5.* ───────────────────────────────

Small to medium-sized, active raptors with narrow wings and rather pointed wing-tips with little or no spreading of primaries when seen soaring or in flight.

**Black-shouldered Kite** *Elanus axillaris* **p. 273**
**Letter-winged Kite** *Elanus scriptus* **p. 274**
**Brown Falcon** *Falco berigora* **p. 275**
**Nankeen Kestrel** *Falco cenchroides* **p. 276**
**Australian Hobby** *Falco longipennis* **p. 277**
**Grey Falcon** *Falco hypoleucos* **p. 278**
**Black Falcon** *Falco subniger* **p. 279**
**Peregrine Falcon** *Falco peregrinus* **p. 280**

## Brahminy Kite *Haliastur indus*

**Identification:** Length 0.5 m. Wingspan to 1.3 m. Wings relatively short but broad with trailing edge often S-shaped and pinched near body when gliding; soars and glides with shallow upswept wings; tail slightly rounded to wedge-shaped. Adult chestnut with white head and breast. Juvenile brown with paler head and breast. Immature similar with chestnut belly; shoulders and underwing (except flight feathers) mottled with chestnut.

**Undersurface Pattern:** Adult — most of underside pale chestnut except for blackish wing-tips; bright chestnut underwing coverts and belly; white head and breast and whitish tail tip. Immature — blackish wing-tips; pale window at base of primaries; pale diagonal band across bases of mainly brownish secondaries; underwing coverts heavily mottled with chestnut; outer tail brownish, rest whitish; pale throat; belly chestnut; head and breast whitish mottled with sandy brown. Juvenile — similar, except that underwing coverts are reddish-brown and breast and belly reddish-brown with cream streaks.

**Flight Pattern:** Soaring and slow gliding — wings are pushed forwards with tips of widely spaced primaries curled upwards. The outer part of the wing may droop when gliding. Sailing and fast gliding — wings held straighter, primaries closed with increasing speed and are flexed back from closed wrist, trailing edge becomes very S-shaped, tail closed or partly fanned. Active flight — loose, rowing wing-beats interspersed with glides.

**Habitat and Range:** Marine and estuarine areas and less commonly near permanent streams, reservoirs and freshwater wetlands. May be encountered throughout region.

Ray Viljoen

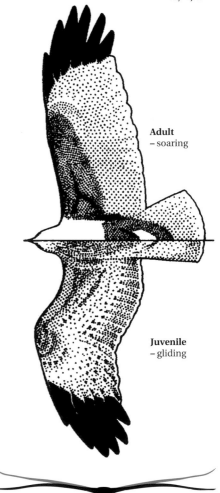

**Adult** – soaring

**Juvenile** – gliding

**Flight profile**

R. Hill

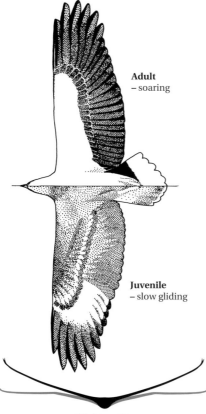

**Adult**
– soaring

**Juvenile**
– slow gliding

**Flight profile**

## White-bellied Sea-Eagle
### *Haliaeetus leucogaster*

**Identification:** Length 0.8 m. Wingspan to 2.2 m. Shape very distinctive irrespective of age — long broad wings with strongly curved trailing edge and very short wedge-shaped tail exaggerated by protruding neck and large beak; female larger than male; soars and glides with strongly upswept wings. Adult white with grey back. Juvenile brown with cream head. Immature stages increasingly resemble adult. Young adults similar to adult but retain traces of brownish plumage.

**Undersurface Pattern:** Adult — primaries, secondaries, lower edge of underwing coverts and base of tail blackish-grey; rest of underparts white. Young adults very similar but may have blackish-grey primaries and secondaries except for pale patch at base of primaries, small inner patch midway through secondaries and a distinct dark band across lower edge of underwing coverts. Juvenile — broad areas of brown and grey through underparts; dark primaries and secondaries except for very obvious pale window at base of primaries; dark band along edge of primary coverts and another narrow band across primary coverts from wrist to armpit; lower third of tail dark tipped with white. Immature — becomes progressively paler below and retains primary patch and covert bands, but loses dark end to tail. Later stages develop dark base to tail and pale bases to secondaries.

**Flight Pattern:** Soaring — wings held straight out from body with primaries spread. Gliding — in slow glide primaries closed, tail closed and strongly wedge-shaped; fast gliding, wrist pushed forward and primaries back. Active flight — powerful, rowing wing-beats interspersed with glides.

**Habitat and Range:** Marine and estuarine areas, also near permanent streams, reservoirs and freshwater wetlands. May be encountered throughout region.

# Black-breasted Buzzard
## *Hamirostra melanosternon*

Greg Czechura

**Identification:** Length 0.6 m. Wingspan to 1.5 m. Long broad wings with nearly parallel leading and trailing wing edges and short squarish to slightly rounded tail. Female slightly larger than male; usually soars with wings upswept; characteristically soars at high altitude followed by long glides with gentle side to side rocking. Adult with black head, breast and back; nape and shoulders rufous; tail buff-grey. Juvenile and immature predominantly reddish except for flight feathers and grey tails. Black feathering increases with age on wings, back and breast.

**Undersurface Pattern:** Adult — throat, breast and upper belly black; sides of neck, leg feathers and lower belly bright rufous; tail grey; secondaries, edge of underwing coverts dark grey; outer coverts with blackish patch, rest mottled brown, rufous and black; wing-tips black contrasting with white window at base of primaries that can also be seen in upper wing. Juvenile — rufous except for black wing-tips; white window; white band along edge of underwing coverts; and grey tail, inner primaries and secondaries. Immature — similar except breast and underwing coverts streaked black, and pale band across lower underwing coverts obscured by black or grey feathers.

**Flight Pattern:** Soaring — wings held out from sides of body or pushed slightly forward and primaries spread. Gliding — in slow glide, wings swept back from wrist and primaries partly or fully closed, a marked "step" present between outer and inner primaries, tail closed, sides straight with square tip; fast gliding, wings sharply swept back from wrists which are pushed further forward. Active flight — bird rarely flaps but when it does so, wings move in shallow beats or in rowing action; near ground bird flaps deeply like a harrier.

**Habitat and Range:** Extremely rare visitor from inland.

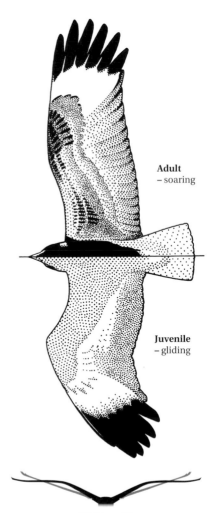

**Adult**
– soaring

**Juvenile**
– gliding

**Flight profile**

Queensland Museum

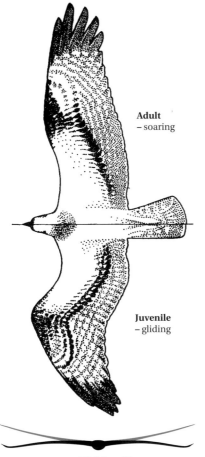

**Adult**
– soaring

**Juvenile**
– gliding

**Flight profile**

## Osprey *Pandion haliaetus*

**Identification:** Length 0.6 m. Wingspan to 1.7 m. Long tapering wings with prominent kink in wrist region, protruding head and neck and short square tail; female slightly larger than male; soars and glides with wings bowed. Adult brown-backed; head and underparts white; distinctive dark "bandit-mask" through eye which joins a brown "necklace" across throat and is darker and more obvious in female. Juvenile similar but more speckled and with darker face and throat markings.

**Undersurface Pattern:** Adult — predominantly white; brown "necklace" across throat; dark brown wing-tips, patch near wrist and lower edge of underwing coverts; lighter brown barring across bases of primaries, secondaries and tail (including broad band near tip); tail-tip edged white. Juvenile — very similar; "necklace" more pronounced; wrist area dark brown and sandy; a double line of dark brown feathers along lower margin of underwing coverts.

**Flight Pattern:** Soaring — wings held straight out from sides of body or slightly forward; wrist pushed forward and primaries held slightly back; tail well spread. Gliding — wrists pushed forward and level with beak; wings strongly angled due to primaries being cranked back; tail closed and square-tipped. Active flight — easy and regular with shallow, powerful strokes interspersed with long glides; heavy flapping accompanied by bobbing of body.

**Habitat and Range:** Marine and estuarine areas and less commonly near permanent streams, reservoirs and freshwater wetlands. May be encountered throughout region.

## Pacific Baza *Aviceda subcristata*

**Identification:** Length 0.5 m. Wingspan to 1.1 m. Slim body, long wings and long tail with conspicuous crest; wings paddle-shaped, pinched near body and broadest in outer wing; soars and glides with wings slightly to strongly bowed and head often held above plane of body. Adult grey with brown wings, breast white with rufous bars and apricot undertail; female with browner tone to head and back. Juvenile similar but darker and browner with variable white eyebrow and other facial markings.

**Undersurface Pattern:** Adult — upper breast grey; armpits and belly white barred rufous; undertail and underwing coverts apricot; lower margin of coverts paler; primaries greyish, strongly barred blackish brown; secondaries also grey with dark band along tips; tail similar with some incomplete barring near base and broad terminal band. Juvenile — similar but paler, lacks broad terminal band on tail and some barring present across secondaries.

**Flight Pattern:** Soaring — wings pushed well forward with wrists at level of beak; primaries well spread forming very round wing-tip; trailing edge of wing S-shaped; tail fanned with rounded tip. Gliding — primaries swept back and closed forming squarer wing-tip; tail closed with square tip, slightly rounded ends and weakly convex sides. Active flight — deep and easy, tending to rowing at speed.

**Habitat and Range:** Forest and woodland, also parks, gardens and bushland corridors. Winter visitor, sometimes in large numbers, to lowlands including suburbs. May be encountered throughout region.

Ray Viljoen

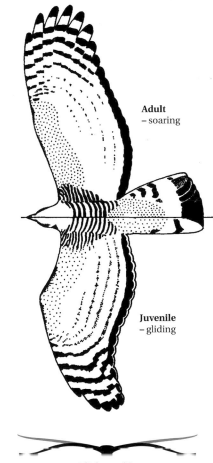

**Adult
– soaring**

**Juvenile
– gliding**

**Flight profile**

Bruce Cowell

## Black Kite *Milvus migrans*

**Identification:** Length 0.5 m. Wingspan to 1.4 m. Long wings, slim body with long forked tail; gregarious; soars and glides with flat or slightly bowed wings, much tail-twisting and side-slipping. Adult dark brown. Juvenile paler brown streaked and spotted with buff.

**Undersurface Pattern:** Adult — dark brown body and underwing coverts; blackish wing-tips, rest of primaries indistinctly barred brownish; lower underwing coverts and secondaries dark brown; tail brownish indistinctly barred. Juvenile — similar but body paler and distinctly streaked; trace of pale patch sometimes discernible at base of primaries.

**Flight Pattern:** Soaring — wings held slightly forward to wrist and primaries slightly backward; trailing edge S-shaped; tail fanned, rather triangular with pointed corners. Gliding — wrists pushed to level of beak and primaries closed and swept back; tail closed, narrow and deeply forked. Active flight — deep, easy strokes interspersed with glides; very agile.

**Habitat and Range:** Open habitats. Rare visitor, sometimes in very large numbers, from inland.

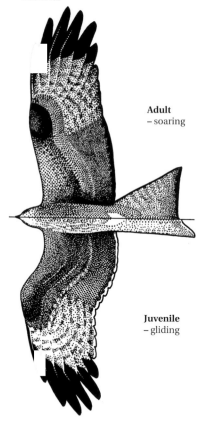

Adult – soaring

Juvenile – gliding

Flight profile

## Whistling Kite  *Haliastur sphenurus*

Queensland Museum

**Identification:** Length 0.6 m. Wingspan to 1.5 m. Rather scruffy with long, broad wings pinched near body and long rounded tail; female larger than male; soars and glides with pronounced droop to wings and some tail twisting. Adult sandy coloured with brown back. Juvenile similar, more reddish with prominently spotted wings.

**Undersurface Pattern:** Adult — predominantly sandy brown with some darker streaking on breast; outer primaries blackish, secondaries dark brown; underwing coverts and inner primaries sandy thus forming a pale M-shaped pattern when seen from below; two parallel broken bands of dark brown across lower half of coverts; obscure dark patch at wrist. Juvenile — similar but darker, underwing coverts and breast quite strongly marked.

**Flight Pattern:** Soaring — wings pushed forward with primaries spread and well rounded wing-tip; leading edge straight or angled and trailing edge S-shaped; tail spread with rounded tip. Gliding — wrist pushed forward and primaries back; tail closed with straight sides and rounded tip. Active flight — deep and lazy with some body movement producing rather jerky, rowing action.

**Habitat and Range:** Marine, estuarine areas, vicinity of permanent streams, reservoirs, freshwater wetlands and farmland. May be encountered throughout region.

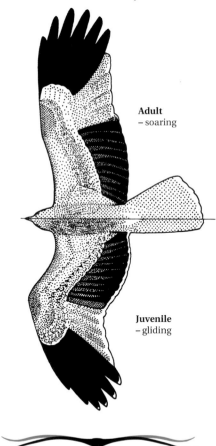

**Adult** – soaring

**Juvenile** – gliding

**Flight profile**

D. Watts (Nature Focus)

**Adult** – soaring

**Juvenile** – gliding

**Flight profile**

## Wedge-tailed Eagle *Aquila audax*

**Identification:** Length 1 m. Wingspan to 2.3 m. Large, dark, broad-winged with protruding head and beak and very distinctive wedge-shaped tail; female larger than male; wings plank-like and upswept in flight. Adult very dark sooty brown to black with paler feathers on back of head and through middle of upper wing; female generally paler. Juvenile paler but remains very dark on breast; crown, back of neck, upper back and band through upper wing rufous. Immatures progressively become less rufous on back of head and upper wing.

**Undersurface Pattern:** Adult — dark sooty brown to black except reddish patch at wrist and hint of reddish line diagonally through underwing coverts; narrow white patch at base of primaries and thin white line across base of secondaries; underside of rump buffish. Juvenile — dark brown below; reddish patch at wrist and trace of narrow, reddish diagonal stripe through underwing coverts; hint of dusky panel at base of primaries; inner primaries, secondaries and tail barred; underside of rump pale yellowish. Immature — intermediate, underside of rump becoming more brownish and developing whitish area at base of primaries.

**Flight Pattern:** Soaring — wings held straight out from body or slightly forward with leading and trailing edges parallel or latter very gently curved; trailing edge may be S-shaped in juveniles; primaries and tail well spread. Gliding — primaries closed, backswept; outer wing lowered to horizontal, inner wing upswept; tail closed and rather pointed looking; fast glide, wrists pushed well forward. Active flight — deep, slow and powerful often short burst of flapping followed by long glide.

**Habitat and Range:** Forest, woodland, fields and edges of suburbia. May be encountered throughout region.

## Little Eagle *Hieraaetus morphnoides*

R. Hill

**Identification:** Length 0.6 m. Wingspan to 1.4 m. Robust, long-winged with rectangular wing shape, inner and outer wings of similar width and square-cut tail; pale translucent trailing edge from inner primaries to body; short, broad head; female larger than male; soars and glides on flat, bowed or slightly upswept wings. Adult light brown above and buff below (light phase) or dark brown (dark phase); pale band through upper wing; female usually darker and more heavily streaked. Juvenile similar but reddish-brown.

**Undersurface Pattern:** Adult — light phase, underwing coverts to wrist reddish in triangular pattern; ends of outer primaries and lower half of secondaries grey barred black; rest of underwing whitish forming an M-shaped pattern; tail light grey with darker barring; body whitish with some streaking on breast. Dark phase, body and underwings darker; M-shaped marking of underwing reduced to dusky panel formed by inner primaries and bases of outer primaries. Juvenile — light phase, similar to adult except for reddish body and more ragged M-shaped underwing pattern due to more reddish feathers in underwing coverts; greyish patch in middle of outer wing panel and series of blackish spots along lower edge of underwing coverts. Dark phase, very similar to adult except body is more rufous.

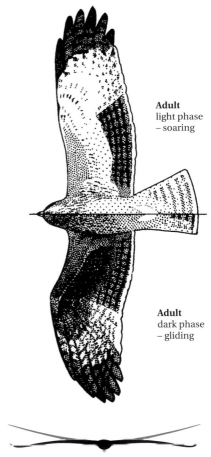

**Adult**
light phase
– soaring

**Adult**
dark phase
– gliding

**Flight Pattern:** Soaring — wings held straight out from body or slightly forward; leading and trailing edges straight (or latter gently S-shaped) and parallel; tail fanned round at tip with sharp corners. Gliding — in slow glide same as soaring but primaries closed and backswept; in fast glide wrist pushed forward to about beak level and primaries strongly backswept, trailing edge S-shaped, tail closed straight and square-tipped. Active flight — deep and slow interspersed with glides; some tail twisting.

**Habitat and Range:** Open forest, woodland and fields. More likely to be seen in western parts of region.

**Flight profile**

Greg Czechura

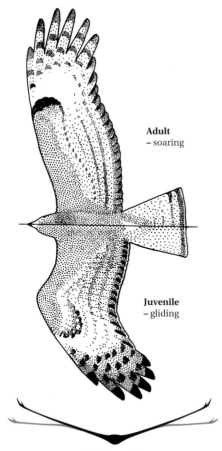

Adult
– soaring

Juvenile
– gliding

**Flight profile**

## Square-tailed Kite *Lophoictinia isura*

**Identification:** Length 0.6 m. Wingspan to 1.5 m. Slim body, rather scruffy with long, broad wings narrowest at base, long primaries, small white panel at base of primaries and square tail; female slightly larger than male; soars and glides in and around treetops with head down, wings upswept and tail-twisting. Adult reddish with brown back, streaked breast, white face and pale band through middle of upper wing. Juvenile reddish with reddish band through upper wing.

**Undersurface Pattern:** Adult — body and underwing coverts reddish; throat and breast streaked; face whitish; inner primaries, secondaries and tail greyish with darker bars and broad terminal band; lower underwing coverts greyish with small crescent of blackish feathers near wrist; primaries grey with broad dark bars except for white bases which form small panel. Juvenile — similar, more reddish; throat and breast unstreaked; broad dusky crescent near wrist; grey lower underwing coverts speckled.

**Flight Pattern:** Soaring — wings held out from sides of body with well spread primaries, rounded outer wing and protruding head and neck; leading and trailing edges of wings straight with slight bulge in the secondaries; tail with sharp corners and rounded when fanned or square when partly closed. Gliding — wrists pushed forward, primaries backswept and closed creating S-shaped trailing edge to wing and more pointed but blunt-tipped outer wing, tail closed; in fast glide wrists pushed further forward and outer wing becomes more pointed. Active flight — deep and rapid or slow and heavy interspersed with long glides.

**Habitat and Range:** Uncommon to rare inhabitant of open forest, woodland and lightly timbered areas. May also be seen along edges of suburbia or older "green" suburbs. Mainly encountered in northern and western parts of region.

## Red Goshawk *Erythrotriorchis radiatus*

**Identification:** Length 0.6 m. Wingspan 1.4 m. Heavy body and rather scruffy; long broad wings with deep primaries; protruding head and neck and square cut or slightly rounded tail; robust, long yellow legs often obvious in flight; female much larger and more robust than male; soars and glides with wings flat, upswept or slightly bowed. Adult grey-brown mottled with rufous and black above and rufous below with whitish face and throat (males), or with whitish face and underparts; rufous flanks, "trousers" and variable breast band (females); face, throat and breast streaked black; legs yellow. Juvenile almost entirely rufous with finer streaking; legs cream to pale grey.

D. Baker-Gabb (Nature Focus)

**Undersurface Pattern:** Adult — underwing coverts rufous streaked black; throat whitish; rest of body rufous (male) or whitish with rufous flanks, "trousers" and breast band (females); throat, breast and belly streaked black; rest of underparts whitish strongly barred brown or black; pale panel may be present at base of outer primaries. Juvenile — similar but more strongly rufous with dark-tipped outer primaries; grey streaked black lower underwing coverts; large whitish outer wing panel extending along bases of secondaries, the ends of which are barred.

**Flight Pattern:** Soaring — wings held out from sides of body with leading and trailing edges nearly parallel; primaries well spread and outer wing rounded; tail closed or fanned with sharp corners; square-cut when closed or round when fanned. Gliding — wrists pushed forward and primaries back-swept and closed but still fingered; trailing edge of wing S-shaped; tail closed; in fast glide wrist pushed further forward to head level; primaries more backswept and wing-tip more pointed but blunt-tipped. Active flight — rapid, deep and powerful interspersed with glides or slower, regular flapping with deep stokes for long periods.

**Habitat and Range:** Rare, declining inhabitant of forests and well timbered areas.

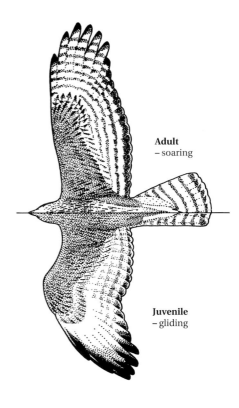

**Adult**
– soaring

**Juvenile**
– gliding

**Flight profile**

R. Hill

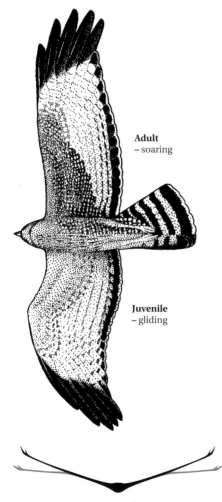

**Adult**
– soaring

**Juvenile**
– gliding

**Flight profile**

## Spotted Harrier *Circus assimilis*

**Identification:** Length 0.6 m. Wingspan to 1.5 m. Broad-winged with rounded outer wing, slim body and long, slender legs; wing-tips barred; face rufous with owl-like disc; tail strongly barred and wedge-shaped at tip; female larger than male; sails with gentle rocking motion above ground with head down, upswept wings and tips of primaries curled up. Adult blue-grey with rufous face, belly and shoulders heavily spotted white. First immature dark grey-brown above and mottled whitish; some develop marked dark hood in post-juvenile moult; underparts streaked reddish-brown. Later immature resembles adult above and is rufous streaked or spotted with white below. Juvenile pale reddish-brown on head, breast and shoulders with darker streaks; wings and tail dark brown; belly whitish; rump pale.

**Undersurface Pattern:** Adult — body and underwing coverts rufous spotted white; wing-tips and tips of secondaries black; rest grey barred brown; tail grey with prominent blackish bars, the last broadest. Immature — similar except breast and belly paler streaked reddish; dark-hooded immature with chest, belly and underwing coverts buff; head and throat heavily streaked reddish-brown. Juvenile similar to dark-hooded immature but breast and belly fully streaked.

**Flight Pattern:** Soaring — wings pushed slightly forward; leading edge slightly angled, trailing edge S-shaped and primaries spread; tail fanned with wedge-shaped tip. Gliding — in slow glide, the wrist is pushed forward and primaries back but still spread; in fast glide, wing strongly angled with wrist in line with head, outer wing nearly horizontal, innerwing still upswept, primaries closed and tail closed. Active flight — deep, regular wing-beats; sometimes bursts of flapping; hovers with deep slow wing-beats.

**Habitat and Range:** Grasslands and open fields, vicinity of freshwater swamps. Irregular visitor, mainly in winter and spring.

## Swamp Harrier *Circus approximans*

**Identification:** Length 0.6 m. Wingspan to 1.5 m. Broad-winged with narrow outer wing, slim body and long, slender legs; wing-tips barred; face with owl-like disc; tail faintly barred and rounded to squarish at tip; white rump in all ages and sexes; female larger than male; soars and glides near ground with head down and strongly upswept wings. Adult male — brown with grey wings, streaked breast and faintly barred tail; female — brown with pale patch in underwing. Juvenile — dark chocolate brown.

**Undersurface Pattern:** Adult — body and underwing coverts whitish or brownish, narrowly or broadly streaked with reddish-brown; ends of outer primaries and secondaries greyish barred black; tips of secondaries dark forming a narrow band along trailing edge; inner half of primaries whitish faintly barred brownish, forming an obscure pale panel; tail greyish with darker middle (male) or obscurely banded dark grey (female). Juvenile — body and underwing coverts dark brown; pale panel present in base of primaries; tips of outer primaries blackish; secondaries and tips of inner primaries dark grey; tail greyish with lower half darker.

**Flight Pattern:** Soaring — wings pushed slightly forward; leading edge slightly angled, trailing edge gently curved or parallel with leading edge (males) or S-shaped (females) and primaries spread; tail fanned or closed with rounded tip. Gliding — in slow glide, wrist pushed forward and primaries back, otherwise similar to soaring; in fast glide, wing strongly angled from wrist in line with beak, primaries closed and backswept, outer wing nearly horizontal, inner wing upswept and long, narrow tail closed. Active flight — wing-beats heavy, deep and fast but still buoyant; often bursts of flapping with long glides on upswept wings.

**Habitat and Range:** Grasslands, open fields and freshwater wetlands. Most sightings are of juveniles in winter. May be encountered throughout region.

Juvenile                    Queensland Museum

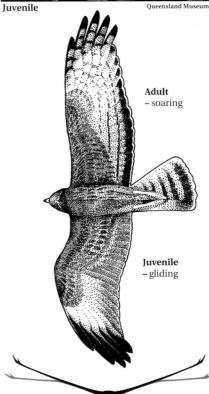

**Adult**
– soaring

**Juvenile**
– gliding

**Flight profile**

Queensland Museum

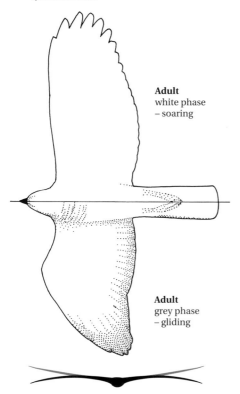

**Adult**
white phase
– soaring

**Adult**
grey phase
– gliding

**Flight profile**

## Grey Goshawk *Accipiter novaehollandiae*

**Identification:** Length 0.6 m. Wingspan to
1.1 m. Robust, short-winged with broad
inner wing and rounded outer wing (trailing
edge bowed in region of outer secondaries);
short, broad tail with square tip when folded;
female larger than male; soars and glides on
flat, slightly upswept or slightly bowed wings.
Adult pure white (white phase) or white with
grey back, faint grey barring on breast (grey
phase) and bright yellow legs and cere.
Juvenile similar to adult (white phase) or
slightly darker and breast more barred; legs
pale yellow and cere yellow.

**Undersurface Pattern:** Adult — white in
both phases, except for faint grey barring on
breast and grey edge to tips of primaries and
secondaries in grey phase. Juvenile — white
phase similar to adult white phase; grey
phase with darker barring on breast and
faint grey barring on tail, primaries, secondaries and some lower underwing coverts.

**Flight Pattern:** Soaring — wrists pushed
slightly forward, trailing edge strongly
bowed along secondaries, pinched at body
and tail spread with rounded tip. Gliding —
in fast glide, wrists pushed well forward,
primaries backswept, tail closed with square
tip. Active flight — loose, rapid with short
bursts interspersed with glides.

**Habitat and Range:** Rainforest, dense open
forest and gallery forest including forest
margins and clearings. Occasionally seen
near mangroves.

## Brown Goshawk *Accipiter fasciatus*

**Identification:** Length 0.6 m. Wingspan 1.0 m. Medium-sized, robust and rather short-winged; rounded wing-tips; protruding head and neck; long tail rounded at tip; marked "frowning expression"; female much larger than male; soars on slightly upswept wings and glides with wings flat or slightly bowed. Adult greyish-brown with rufous collar and underparts barred in pale rufous and white. Immature similar to adult; collar incomplete; breast and belly broadly barred reddish-brown and white with paler finely barred "trousers". Juvenile dark brown above; breast heavily streaked dark brown; rest of underparts broadly barred dark brown and white.

**Undersurface Pattern:** Adult — throat pale; rest of body and underwing coverts finely barred rufous and white; tail light brownish-grey; outer primaries whitish but darker near tips; dark grey to blackish barring present; secondaries and inner primaries light greyish-brown with darker barring. Immature — darker barring, contrasting paler "trousers" and some barring on tail. Juvenile — throat with indication of brownish streak; breast broadly streaked dark brown; rest of underparts broadly barred dark brown except for trousers which are barred rufous; underwing coverts barred brown, more broadly along lower margin; inner primaries, secondaries and tail with greyish to buff wash and dark barring; outer primaries similar to adult but duller.

**Flight Pattern:** Soaring — wings held straight out from sides of body; leading edge straight lacking an obvious bend at wrist; trailing edge S-shaped; primaries well spread; wing-tip blunt; tail spread or partly closed with rounded tip. Gliding — wings held straight from body but primaries closed and angled backwards; wing-tip blunt; trailing edge appears straight; tail closed with well-rounded tip; in fast glide, wrist pushed forward (to cheek level) primaries backswept and closed; wing-tip blunt. Active flight — bursts of deep but rapid wing-beats followed by glides.

**Habitat and Range:** Open forest, woodland, farmland, parks and gardens.

Juvenile         Queensland Museum

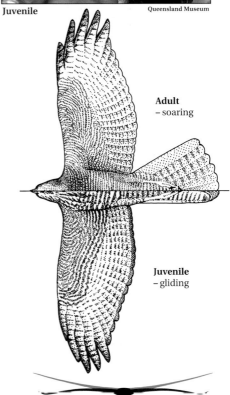

Adult – soaring

Juvenile – gliding

**Flight profile**

Peter Slater

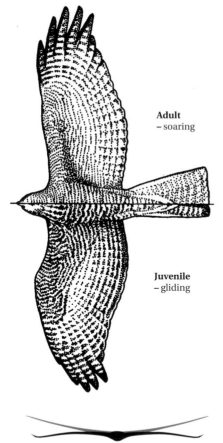

**Adult**
– soaring

**Juvenile**
– gliding

**Flight profile**

# Collared Sparrowhawk
## *Accipiter cirrhocephalus*

**Identification:** Length 0.4 m. Wingspan 0.8 m. Smallish and rather finely built; rather short-winged with rounded wing-tips; protruding head and neck; long tail square or notched at tip; staring facial expression; female much larger than male; soars on slightly upswept wings and glides with wings flat or drooped from near the body. Adult and juvenile identical to Brown Goshawk, see p. 271. No immature plumages have been recorded. Undersurface of adult and juvenile as for Brown Goshawk except bases of outer primaries usually more dusky and tail of adult barred.

**Flight Pattern:** Soaring — wrists pushed forward giving an angled leading edge and trailing edge prominently S-shaped; primaries spread and wing-tip blunt; tail closed or partly spread with square tip. Gliding — wrists well forward and primaries closed and backswept producing a pointed outer wing with blunt wing-tip; tail closed with square or notched tip. Active flight — usually bursts of rapid wing-beats interspersed with glides; also slow rowing flight and flicking, erratic, undulating flight.

**Habitat and Range:** Widespread — open forest, woodland, parks and gardens. Also margins of roads and clearings in dense forest. May be encountered throughout region but less common at higher altitudes.

## Black-shouldered Kite *Elanus axillaris*

**Identification:** Length 0.4 m. Wingspan to
1 m. Small, active during the day; wings
rather broad but long with pointed wing-tip;
somewhat large head with square or notched
tail-tip. Hovers frequently with deep, fast
wing-beats; soars and glides with upswept
wings. Adult grey above, white below with
black shoulders; black patch in front of eye
and short, black streak behind eye. Juvenile
— similar but with reddish-yellow wash to
head, breast and back; back with pale edged
feathers.

**Undersurface Pattern:** Adult — white
except for dark grey primaries and black
patch between wrist and base of outer primaries. Juvenile — similar except for reddish-
yellow band across throat.

**Flight Pattern:** Soaring — wings and wrists
pushed forward giving angled leading edge;
trailing edge straight; primaries spread
giving blunt wing-tip; tail spread and squarish. Gliding — wrists pushed well forward
and primaries angled back with pointed
wing-tip; tail closed with notched tip. Active
flight — direct with rapid, shallow action;
flapping often interspersed with long glides
with gentle rocking of body.

**Habitat and Range:** Margins of forest, woodland, lightly timbered country, grasslands
and parks in urban areas. Numbers subject
to fluctuation for as yet unknown reasons.
Some evidence for interaction with Nankeen
Kestrel. Found throughout region.

Queensland Museum

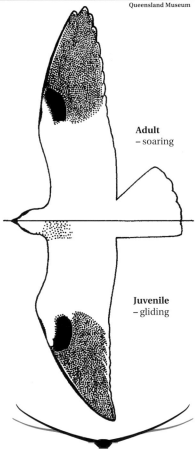

**Adult**
– soaring

**Juvenile**
– gliding

**Flight profile**

**Juvenile** R. Brown (Nature Focus)

## Letter-winged Kite *Elanus scriptus*

**Identification:** Length 0.4 m. Wingspan to 1 m. Small, active at night and roosts during day; wings rather broad but long with pointed wing-tip; somewhat large head with square or notched tail-tip; hovers frequently with deep, slow wing-beats or hangs motionless on slightly upswept wings in breeze; soars and glides with upswept wings. Adult grey above, white below with black shoulders; black patch in front of eye; male with whiter head than female. Juvenile similar but with red-dish-yellow wash to head, breast and back.

**Undersurface Pattern:** Adult — white except for greyish wing-tips and broad black band down centre of underwing from near wrist to armpit. Juvenile — similar except for yellowish-red band across breast.

**Flight Pattern:** Soaring — wings and wrists pushed forward giving angled leading edge; trailing edge straight; primaries spread giving blunt wing-tip; tail spread and squarish. Gliding — wrists pushed well forward and primaries angled back with pointed wing-tip; tail closed with notched tip. Active flight — slow and buoyant with deep, easy wing-beats; often interspersed with gliding and diving.

**Habitat and Range:** Extremely rare visitor from inland. Presence linked with end of major rat plagues in arid, western regions.

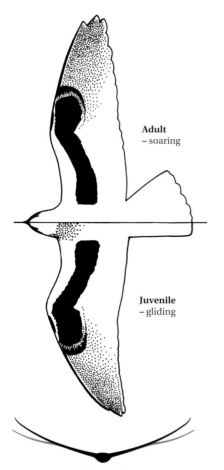

**Adult** – soaring

**Juvenile** – gliding

**Flight profile**

## Brown Falcon *Falco berigora*

**Identification:** Length 0.5 m. Wingspan 1.2 m. Medium-sized, large head, long legs; rather scruffy and tail heavy; long wings with rounded tips; tail long, gently rounded at tip; female larger than male; soars and glides on upswept wings with outer wing flatter than inner wing; rowing action in active flight; hovers clumsily. Adult (several colour phases exist) — shades of brown, ranging from reddish-brown to almost black; underparts uniformly whitish or brown, or streaked, speckled or blotched; lower half of trousers dark; moustachial and double cheek stripe. Juvenile — all forms are uniformly dark and resemble dark adults but often have paler markings on forehead, cheeks, eyebrow, throat and underside of rump; darkest juveniles lack reddish spotting on flanks.

**Undersurface Pattern:** Adult and juvenile — tail, primaries and secondaries pale barred in shades of brown; tips of primaries dark; pale panel present in outer wing (dusky in juveniles and reduced in dark phase); always contrasting between dark underwing coverts and paler underwing; throat and underside of rump pale (not dark phase); underwing coverts brown and paler near base of primaries.

**Flight Pattern:** Soaring — wrists pushed forward and primaries spread; outer wing broad with rounded wing-tip; trailing edge curved or with slight kink at junction of primaries and secondaries; tail spread with rounded tip. Gliding — wrists pushed forward and primaries backswept; wing-tip more pointed but tips of longest primaries evident; tail closed, broad with squarish tip. Active flight — slow and heavy with definite rowing action; flapping interspersed with glide; wing-beats in faster pursuit flights short and stiff; hovers in clumsy manner; displays with much jinking and side-slipping.

**Habitat and Range:** Margins of forest, woodland, lightly timbered country and grasslands.

Queensland Museum

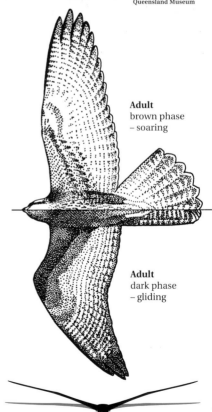

**Adult**
brown phase
– soaring

**Adult**
dark phase
– gliding

**Flight profile**

R. Hill

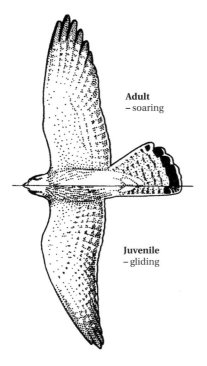

**Adult**
– soaring

**Juvenile**
– gliding

**Flight profile**

## Nankeen Kestrel *Falco cenchroides*

**Identification:** Length 35 cm. Wingspan 80 cm. Small, finely built with long tail; wings long and narrow with blunt tips; tail rounded or weakly wedge-shaped at tip. Soars and glides with wings flat or outer wing drooped; hovers with little or no flapping. Adult chestnut above and white below with some streaking on breast; black upper surface of outer wing; short black moustachial stripe; head, neck and tail of male, blue-grey and in female, chestnut. Juvenile similar to adult female but more heavily streaked on breast.

**Undersurface Pattern:** Adult — whitish with brownish barring on primaries and secondaries which are dark tipped; tail whitish in male and buffish in female, barred (often obscurely so in male) with broad black subterminal band and whitish tip; variable amounts of streaking on breast, least in male. Juvenile — similar to adult female.

**Flight Pattern:** Soaring — wings outstretched and wrists held forward; trailing edge of wing curved forward; wing-tip blunt; tail spread with rounded tip. Gliding — wings backswept and scimitar shaped; wrists pushed to beak level; wing-tip blunt; tail closed with rounded or weakly wedge-shaped tip. Active flight — direct, shallow, "winnowing" action interspersed with sweeping glides; hovers with lowered and fanned tail and little or no flapping except for short bursts in breezy conditions; capable of hanging motionless for long periods.

**Habitat and Range:** Margins of forest, woodland, lightly timbered country, grasslands and parks in urban areas. Numbers subject to fluctuation for as yet unknown reasons. Some evidence for interaction with Black-shouldered Kite. Found throughout region.

## Australian Hobby *Falco longipennis*

**Identification:** Length 36 cm. Wingspan 90 cm. Small, finely built with fine square-tipped tail; wings long, narrow and scythe-shaped with sharp tips; female larger than male; soars and glides on flat or slightly drooped wings; very dashing and agile in active flight with rapid flickering wing-beats. Adult head dark with black cheeks and contrasting white throat and pale half-collar; rest of upper parts blue-grey with blackish upper wing-tips; underparts rufous. Juvenile similar but more reddish-brown overall with rufous tipped feathers on back and shoulders.

**Undersurface Pattern:** Adult — mainly rufous; throat white contrasting with edges of black cheeks and rest of underparts; tail, primaries and secondaries with darker barring and dark tips; margin of tail-tip pale edged; some streaking on breast and lower body paler rufous; also paler speckling on underwing coverts. Juvenile — similar but darker and more reddish-brown.

**Flight Pattern:** Soaring — wings outstretched, primaries partly backswept and wrists held slightly forward; blunt wing tip; leading and trailing edges of wings angled (curved or bent wing shape results); tail at most partly spread with square or slightly rounded tip. Gliding — wrists pushed well forward, primaries backswept with sharply pointed wing-tip and curved trailing edge produce a scythe-like shape to wing; tail closed, appears long and narrow with square tip. Active flight — fast and direct with rapid, shallow, "winnowing" wing-beats; also short glides, zig-zags, swoops and stoops, especially in pursuit of prey.

**Habitat and Range:** Woodland, lightly-timbered country, open areas, parks and gardens; also frequents freshwater wetlands. Found throughout region.

Robert Ashdown

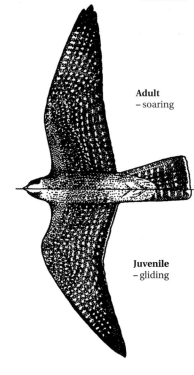

**Adult** – soaring

**Juvenile** – gliding

**Flight profile**

D. Hollands (Nature Focus)

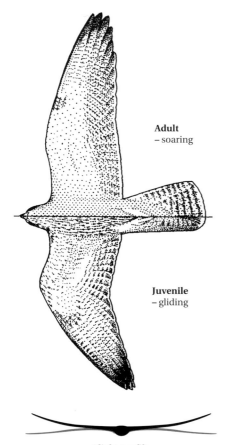

**Adult**
– soaring

**Juvenile**
– gliding

**Flight profile**

## Grey Falcon   *Falco hypoleucos*

**Identification:** Length 0.5 m. Wingspan to 1 m. Medium-sized, heavy-chested with longish, square-tipped tail; wings long with broad base, short inner wing and pointed wing-tip; female larger than male; soars and glides with wings level, slightly drooped from outer wing or with outer wings raised and primaries curled; stoops on prey from nearly vertical power-dives. Adult blue-grey above and whitish below with wispy, black moustachial streak and very fine streaking on underparts. Juvenile similar but with darker cap and moustachial streak; more whitish below with obvious fine streaking.

**Undersurface Pattern:** Adult — whitish except for greyish body and faint barring on primaries and secondaries and slightly stronger barring on tail; barring more noticeable towards tips, especially outer primaries; tail thinly edged with white. Juvenile — similar but more strongly barred and body and underwing coverts whitish finely streaked with grey.

**Flight Pattern:** Soaring — wings held straight from body and wrists pushed slightly forward; trailing edge almost straight and wing-tip rounded, giving impression of somewhat elliptical wing shape; tail usually spread and may seem short; tail-tip rounded. Gliding — wrists pushed well forward and primaries backswept; wing-tips pointed; tail closed, tapering with square or pointed end. Active flight — fast and direct with shallow, flickering wing-beats; deeper and faster in pursuit; easy leisurely flight with rowing action; flapping may be interrupted by short glides; sudden changes of direction and vertical stoops when hunting.

**Habitat and Range:** Extremely rare visitor from inland.

## Black Falcon *Falco subniger*

**Identification:** Length 0.6 m. Wingspan to 1.2 m. Medium-sized, small head, neat, streamlined with tapering tail; long broad wings tapering to sharp tips; tail long narrow with square tip when closed, but when fanned outermost feathers short producing a step at the corners; female larger than male; soars and glides with wings level or drooped from near wrist; rapid, stiff, shallow action in active flight; in pursuit, high speed low level dashes and high speed stoops. Adult uniformly dark brown to blackish-brown with some white on chin, throat and ear region. Juvenile similar but darker with some pale fringing to feathers on back.

R. Brown (Nature Focus)

**Undersurface Pattern:** Adult — almost uniformly dark, blackish-brown with variable amounts of white on chin and throat; some white barring present at bases of primaries and underside of rump; suggestion of two-tone pattern in underwing with darker underwing coverts and slightly lighter rest of underwing; some faint barring may be present on tail. Juvenile — similar to darkest adults.

**Flight Pattern:** Soaring — wings held out from body and wrists slightly forward; trailing edge of wing straight; primaries slightly backswept with pointed wing-tip; tail usually closed appears long and narrow with square tip or tapering to rounded tip; if fanned, corners are stepped and tip squarish or slightly rounded. Gliding — wrists well forward and primaries strongly backswept and tapering to points; tail closed. Active flight — direct and rapid with stiff, shallow wing-beats interrupted by glides; in pursuit, faster and deeper; also slow, leisurely flight like crows; in pursuit, low level dashes and vertical stoops.

**Habitat and Range:** Occasional visitor from inland. Presence sometimes linked with eruptions of quail through Brisbane Valley. Mainly encountered in western parts of region.

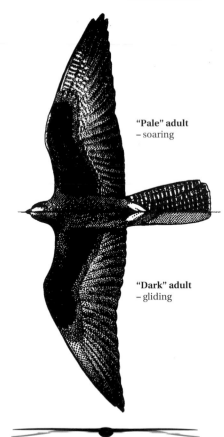

"Pale" adult
– soaring

"Dark" adult
– gliding

**Flight profile**

Queensland Museum

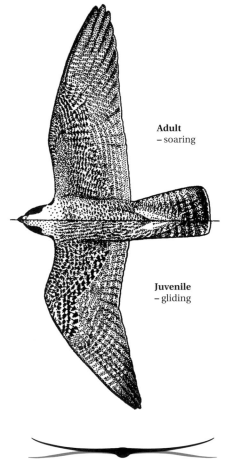

**Adult**
– soaring

**Juvenile**
– gliding

**Flight profile**

## Peregrine Falcon *Falco peregrinus*

**Identification:** Length 0.5 m. Wingspan to 1.1 m. Medium-sized, heavy-set and deep chested; long wings with broad base and short inner wing tapering to pointed wing-tip; female larger and more robust than male; soars and glides with wings level or very shallowly drooped; in active flight wing-beats rapid and shallow; in pursuit faster and deeper also high speed vertical stoops. Adult black cap with cheeks with rest of upper parts blue-grey except for dark upper surface to wing-tips; under parts whitish, greyish or buff with fine black barring; throat and breast white. Juvenile dark brown above and buff below streaked with brown.

**Undersurface Pattern:** Adult — whitish to buff, finely barred with black except for white throat and breast; edges of black cap obvious; tips of primaries, secondaries blackish; tail barred and tip edged with white. Juvenile — similar, more brownish with body streaked and underwing coverts barred and streaked often forming arrowhead pattern.

**Flight Pattern:** Soaring — wings held straight with wrists slightly forward and primaries slightly backswept; leading edge angled and trailing edge straight or with forward curve and wing-tip blunt, giving rather triangular wing shape; tail spread with round tip and corners; outermost tail feathers may contact trailing edge of wing at times. Gliding — wrists pushed forward and primaries backswept with pointed wing-tip; leading and trailing edges angled; tail closed appears broad with squarish or slightly rounded tip. Active flight — direct and steady with shallow elastic wing-beats interspersed with short glides; faster and deeper in pursuit, also high-speed vertical stoops with wings closed or fast, shallow swoops.

**Habitat and Range:** Recorded from most forested, open and wetland habitats and urban areas. Occasionally seen resting on skyscrapers in city area. May be encountered throughout region.

# Monotremes and Marsupials

Steve Van Dyck

The Greater Brisbane Region is home to a remarkable 36 percent of the State's monotreme and marsupial fauna. Almost all of the species not found principally in either the arid Queensland interior (19 species) or the tropical north (27 species) can be found in or around Brisbane (29 species). No one marsupial is endemic to the Brisbane area. Some such as the Common Brushtail Possum, Common Ringtail Possum and Northern Brown Bandicoot take the urban sprawl in their stride, and the Squirrel Glider, while considered rare to endangered elsewhere in Australia, is found nowhere else in such prolific numbers as in Brisbane. Others however like the Koala, Greater Glider, Yellow-bellied Glider, Brush-tailed Phascogale and Rufous Bettong hang on by the skin of their teeth, totally dependent on what little remains of tall, mature open forest. There is little doubt that the cream of Brisbane's wildlife is being skimmed off to the limits of both the city's boundaries and the animals' tolerance of interference.

# Monotremes

Bruce Cowell

## Platypus *Ornithorhynchus anatinus*

**Identification:** Body length 370 mm, tail length 130 mm. Duck-bill, webbed feet. Male has venom-delivering spur on hind foot.

**Habitat and Range:** Reasonably common but secretive. Freshwater (occasionally brackish) streams, some dams and lakes.

**Similar species:** Distinguished from Water Rat when swimming by absence in Platypus of visible ears, (see p. 307).

**Notes:** Active dawn, dusk, all day if overcast.

**Threats:** Set fishing nets, dogs, foxes, chemical pollution, dredging, dams.

**Traces:** Hen egg-sized burrow entrance just above water level and among tree roots.

Queensland Museum

## Echidna *Tachyglossus aculeatus*

**Identification:** Body length up to 450 mm; weight up to 7 kg. Young females and males have small non-functional spur on inside of each ankle.

**Habitat and Range:** Absent from inner city suburbs but reasonably common in shires. Anywhere with ground cover and ants.

**Similar species:** Australia has no porcupines, hedgehogs or tenrecs to confuse with the Echidna.

**Notes:** Active day or night. Eats only ants, termites, dirt.

**Threats:** Cars, dogs.

**Traces:** Shed quills; droppings long (up to 130 mm by 18 mm wide), cigar-shaped, smelly, clay-like and filled with shiny ant remains.

## Tiger Quoll  *Dasyurus maculatus*

Bruce Cowell

**Identification:** Body length 500 mm; tail length 450 mm; weight 5 kg. Cat-sized, ginger-tan with white spots on body and tail. Cat-like teeth; inner "big" toe on hind foot has no nail. Female has poorly developed pouch.

**Habitat and Range:** Almost certainly extinct in Brisbane area. Wet eucalypt forest and rainforest. Old records from Zillmere (1923), Oxley (1927). Last recorded at Upper Brookfield in 1957.

**Similar species:** Northern Quoll — much smaller and lacks tail spots.

**Notes:** Dogs, foxes, land clearing, cane toads, toxoplasmosis and humans are the main causes of Tiger Quoll's demise in region. Mostly nocturnal.

**Traces:** Birds — turkeys to pigeons — decapitated or throttled. Droppings large (70 mm long by 20 mm wide) and cigar-shaped.

## Brush-tailed Phascogale
*Phascogale tapoatafa*

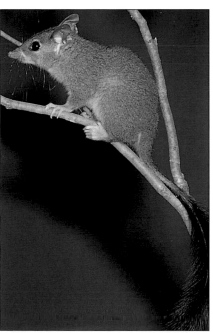

Queensland Museum

**Identification:** Body length 200 mm; tail length 190 mm; weight 180 g. Rat-sized, grey with black "bottle-brush" tail. Cat-like teeth; inner "big" toe on hind foot has no nail. Female has poorly developed pouch.

**Habitat and Range:** Rarely encountered. Dry eucalypt to rainforest.

**Similar species:** Squirrel and Sugar Gliders with prominent, black faces and body stripes and tails fluffy to base (see p. 288).

**Notes:** Nocturnal. Eats insects and small vertebrates. Mostly arboreal.

**Threats:** Cats, destruction of large trees with hollows, maybe cane toads.

**Traces:** Droppings usually large (35 mm long by 6 mm wide) and pointed. Fowls usually throttled and badly gashed about the throat.

Queensland Museum

## Yellow-footed Antechinus
*Antechinus flavipes*

**Identification:** Body length 110 mm; tail length 90 mm; weight — male 47 g, female 28 g. Small rat-sized. Flattish, broad head; pointed snout; cat-like teeth; inner "big" toe on hind foot has no nail. Colourful — grey head; white eye ring; orange-brown sides, belly, rump and feet; black tail-tip. Broad "Charlie Chaplin" hind feet. Poorly developed pouch.

**Habitat and Range:** Absent from inner city, uncommon elsewhere. Non-rainforest, but often in moist bracken, lantana, creek verges. Also found in dry eucalypt forest.

**Similar species:** Brown Antechinus which lacks eye rings, orange-brown fur and black tip to tail (see below).

**Notes:** Mainly nocturnal.

**Threats:** Cats

**Traces:** Calls ("tssst-tssst,") of nestling young around December-January. Droppings of adults long (up to 22 mm by 3 mm wide), pointed, often very tarry.

## Brown Antechinus   *Antechinus stuartii*

**Identification:** Body length 95 mm; tail length 90 mm; weight — male 60 g, female 28 g. Small rat-sized. Flattish, broad head; pointed snout; cat-like teeth; inner "big" toe on hind foot has no nail. Body and head uniformly brown, tail uniformly brown. Broad "Charlie Chaplin" hind feet.

**Habitat and Range:** Very common in restricted habitat. Rainforest.

**Similar species:** Yellow-footed Antechinus — same size but has eye rings, orange-brown sides and feet, black-tipped tail. Poorly developed pouch (see above).

**Notes:** Nocturnal except in breeding season.

**Threats:** Cats

**Traces:** As for the Yellow-footed Antechinus.

Queensland Museum

## Common Dunnart *Sminthopsis murina*

**Identification:** Body length 90 mm; tail length 80 mm; weight 22 g. Large mouse-sized. Sharply pointed snout; large, bulging black eyes; delicate white hind feet; grey-brown head and body; belly pure white; cat-like teeth; inner "big" toe on hind leg has no nail. Female has "kangaroo-type" pouch.

**Habitat and Range:** Uncommon despite its name. Dry forests and woodlands, often with blady or kangaroo grass.

**Similar species:** Smaller and more delicate than antechinuses which have much broader hind feet, smaller eyes and poorly developed pouches (see p. 284).

**Notes:** Nocturnal.

**Threats:** Cats.

**Traces:** Droppings smaller version (15 mm long by 2.5 mm wide) of antechinus scat.

Queensland Museum

## Common Planigale *Planigale maculata*

**Identification:** Body length 70 mm; tail length 60 mm; weight up to 11 g. Mouse-sized; mouse-coloured; male larger than female. Flat head; pointed snout; cat-like teeth; inner "big" toe on hind foot has no nail. Female has "kangaroo-type" pouch.

**Habitat and Range:** Reasonably common in outer suburbs. Dry forests and woodlands, often with blady or kangaroo grass.

**Similar species:** House Mouse which lacks pendulous scrotum, pouch, cat-like teeth and clawless "big" toe.

**Notes:** Nocturnal.

**Threats:** Cats.

**Traces:** Very small pointed droppings (4 mm long by 1 mm wide).

Queensland Museum

Bruce Cowell

## Northern Brown Bandicoot
### *Isoodon macrourus*

**Identification:** Body length 400 mm; tail length 170 mm; weight 2 kg. Large male may be size of miniature Fox Terrier. Brown with very harsh fur. Posture humped; snout very long and pointed; movements jerky. Forefeet with only 3 long-nailed toes. Tail often absent.

**Habitat and Range:** Common. Inner suburbs with protective daytime cover (eg long grass, thick shrubs, rubbish piles). Outer suburbs — dry and wet eucalypt forests, open paddocks.

**Similar species:** Long-nosed Bandicoot has soft fur, pointed ears, a much larger gap between the 4th and 5th upper incisor and is generally restricted to rainforest and very moist patches (see below).

**Notes:** Nocturnal. Non-climbing. Infamous for small holes it digs in lawns and gardens. Explosive "balloon screech" call if disturbed.

**Threats:** Dogs, cats, cars.

**Traces:** Small holes (7 cm diameter) in lawns, usually in winter and spring, large excavations in gardens for roots and insect larvae. Droppings like peanut pods (25 mm long by 10 mm wide).

Brisbane Forest Park

## Long-nosed Bandicoot *Perameles nasuta*

**Identification:** Body length 400 mm; tail length 140 mm; weight 1.5 kg. Snout very long and pointed; posture hunched; ears pointed; fur soft; large gap between 4th and 5th upper incisors; 3 long-clawed toes on forefeet.

**Habitat and Range:** Common only on D'Aguilar Range and slopes. Rainforest and moist gullies.

**Similar species:** Northern Brown Bandicoot has more rounded ears and much harsher fur.

**Notes:** Nocturnal. Non-climbing, omnivorous, common at backyard composts. Shrill "toy trumpet" squeek when disturbed.

**Threats:** Dogs, cats, cars.

**Traces:** Small conical holes in lawns and gardens, droppings like peanut pods (35 mm long by 10 mm wide).

## Koala *Phascolarctos cinereus*

Queensland Museum

**Identification:** Body length 90 cm; weight 6 kg. Male larger and more "coarse-looking" (Roman-nosed, "dirty" chest gland) than female.

**Habitat and Range:** Uncommonly seen. Dry open eucalypt forests.

**Notes:** Nocturnal. Favoured local food trees include Grey Gum, Tallowwood, Queensland Blue Gum, Blackbutt, Spotted Gum, Flooded Gum, Swamp Mahogany, Scribbly Gum, Brush Box. Some Melaleuca leaves also eaten. Breeding season October-January.

**Threats:** Land clearing, dogs, guns, cars.

**Traces:** Scratch marks on trunks; strong eucalyptus smell. Droppings avocado-shaped (22 mm long by 13 mm at widest point).

## Yellow-bellied Glider *Petaurus australis*

Queensland Museum

**Identification:** Body length 280 mm; tail length 420 mm; weight 550 g. Black fore and hind paws; ears naked and black; claws white. Belly buff-yellow, orange or white depending on age. Gliding membrane extends from wrist to ankle.

**Habitat and Range:** Rare. Tall open mature eucalypt forest (most generally wet forest).

**Similar species:** Greater Glider — very furry ears and gliding membrane that extends from elbows to ankle (see p. 289).

**Notes:** Nocturnal. Noted for its long glides (over 100 m recorded), loud gurgling calls, and habit of slashing tree trunks to obtain exuded gums. Incisions resemble human "kiss" marks on trunks. Locally favoured trees include Scribbly Gum, Sugar Gum, Blue Gum and Grey Gum. Insects, nectar and pollen also eaten.

**Threats:** Land clearing, felling of old hollow nest trees.

**Traces:** Weeping incisions on feed trees. Call "ooo-cree-cha-cree-cha-chigga-woo-ja". Droppings like small, rough-skinned avocados indented on the side of the narrow end (20 mm long by 9 mm at widest end).

Queensland Museum

## Sugar Glider *Petaurus breviceps*

**Identification:** Body length 170 mm; tail length 190 mm; weight 130 g. Rat-sized body; soft grey with black stripe on head and body. Tail as thick or slightly thicker than a person's thumb, usually white-tipped.

**Habitat and Range:** Common in restricted range, generally wetter or higher altitude habitats or rainforest remnants.

**Similar species:** Squirrel Glider — usually larger (HB: 210 mm, T: 270 mm , Wt: 230 g), very bushy tail that is never white-tipped (see below).

**Notes:** Nocturnal. Feeds on wattle exudates, gum sap, nectar, and insects. Lives in groups of up to 10, nesting in tree hollows.

**Threats:** Cats, clearing of wattles.

**Traces:** Loud "yip-yip-yip". Droppings (12 mm long by 4 mm wide) blackish, pointed at one end, sometimes joined by hairs.

Bruce Cowell

## Squirrel Glider *Petaurus norfolcensis*

**Identification:** Body length 210 mm; tail length 270 mm; weight 230 g. Large rat-sized body; soft grey with black stripe on head and body. Tail very thick especially where it joins body; tail never white-tipped.

**Habitat and Range:** One of Brisbane's more common nocturnal marsupials, yet rare to endangered through the rest of its eastern Australia range. Dry forests, woodlands, parks and gardens.

**Similar species:** Sugar Glider — smaller (BL: 170 mm; T: 190 mm; W: 130 g); very narrow tail that is often white-tipped. Does not "yip" like Sugar Glider (see above).

**Notes:** Nocturnal. Feeding and nesting same as for Sugar Glider.

**Threats:** Cats, clearing of wattles.

**Traces:** Droppings — knobbly pointed cylinders (15 mm long by 5 mm wide), often with gum bands.

## Greater Glider *Petauroides volans*

**Identification:** Body length 400 mm; tail length 500 mm; weight 1.5 kg. Body colour may be charcoal-brown to creamy-white. Fluffy ears; shaggy fur; long pendulous non-gripping tail; no body or head stripes. Gliding membrane stretches from elbow to ankle.

**Habitat and Range:** Uncommon but widespread in southern suburbs, probably gone from northern and western suburbs. Tall, mature eucalypt forests and woodlands.

**Similar species:** Yellow-bellied Glider has naked ears, dark body-stripe, never creamy-white. (see p. 287).

**Notes:** Silent, solitary, nocturnal. Eats gum leaves. Entirely dependent on large tracts of undisturbed, tall open forest with suitably large nesting hollows. Each animal requires approximately 1.5 hectares.

**Threats:** Land clearing, dogs.

**Traces:** Landing scratches on tree trunks. Droppings are size and shape of slightly flattened peas.

Dept of Environment and Heritage

## Common Ringtail Possum
### *Pseudocheirus peregrinus*

**Identification:** Body length 350 mm; tail length 350 mm; weight 1 kg. Small cat-sized; silver-grey back; rusty red flanks, face, arms and legs. Tail thin, with white tip but no brush. Eyes caramel-brown.

**Habitat and Range:** Common even in inner city suburbs. Rainforest, thick vegetation along watercourses, parks, backyard gardens.

**Similar species:** Common Brushtail Possum — grey with a bushy, black-tipped tail. Water Rat — does not climb trees (see pp. 290, 307).

**Notes:** Nocturnal, feeding on flowers and leaves. Builds tidy, basketball-sized nests of twigs, ferns and bark in mango trees, palms, bottle-brushes, dense vegetation and occasionally in verandah blinds or awnings. Avoids ceilings and rubbish bins. Usually silent.

**Threats:** Dogs, cats.

**Traces:** Large nests. Droppings (15 mm long by 6 mm wide) like roughly textured jellybeans.

Bruce Cowell

Queensland Museum

## Mountain Brushtail Possum
*Trichosurus caninus*

**Other Names:** Bobuck.

**Identification:** Body length 500 mm; tail length 400 mm; weight 4 kg. Cat-sized; commonly dark slate grey but may be pure black. Short round ears; tail not bushy near tip; black paws.

**Habitat and Range:** Mostly rainforest or thick vegetation bordering watercourses. Some isolated populations in southern and western Brisbane suburbs.

**Similar species:** Common Brushtail Possum — longer pointed ears, light grey paws, bushy tail-tip and fur of a lighter grey (see below).

**Notes:** Nocturnal.

**Threats:** Land clearing.

**Traces:** Droppings like large jellybeans (25 mm long by 10 mm wide), coarse and smooth-ended.

Bruce Cowell

## Common Brushtail Possum
*Trichosurus vulpecula*

**Identification:** Body length 500 mm; tail length 380 mm; weight 4 kg. Cat-sized; light grey; black tail bushy to tip; paws light grey; ears large.

**Habitat and Range:** Most commonly encountered Brisbane marsupial. Dry and wet forests — usually anywhere Mountain Brushtail Possum is not found. In the inner suburbs almost anywhere with a tree and a ceiling.

**Similar species:** Mountain Brushtail Possum — dark slate grey to pure black fur, short round ears, tail not bushy near tip, black paws (see above).

**Notes:** Nocturnal.

**Threats:** None

**Traces:** Urine stains on the ceiling; heavy breathing (a throaty "ha-ha-ha") in breeding season. Droppings (22 mm long by 7 mm wide) like thin jellybeans with one pointy end.

## Feathertail Glider *Acrobates pygmaeus*

Queensland Museum

**Identification:** Body length 80 mm; tail length 80 mm; weight 13 g. Mouse-sized; grey-brown back; white belly; tail like a small feather (a feature found in no other Australian mammal).

**Habitat and Range:** Rarely seen, but reasonably common in bushy outer suburbs. Wet and dry eucalypt forests, parks and backyard gardens.

**Similar species:** House Mouse — lacks a feather-like tail (see p. 312).

**Notes:** Nocturnal. A miniscule gliding possum, living in family groups (parents plus last one or two litters) numbering up to a dozen. While feeding on nectar, gum, sap, and insects, it careers around treetops and trunks more like a large insect than a marsupial. Commonly nests in electricity meter boxes, telephone junction covers and banana bags.

**Threats:** Cats.

**Traces:** Difficult to detect in wild; droppings like House Mouse scats (5 mm long by 2 mm wide) but pointed at both ends.

## Rufous Bettong *Aepyprymnus rufescens*

Queensland Museum

**Identification:** Body length 38 cm; tail length 36 cm; weight 3 kg. Very small, long-clawed wallaby with silvery-ginger fur, blunt face, white (to off-white) tail, and delicately thin long hind legs.

**Habitat and Range:** Rare. Dry open forest with dense grassy ground cover (blady, kangaroo, wiregrass etc).

**Similar species:** Long-nosed Potoroo which has black tail, short and wide hind feet, pointed snout (see p. 292).

**Notes:** Nocturnal, usually solitary. Builds grassy nest under tussock, carries nesting material curled in tail.

**Threats:** Dogs, cats.

**Traces:** Droppings are shape and size of pea, or more oval (17 mm long by 10 mm at widest point).

H. and J. Beste (Nature Focus)

## Long-nosed Potoroo
### *Potorous tridactylus*

**Identification:** Body length 36 cm; tail length 23 cm; weight 1 kg. Dark brown-grey body; dark tail; very long narrow nose. Hops with body almost horizontal.

**Habitat and Range:** Rarely seen and then only when animal is dashing across road. Generally restricted to wetter or higher altitude habitats in thick, wet eucalypt forests with heavy ground cover.

**Similar species:** Short and Long-nosed Bandicoots — very similar but never hop bipedally and have only 3 toes on forepaws (see p. 286).

**Notes:** Nocturnal.

**Threats:** Foxes, dogs, cats, land clearing.

**Traces:** Bandicoot-like holes in ground. Droppings vary according to food eaten, usually dark and oval (10 mm long by 4 mm wide).

Queensland Museum

## Agile Wallaby  *Macropus agilis*

**Identification:** Body length 80 cm; tail length 77 cm; weight 15 kg. Medium-sized, light yellowish-brown. Prominent white face stripe leading back from upper lip to under eye; white thigh stripe.

**Habitat and Range:** Uncommon and perhaps dying out. Dry open forests, heath, woodlands and adjoining grasslands. North and South Stradbroke Islands, Peel Island and a 1924 record from Russell Island.

**Similar species:** Red-necked Wallaby and Black-Striped Wallaby — ranges do not extend to Bay islands (see p. 293).

**Notes:** Bay population is precious remnant of now extinct pre-European southern distribution. Elsewhere species is found abundantly north of Rockhampton.

**Traces:** Droppings pear-shaped, slightly pointed at broader end (25 mm long by 15 mm at broadest end).

## Black-striped Wallaby
### *Macropus dorsalis*

Dept of Environment and Heritage

**Identification:** Body length 80 cm; tail length 60 cm; weight 12 kg. Black gloves; white face stripe; white thigh stripe; distinct black brush-stroke down mid neck and back.

**Habitat and Range:** Absent from inner Brisbane, uncommon on outskirts, common elsewhere in Qld. Densely understoreyed eucalypt and acacia forests, often in areas infested with lantana.

**Similar species:** Red-necked Wallaby — no black stripe down back (see below).

**Notes:** Mostly nocturnal.

**Threats:** Land clearing

**Traces:** Well defined paths through dense vegetation leading to grazing areas.

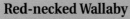

## Red-necked Wallaby
### *Macropus rufogriseus*

Queensland Museum

**Identification:** Body length 82 cm; tail length 80 cm; weight 15 kg. Weak face stripe; weak to absent thigh stripe; rust-red shoulders and upper back; rest silver-tipped grey.

**Habitat and Range:** Most abundant wallaby. Commonly seen early mornings, late evenings feeding along sides of roads. Dry open forests with some brushy undergrowth, grasslands, roadside verges, paddocks and backyards.

**Similar species:** Black-striped Wallaby has distinct black stripe down neck and back (see above).

**Threats:** Creekside clearing.

**Traces:** Droppings pear-shaped, slightly pointed at broader end (25 mm long by 15 mm at broadest end).

Queensland Museum

## Whiptail Wallaby *Macropus parryi*

**Other Names:** Pretty-faced Wallaby.

**Identification:** Body length 90 cm; tail length 94 cm; weight 16 kg. Uniform grey above; white below; very prominent white face stripe; white ear-tip patches; and long thin tail.

**Habitat and Range:** Common on ranges and steeply grassed slopes of outer Brisbane. Hilly to mountainous dry open forests and woodlands with grassy understorey.

**Similar species:** Red-necked Wallaby — red neck and indistinct stripe on face and thigh. Black-striped Wallaby has black stripe down neck and back (see p. 293).

**Notes:** Diurnal and usually in mobs. Rarely drinks.

**Threats:** Habitat destruction.

Bruce Cowell

## Grey Kangaroo *Macropus giganteus*

**Identification:** Body length 1 m; tail length 90 cm; weight 50 kg. Uniform woolly grey-brown (slightly darker on shoulders and mid back), without face stripes or thigh stripes. Tail black-tipped.

**Habitat and Range:** Uncommon. Open forests and woodland with grassy understorey, roadside verges, paddocks, grasslands, parkland.

**Similar species:** Only local large kangaroo with no adornments such as red neck, stripes, white flashes or black stripes.

**Notes:** Grazes on grasses and forbes, late afternoon to early morning.

**Threats:** Habitat destruction.

**Traces:** Droppings pear-shaped (26 mm long by 21 mm at widest).

## Swamp Wallaby (including "Golden" Wallaby) *Wallabia bicolor*

Jeff Wright

**Identification:** Body length 75 cm; tail length 75 cm; weight 15 kg. Very dark, thickly-set wallaby. Back charcoal; belly orange; black "robber's" mask; yellow face stripe; ears ginger at bases; black fore and hind feet; white tail tip.

**Habitat and Range:** Reasonably common. Wide variety of habitats including swamps, ferny gullies, open forest, woodland, lantana thickets, heathlands and shrubby water-courses.

**Similar species:** No other local wallaby is as dark on back, none is as ginger on belly, and no other has white-tipped tail.

**Notes:** Isolation on Stradbroke Islands has favoured preservation of a golden colour phase, particularly frequent on South Stradbroke.

**Threats:** Dogs.

**Traces:** Droppings round and coarse (25 mm diameter); green grass is compressed into long cigar shape (6 cm long by 18 mm wide).

## Red-legged Pademelon *Thylogale stigmatica*

Lone Pine Sanctuary

**Identification** Body length 48 cm; tail length 42 cm; weight 5 kg. Very small, brownish wallaby with brightly coloured rust-red legs and face. No red on neck.

**Habitat and Range:** Rainforest and vine thickets. Throughout D'Aguilar Range.

**Similar species:** Red-necked Pademelon which does not have red legs (see p. 296).

**Notes:** Reasonably common in restricted habitat. Less often seen than Red-necked Pademelon because of tendency to use thickest parts of forest rather than edges.

**Threats:** Dogs, cats

Heather Janetzki

## Red-necked Pademelon
*Thylogale thetis*

**Identification:** Body length 50 cm; tail length 40 cm; weight 6 kg. Very small greyish-brown wallaby, unadorned but for distinct red neck and shoulders.

**Habitat and Range:** Common in restricted habitat. Rainforest and vine thickets.

**Similar species:** Red-legged Pademelon which has bright rust-red thighs and grey-brown neck (see p. 295).

**Notes:** Common in restricted habitat. Nocturnal. More often encountered than Red-legged Pademelon because of tendency to graze on grass at edge of dense cover. Cautious animal which betrays presence of an observer by loud warning thumps made by the hind feet.

**Threats:** Dogs, cats.

# Bats

Dr Les Hall and Dr Len Martin

B ats are found in most parts of Australia and in the summer months they can be seen flying around city street lights, foraging for insects over ponds and streams, feeding on native blossoms and figs and backyard fruit trees.

Bats belong to the order Chiroptera which is divided into two sub-orders — the Megachiroptera and the Microchiroptera. The Megachiroptera contains the larger bats such as flying foxes or fruit bats and several small blossom bats. All Megachiroptera are fruit, blossom or nectar feeders. They have large eyes, small ears and their facial features resemble foxes or dogs. They use their excellent night vision and sense of smell to find food.

The Microchiroptera are small bats which, in Australia, are all insectivorous except for one carnivorous species. They usually have complex ears and all use echo-location for navigating and to detect and catch small insects. Although their eyes tend to be small, most have good vision and it is probable that some also use sight for navigation.

## Black Flying Fox  *Pteropus alecto*

**Identification:** Very large. Body 240–260 mm. Weight 500–700 g. Wingspan 1 m plus. Short black fur, often tipped with white. Eyes large, dark brown — sometimes "spectacles" of pale brown fur. Some have a shoulder mantle of dark orange or brown fur. Mantle does not encircle neck. Legs black and hairless. Wings black, opaque against bright light.

**Habitat and Range:** Roosts high in trees, especially mangroves. Camps in Brisbane area at Indooroopilly Island, Bulimba Creek, Norman Creek, Sparkes Hill, Woodend-Ipswich and Pine River. Far north-eastern NSW, coastal Qld, NT and northern WA.

**Fly-out Pattern:** Almost random — direction can change nightly. Flies at 25–35 km per hour. Does not echo-locate, finding its food and navigating by sight and smell.

**Notes:** One of world's largest bats. Frequently seen electrocuted on powerlines. Noisy when feeding at night.

Clancy Hall

Clancy Hall

Dr L. Hall

## Grey-headed Flying Fox,
*Pteropus poliocephalus*

**Identification:** Very large. Body 230–280 mm. Weight 600–800 g. Wingspan over 1 m. Fur long, almost fluffy; silver-grey in summer; may thicken and darken to grey-brown in winter. Head silver-grey/grey-brown. Large, dark brown eyes. Shoulder mantle thick ginger to orange-brown encircling neck. Legs covered with silver-grey/grey-brown fur to ankle. Wings black, opaque against bright light.

**Habitat and Range:** Roosts in trees often beside water. Brisbane camps at Indooroopilly Island, Norman Creek, Woodend-Ipswich, Pine River-Griffin. From Vic., through NSW and South-East Qld to about Rockhampton, mainly coastal.

**Fly-out Pattern:** As for Black Flying Fox.

**Notes:** As for Black Flying Fox. Both species mate in autumn; single young born in spring (Oct.–Nov.).

## Little Red Flying Fox
*Pteropus scapulatus*

**Identification:**  Body 195–235 mm. Weight 200–500 g. Wingspan less than 1 m. Short red-brown fur; occasionally "blonde" to pale fawn fur. Eyes large, red-brown; sometimes "spectacles" of pale fur.  Shoulder fur pale, no distinct mantle. Legs red-brown, hairless. Wings red-brown, black in poor light, translucent in bright light with wing bones visible.

**Habitat and Range:** Animals roost close together, often near the ground.  Brisbane camps are usually at Indooroopilly Island, Woodend-Ipswich, Pine River-Griffin. Forms temporary camps. Found over most of eastern and northern Australia.

**Fly-out Pattern:** Distinct columns, clouds of animals spiral upwards from canopy.  Does not echo-locate.

**Notes:** Arrives in south-eastern Qld in summer,  moves up central Qld coast in autumn and goes inland for winter. Mates in spring; single young born in autumn.

## Queensland Tube-nosed Bat
*Nyctimeme robinsoni*

**Identification:** Small fruit bat. Body 100–110 mm. Weight 30-50 g. Forearm 60-70 mm. Short brown-grey fur, slightly darker stripe from head down centre of back, short tail. Nostrils tubular and protrude above muzzle. Large brown eyes. Ears and wings brown with yellow to yellow-green splotches.

**Habitat and Range:** Dense forest, rainforest, regrowth areas, riparian forests, particularly if figs are present. Coastal, from far north-eastern NSW to Cape York.

**Flight Pattern:** Swift and often high in the canopy between emergent figs. Has high pitched whistle uttered while flying. Does not echo-locate.

**Notes:** Found around fruiting figs or flying along pathways in forest. Roosts singly in dense vegetation where it resembles a hanging dead leaf.

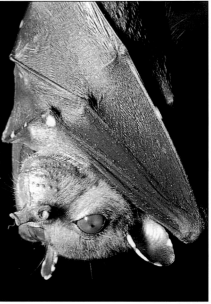

Dr L. Hall

## Queensland Blossom Bat
*Syconycteris australis*

**Identification:** Miniature blossom bat. Body 48–52 mm. Weight 12–18 g. Forearm 38–43 mm. Body covered with soft fawn to reddish fur. Large brown eyes. Nostrils slightly raised above muzzle. Wings reddish-brown. No tail.

**Habitat and Range:** Found in heathlands, paperbark swamps, riparian forest and rainforest. Coastal eastern Australia from about Coffs Harbour, NSW, to Cape York.

**Flight Pattern:** Generally 1–3 m above ground, along natural pathways and through dense vegetation. Does not echo-locate.

**Notes:** Feeds on banksias and paperbarks. Can be quite common in an area when plants are flowering. Roosts singly in dense vegetation.

Dr L. Hall

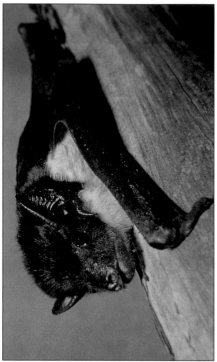

Dr L. Hall

## Yellow-bellied Bat
*Saccolaimus flaviventris*

**Identification:** Body 80–85 mm. Weight 30–60 g. Forearm 74–77 mm. Fur on back is jet black, belly pure white. Males have a throat pouch which is rudimentary in females.

**Habitat and Range:** Roosts in hollows of live or dead trees. Seems to prefer cleared land and open forest. Northern and eastern Australia.

**Flight Pattern:** Fast and direct above the canopy level. Produces audible calls while flying. Echo-locates at 19–24 kHz.

**Notes:** Old bats are often found on ground or clinging to walls in state of exhaustion.

Dr L. Hall

## Eastern Horseshoe Bat
*Rhinolophus megaphyllus*

**Identification:** Body 42–58 mm. Weight 9–14 g. Forearm 44–50 mm. Small grey-brown bat with large pointed ears and a fleshy "horseshoe" shaped area of skin on nose. Occasional individuals have rusty orange fur.

**Habitat and Range:** Roosts in caves, mines, tunnels, stormwater drains and dark over-hangs. Eastern Australia from Vic. to Cape York, generally east of the Great Dividing Range.

**Flight Pattern:** Swift and direct, but can be manoeuvrable in dense vegetation. Usually flies 1–3 m above ground. Echo-locates at 67–68 kHz.

**Notes:** Always hangs free by toes and twitches ears when approached.

## White-striped Free-tail Bat
### *Tadarida australis*

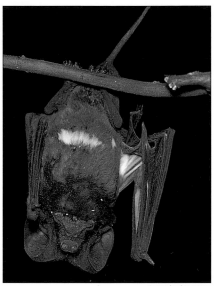

**Identification:** Body 85–100 mm. Weight 25–40 g. Forearm 57–63 mm. Tail protrudes from end of membrane. Chocolate to dark brown fur on back; underbody slightly lighter; fur very soft. Distinct white stripe down junction between wings and belly fur. Ears not joined over forehead. Neck pouch in both sexes — male pouch contains tuft of bristly hairs. Face bull-doggish. Lips prominently wrinkled.

**Habitat and Range:** Can be found flying above cleared land, open forest and rainforest. Found in southern Australia below Tropic of Capricorn.

**Flight Pattern:** Swift, direct, usually high above canopy. Echo-location calls can be heard by humans (11–15 kHz).

Queensland Museum

**Notes:** Tree-dweller which occasionally lands on the ground to forage for invertebrates. Docile when captured. Meticulous when grooming. Often solitary, but sometimes in groups of 2–5. Maternity colonies of more than 100 females have been found in Brisbane in tree hollows.

## Little Northern Free-tail Bat
### *Mormopterus loriae*

**Identification:** Body 43–53 mm. Weight 6–10 g. Forearm 29–35 mm. Short, light greyish-brown fur with paler base. Neck pouch in males. Large ears which can be pulled down over their eyes. Tail protrudes from end of membrane. Lips thick and wrinkled.

**Habitat and Range:** Fairly common. Wide range of habitats from urban to arid inland. Found in north-eastern NSW and coastal Qld.

**Flight Pattern:** Fast and direct, usually above the canopy. Echo-locates at 30–35 kHz.

Dr L. Hall

**Notes:** Roosts in tree hollows, old posts and under roofs. Colonies of several hundred known.

Dr L. Hall

## Beccari's Free-tail Bat
### *Mormopterus beccarii*

**Identification:** Body 55–65 mm. Weight 13–19 g. Forearm 34–41 mm. Short, light grey fur, paler on belly. Distinct musty smell. Tail protrudes from end of membrane. Large thick ears which can be lowered over face. Thick fleshy lips which are wrinkled.

**Habitat and Range:** From coastal forests, cleared land to arid rangelands. Far northern NSW, Qld and NT.

**Flight Patterns:** Fast and direct, usually high and above tree height. Echo-locates at 20–22 kHz.

**Notes:** Roosts in tree hollows as well as in roofs of houses. Colonies of more than 100 have been found in Brisbane houses. Can move quite quickly along the ground and is known to feed on ground-dwelling insects.

Dr L. Hall

## Large-footed Myotis
### *Myotis moluccarum*

**Identification:** Body 52–56 mm. Weight 7–12 g. Forearm 38–41 mm. Ears funnel-shaped. Fur grey-brown on back; belly slightly lighter and tipped with grey. Old bats have ginger fur; albinism and partial albinism are occasionally seen. Calcaneum (cartilaginous thickening of edge of tail membrane) extends 3/4 of distance from ankle to tail. Feet long (10–14 mm).

**Habitat and Range:** Distributed across northern coastal Australia.

**Flight Pattern:** Often flies in fixed circuit over a pond, dipping down to the water surface where it captures prey. Echo-locates at 40–55 kHz.

**Notes:** Roosts in caves, mines, disused railway tunnels, old buildings and dense foliage. Colonies can number several hundred. At dusk can be seen raking surface of water for insects. Bats cluster and can be found in a semi-torpid state in winter.

## Hoary Bat
*Chalinolobus nigrogriseus*

**Identification:** Body 45–55 mm. Weight 7–10 g. Forearm 32–38 mm. Blackish-grey fur on back; slightly lighter on belly. White "frosting" on fur of animals from north-western Qld. Very small ear lobe at corner of mouth.

**Habitat and Range:** Reasonably common. Found in a variety of habitats from open dry country to rainforest. Northern Australia north of Tropic of Capricorn; south-eastern Qld and far north-eastern NSW.

**Flight Pattern:** Quick and manoeuvrable with lots of twists and turns. Often chase each other over the surface of water. Echolocates at 40–50 kHz.

**Notes:** One of the first bats seen at dusk, usually near waterholes. Roosts in tree hollows. Uncommon in south-eastern Qld.

Dr L. Hall

## Gould's Wattled Bat
*Chalinolobus gouldii*

**Identification:** Body 65–75 mm. Weight 10–18 g. Forearm 40–48 mm. Dark chocolate-brown fur on back; belly slightly lighter; head and shoulders dark brown. Prominent lobe of skin on mouth corner, ear terminates in loose flap at corner of mouth.

**Habitat and Range:** One of most common bats in south-eastern Australia. Found in arid sandhill country, cleared grazing land, open forest, urban areas, but rare in rainforest. Widespread throughout Australia, but not recorded from Cape York Peninsula.

**Flight Pattern:** Swift and direct unless feeding, when the bat circles and dives. Echolocates at 35–40 kHz.

**Notes:** Frequently seen around waterholes and cattle troughs at dusk. Small colonies of up to 30 are found in tree hollows and under roofs. Single specimens are sometimes found under bark and inside buildings.

Dr L. Hall

Jack Pettigrew

## Little Cave Bat *Vespadelus troughtoni*

**Identification:** Body 35–45 mm. Weight 5–7 g. Forearm 33–37 mm. Dark brown on back; underbody slightly lighter. Muzzle broad, often swollen appearance due to glandular pads at sides. Short ears (under 15 mm) meet when folded across crown of head; long narrow pointed tragus (flap of skin in the entrance of the ear).

**Habitat and Range:** Generally found in forested areas and rocky country. Eastern Australia from Vic. to central Qld.

**Flight Pattern:** Often flies in a repeated circuit around trees and bushes. Flight consists of many twists and turns of small radius while chasing small insects such as mosquitoes. Echo-locates at 50–55 kHz.

**Notes:** Inhabits caves, mines or similar cave substitutes and also buildings. Winter colonies small, summer maternity colonies can contain up to 500 individuals.

## Northern Broad-nosed Bat
*Scotorepens greyi*

**Identification:** Body 45–55 mm. Weight 6–12 g. Forearm 28–34 mm. Brown fur with a reddish tinge on back; lighter brown belly with a dark brown base.

**Habitat and Range:** Cleared farmland, open forests and urban areas. Widespread through Qld, NT and WA.

**Flight Pattern:** Erratic with many twists and turns as they chase small insects. Echo-locates at 38–40 kHz.

**Notes:** Roosts in tree hollows, fence posts and buildings. Colonies of several hundred individuals are known from houses in Brisbane. Young are born in November.

Bruce Cowell

---

In February 1994, a single specimen of the rare and beautiful **Golden-tipped Bat** (*Kerivoula papuensis*) was caught at Mt Nebo. This bat, named for the colourful tips to the hair of its body and wings, was presumed extinct for more than 90 years until an individual was caught near Cairns in 1981. Since then they have been found at scattered locations down the east coast as far as southern NSW.

## Common Bent-wing Bat
*Miniopterus schreibersii*

Dr L. Hall

**Identification:** Body 52–58 mm. Weight 13–17 g. Forearm 45–49 mm. Uniform dark chocolate-brown on back; belly slightly lighter brown. Areas of rufous fur appear during moulting. Old bats appear gingerish.

**Habitat and Range:** Reasonably common. Found in well-timbered valleys, rainforest, coastal swamps, and open forest from south-east SA, Vic., NSW and Qld.

**Flight Pattern:** Usually high and fast above the canopy but will hunt insects in closed forest where it needs to be highly manoeuvrable. Echo-locates at 45–47 kHz with a loud call.

**Notes:** Dominant cave dwelling species in south-eastern Australia. Forms large "maternity" colonies in summer. Clusters of torpid bats found in winter; bats pack tightly — up to 1500 per sq m — on ceilings of caves, mines, disused railway tunnels, stormwater drains and old cement buildings. Should not be disturbed when in a torpid state.

## Little Bent-wing Bat
*Miniopterus australis*

Dr L. Hall

**Identification:** Body 43–48 mm. Weight 7–8 g. Forearm 36–40 mm. Similar to Common Bent-wing Bat (see above) except smaller and moult phase is not as pronounced.

**Habitat and Range:** Reasonably common. Likes well-timbered valleys and ranges. Found on the coast and ranges of eastern Australia, from Kempsey NSW to Cape York.

**Flight Pattern:** Fast and manoeuvrable. Found above, in and below canopy. Echo-locates at 58–60 kHz.

**Notes:** Cave-dwelling bat found in mines, disused railway tunnels, stormwater drains and old cement buildings. Forms clusters up to 1800 per sq m Large maternity colonies form in summer months. Males often use caves in different localities from females and young during summer months.

Jack Pettigrew

## Lesser Long-eared Bat
*Nyctophilus geoffroyi*

**Identification:** Body 40–50 mm. Weight 6–8 g. Forearm 33–39 mm. Light grey-brown fur on back; belly light grey. Fur long and "fluffy" with light tips. Pale forms known (generally from inland); patches of white fur occasionally. Ears long, joined over head, strongly ribbed, can be folded when at rest. Small, low Y-shaped protuberance on muzzle behind nostrils.

**Habitat and Range:** Widespread throughout Australia (not Cape York) in all types of habitat. Will enter houses at night when searching for insects and roosts under bark, in tree hollows and in sheds.

**Flight pattern:** Fluttery and close to the ground. Echo-locates at 100–35 kHz. Calls are very weak and faint.

**Notes:** Feeds low to, and even lands on, ground in search of insects. Females often give birth to twins and carry them for a week or so after birth while hunting.

Dr L. Hall

## Gould's Long-eared Bat
*Nyctophilus gouldi*

**Identification:** Body 55–65 mm. Weight 7–12 g. Forearm 39–45 mm. Fur is an olive-grey, slightly paler on the belly. Ears are long and prominently ribbed; can be folded down but are always erect when bat is active or flying. Low transverse ridge on the muzzle behind the nostrils.

**Habitat and Range:** Tends to be found in wetter and more dense vegetation than the Lesser Long-eared Bat, see above. Likes riparian forest, swamps and mangroves. Roosts under bark, in tree hollows and occasionally in buildings. South-eastern Qld, eastern NSW and Vic.

**Flight Patterns:** Slow and jerky, low to the ground at 1–1.5 m. Echo-location calls are very faint at 95–40 kHz.

**Notes:** Gleans insects off vegetation and ground. Feeds around houses and orchards. Females give birth to twins in early summer.

# Rats and Mice

Steve Van Dyck

The Greater Brisbane Region is home to seven species of native rodents and three introduced species. All but the House Mouse and the Water Rat are look-alikes and can be hard to identify. With the exception of the introduced House Mouse, Ship Rat and Sewer Rat, all the rodents listed here are protected.

## Water Rat  *Hydromys chrysogaster*

Queensland Museum

**Identification:** Body length 300 mm; tail length 270 mm; weight 700 g. Very large (rabbit-sized); brown-black back, golden belly; small ears; flattish "square" head; white-tipped tail.

**Habitat and Range:** Reasonably common, though rarely seen. River banks, estuaries, beaches, mangroves, wharves, lakes, dams, creeks and polluted watercourses.

**Notes:** Active day or night. Eats mainly yabbies, mussels and fish although poultry, frogs and snails may be taken. Builds nest at end of complex burrow along waterside.

**Similar species:** Platypus which has no visible ears or white-tipped tail (see p. 282) and Common Brushtail Possum (see p. 290).

**Threats:** Tough and resilient — threatened only by localised habitat destruction (swamp drainage, land reclamation)

**Traces:** Distinctive strong fishy scent; "runway" tracks along water's edge; feeding "tables" scattered with shells and other leftovers. Droppings torpedo-shaped (25 mm long by 8 mm wide); dead poultry with throats and heads roughly skinned.

Queensland Museum

## Water Mouse *Xeromys myoides*

**Other Names:** False Water Rat

**Identification:** Body length 100 mm; tail length 80 mm; weight 40 g. Very small (large mouse-sized); silky, slate-grey back sharply defined by pure white belly; tail short and sparsely haired, without white tip.

**Habitat and Range:** One of Brisbane's rarest mammals and one of Australia's rarest rodents. Intertidal sedgeland zones adjacent to mangrove forests, also freshwater swamps and reedy lakes close to foredunes. Bribie Island (3 km north of Post Office), Pumicestone Passage, North and South Stradbroke Island, Pimpama and Coomera Rivers.

**Notes:** Active at night. Known to eat crabs, shellfish, mud lobsters and marine flatworms. Constructs "volcanic" mounds of peat and mud up to 60 cm high. Rarely climbs; has been seen swimming in the wild but does not pursue active aquatic lifestyle.

**Similar species:** Grassland Melomys which has longer, harsher fur with indistinct line of demarcation between brown back and white belly and a longer tail (see p. 309). Cannot be confused with Water Rat which is 14 times bigger and has white tail-tip (see p. 307).

**Threats:** Direct or indirect interference with mangroves, swamps, and freshwater lakes.

**Traces:** Droppings relatively large (11 mm long by 4 mm wide), cylindrical, ends rounded, often in threes connected by hair, smelly. Large mud nest structures in sedgeland. Feeding scraps (crab and mud lobster shell fragments) at hollow bases of mangrove trees.

## Fawn-footed Melomys
### *Melomys cervinipes*

Heather Janetzki

**Identification:** Body length 114 mm; tail length 160 mm; weight 70 g. Rat-sized; variable in colour, but adults usually brown rather than grey. Tail virtually hairless with small scales arranged like mosaic bathroom tiles.

**Habitat and Range:** Common in restricted habitat. Rainforest and moist lantana, bracken, creek verges.

**Notes:** Nocturnal and partly arboreal.

**Similar species:** Grassland Melomys — usually smaller (rough rule to use is a hind foot length less than 26 mm), and first and second molars bear 5 roots (see below).

**Threats:** Cats, land clearing.

**Traces:** Droppings often very small, knobbly and mouse-like (5 mm long by 2 mm wide).

## Grassland Melomys
### *Melomys burtoni*

Queensland Museum

**Identification:** Body length 100 mm; tail length 120 mm; weight 55 g. Large mouse-sized; usually reddish-brown with tail that is dark on top and off-white underneath. Tail virtually hairless with small scales arranged like mosaic bathroom tiles.

**Habitat and Range:** Rarely encountered. Grasslands and heath fringes bordering swamps and mangroves. North Stradbroke and Moreton Islands.

**Notes:** Nocturnal, solitary, aggressive with its own kind. Agile climber. Builds nest like that of a wren, placed in long grass or in thick vegetation (such as Pandanus leaves).

**Similar species:** Fawn-footed Melomys — usually bigger (a rough rule is a hind foot length greater than 26 mm), and first and second molars bear 4 roots (see above).

**Threats:** Cats, land clearing and reclamation.

**Traces:** Droppings like those of House Mouse.

Bruce Cowell

## Bush Rat  *Rattus fuscipes*

**Identification:** Body length 160 mm; tail length 150 mm; weight 120 g. Rat-sized; brown-grey; tail ringed with bands of scales and shorter than head-body length.

**Habitat and Range:** Common along D'Aguilar Range and its associated gullies. Rainforest and thickly vegetated moist gullies, lantana and bracken patches, creekside verges.

**Notes:** Nocturnal, feeding on insects as first choice, but anything else as second.

**Similar Species:** In Brisbane district can be confused with Fawn-footed Melomys, Ship Rat and Sewer Rat, but all have tail longer than head-body length. Most easily confused with Pale Field Rat — light yellow with more bulging eyes. Also similar to Swamp Rat — very dark charcoal with a very short tail.

**Threats:** Cats.

**Traces:** Messy feeder, leaving droppings and smelly urine. Droppings torpedo-shaped, usually pointed at one end (17 mm long by 4 mm wide). Often digs burrows alongside building footings.

## Swamp Rat  *Rattus lutreolus*

**Identification:** Body length 160 mm; tail length 110 mm; weight 120 g. Very dark, stocky rat with black feet, blackish-brown fur and very short tail.

**Habitat and Range:** Uncommon, requiring more specialised habitat. Swamps, thick vegetation along watercourses and dense island vegetation above high water mark.

**Notes:** Active day and night. Feeds on reeds, swamp-grass stems and seeds. Cuts complex runways through thick vegetation.

**Similar species:** Black phase of Ship Rat which has tail much longer than head-body length.

**Threats:** Cats, land clearing and swamp reclamation.

**Traces:** Cuts runways through reeds and sedges. Droppings large (17 mm long by 5 mm wide) and coarsely granular.

Queensland Museum

## Pale Field Rat  *Rattus tunneyi*

Queensland Museum

**Identification:** Body length 140 mm; tail length 120 mm; weight 80 g. Very attractive and gentle rat. Yellow-brown above with bulging eyes. Tail shorter than head-body length.

**Habitat and Range:** Mainland — grassy or tussocky open forest, cultivated pasture, pine plantations and canefields. Islands — wallum swamps.

**Notes:** Nocturnal. Builds runways through dense grass.

**Similar species:** Can be confused with Fawn-footed Melomys, Ship Rat and Sewer Rat ( see pp. 309, 312 and below). Most easily confused with Bush Rat (see p. 310).

**Traces:** Trackways through tussock grass. Droppings torpedo-shaped, usually pointed at one end (17 mm long by 4 mm wide).

## Ship Rat  *Rattus rattus*

Queensland Museum

**Identification:** Body length 190 mm; tail length 230 mm; weight 280 g. Smart, sleek-looking; may be any colour from all-over black to pure white, but generally steel grey with white belly. Tail much longer than head and body

**Habitat and Range:** Commonest rat; immigrant from South-East Asia. Anywhere around human habitation, but typically an animal of altered or degraded habitats.

**Notes:** Found in ceilings, verandahs, dumps, gardens, shops, warehouses and fowl houses. Nocturnal. Accomplished climber, rarely seen on ground. Suprisingly gentle disposition.

**Similar species:** Sewer Rat, in which ear when pulled forward just reaches eye: in Ship Rat it extends past middle of eye (see p. 312).

**Threats:** Thrives on all forms.

**Traces:** High-pitched calls, "sitt-sitt", or more raucous "ehh-ehh-ehh". Night-time grinding on woodwork, loud pitter-pattering over the ceiling. Hollowed-out macadamia nuts, emptied papaws, scalped seedlings, empty snail shells assembled in caches. Droppings — blunt pellets (10 mm long by 3 mm wide).

Queensland Museum

## Sewer Rat *Rattus norvegicus*

**Identification:** Body length 240 mm; tail length 200 mm; weight 300 g. Shaggy, small-eared rat, with thick tail and very unpleasant disposition. Can be black to white, but generally brown on back and dirty white on belly.

**Habitat and Range:** Common. Human habitation, in particular wharves, warehouses, tunnels, drains and sewers.

**Notes:** Nocturnal. Non-climbing, burrowing. Feeds chiefly on meat (insects, prawns, birds, eggs, mice ) and scraps. Wary and difficult to trap.

**Similar species:** Ship Rat in which ear, when pulled forward, extends past middle of eye.

**Threats:** None sufficiently effective to exterminate it.

**Traces:** Trackways along creeks, riverbanks and in vegetation near rubbish tips and sewerage depots. Droppings large, pointed at one end (16 mm long by 5 mm wide).

Queensland Museum

## House Mouse *Mus musculus*

**Identification:** Body length 75 mm; tail length 80 mm; weight 15 g. Typical mouse, usually olive-brown and unremarkable. Very strong musky-mouldy scent. Small notch on inner side of upper incisors is characteristic.

**Habitat and Range:** Very common immigrant from central Asia. Everywhere, from refrigerators to swamps, wallum to food warmers.

**Notes:** Generally nocturnal. Capable of breeding in temperatures from below freezing to 40 deg. C. This is the "Field Mouse" sometimes said to be encountered in Brisbane.

**Similar species:** Common Planigale and Feathertail Glider (see pp. 285, 291).

**Threats:** Reproduces and expands its range regardless of all threats and in spite of predation at all levels.

**Traces:** Musty smell; screeches while fighting; droppings usually pointed (5 mm long by 2 mm wide), produced in enormous numbers.

# Dugongs

Dr Anthony Preen

Dugongs are big, docile marine mammals which, together with their fresh-water and estuarine cousins the manatees, form a unique group of animals known as the Sirenia. This name relates to the dugong being a possible source of the mermaid legend and the belief that as sirens they lured mariners to a watery grave. Moreton Bay supports a population of more than 600 dugongs. This population is unusual, if not unique, because it exists in such close proximity to a large human population and because the dugongs are found in large herds (typically of about 50 animals), a rare occurrence elsewhere.

Anthony Preen

**Feeding trail through seagrass beds.** Anthony Preen

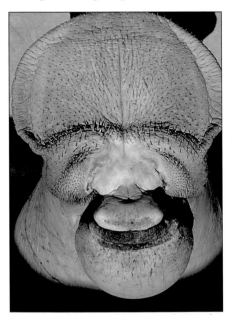

**Front view of downward facing mouth. Note the enlarged upper lip (top) and sensory bristles that allow the dugong to forage in dirty water.**

Anthony Preen

## Dugong  *Dugong dugon*

**Identification:** Length to 3 m; weight to more than 400 kg; light brown to light grey on upper back, paler underneath; no dorsal fin; large head with highly modified skull and facial musculature adapted for feeding on seagrasses. Sexually mature after 10 years, and may live to 70 years.

**Status:** Listed as vulnerable to extinction by the World Conservation Union.

**Habitat and Range:** Moreton Bay distribution is closely tied to seagrass beds — most occur in the central eastern part of the Bay, west of Amity. There is now relatively little use of seagrass beds along mainland shore (Pumicestone Passage, Deception Bay, Fisherman Islands, Tingalpa Creek, Wellington Point, Toondah Harbour and Redland Bay). This is apparently due to higher levels of boat traffic. Dugongs have a tropical and subtropical coastal distribution, with discontinuous populations ranging from south-eastern Africa around the Arabian Peninsula, India, South-East Asia, Vanuatu to Moreton Bay (southern limit).

**Threats:** Few natural predators, although sharks may take calves. Hunting by humans has reduced or exterminated populations in some areas and may impact on the Moreton Bay population in future. Easily disturbed by speed boats. Strikes by boats are the most common cause of death for the related Florida Manatee. Recent loss of seagrass and dugongs from Hervey Bay has highlighted dependence of dugong populations on good water quality and integrated catchment management.

# Whales

Dr R. A. Paterson

Whales are the largest of the marine mammals. Like dolphins, porpoises and the sirenians (dugong and manatee), whales are warm-blooded, air-breathing and nurse their young on milk.

Whales are divided into two groups: baleen whales — such as the Humpbacks which filter shrimp-like krill through curtains of mineralised hair (baleen) in their mouths; and toothed whales — such as the Killer Whale which has single-rooted, undifferentiated teeth and which eats large mammals, fish and birds.

In the past, over-exploitation of whales by many countries led to the near extinction of many species. The 1981 Whale Protection Act protects whales within a zone of 320 km from the Australian coast.

## Humpback Whale
*Megaptera novaeangliae*

**Identification:** Adult length 13–14 m; juvenile 4–4.5 m at birth; females slightly longer. Species characterised by extremely long pectoral flippers (one-third body length). Body — back black, belly white. Pigmentation varies between individuals and areas; Southern Hemisphere stocks — back of pectoral flippers black. At least one "all white" individual, possibly an albino, has been seen off Qld coast in recent years.

**Habitat and Range:** Worldwide. Long migration between summer feeding grounds in Antarctic waters and breeding grounds in sheltered central Barrier Reef waters.

**Notes:** This species is mainstay of whale-watching in Qld. Term "humpback" derives from the tendency of the whale to arch its back before deep diving. Whaling during 1952–1962 severely depleted estimated eastern stock of 10,000; slow recovery to 2000–2500 individuals (in 1994), with annual increase at approximately 10–12%.

Stephen Poole

## Minke Whale
*Balaenoptera acutorostrata*

**Identification:** Adult length 6–8 m. Pencil-shaped body; back grey-blue.

**Habitat and Range:** Worldwide. In Queensland the "dwarf" form is also seen. An "inquisitive" whale, often approaches boats. May enter river systems.

**Notes:** Minkes are not easily seen from shore because of their small size (varying between normal and "dwarf" forms) and tendency to exhale before surfacing. Smallest of baleen whales and most common. Southern Hemisphere population about 800,000.

## Bryde's Whale *Balaenoptera edeni*

**Identification:** Adult length 14–15 m. Back grey. Three distinct longitudinal grooves on upper part of head.

**Habitat and Range:** May frequent southern Queensland waters year-round, most sightings August–October. Does not migrate to Antarctic waters.

**Notes:** Blow is tall and "thin" and does not last as long as that of Humpback. Capable of very rapid speed. Considered relatively abundant. Feeds on schooling bait-fish.

## Killer Whale *Orcinus orca*

**Identification:** Adult length 6–8 m. Tall dorsal fin (especially in males) 1.5–2 m. Body black and white

**Habitat and Range:** Worldwide; Southern Hemisphere — more common in cooler waters.

**Notes:** Largest toothed whale seen from shore in southern Qld. Observed in Cape Moreton/Point Lookout region. Group sizes up to eight.

# Dolphins

Dr Peter Corkeron

Brisbane is unique among the major cities of Australia in having an abundance of dolphins in local waters. In the past Aboriginal people on North Stradbroke Island fished for mullet in co-operation with local dolphins. Although this tradition has died, interactions with people still occur in Moreton Bay. For a few days in the mid-1980s, a female Bottlenose Dolphin and her calf stayed close to the beach at the Tangalooma wrecks, where campers fed her on squid and children played with the calf. Now, on most evenings, Bottlenose Dolphins visit the shore at the Tangalooma resort where they are fed fish by guests.

Dolphins are not fish but, with whales and porpoises, cetacean (marine) mammals. They are warm-blooded and bear live young.

Bottlenose Dolphins (*Tursiops truncatus*) and Indopacific Humpback Dolphins (*Sousa chinensis*) are the only species found within Moreton Bay. Common Dolphins (*Delphinus delphis*), Pantropical Spotted Dolphins (*Stenella attenuata*) and Spinner Dophins (*Stenella longirostris*) occur in oceanic waters near Brisbane.

Peter Corkeron

## Bottlenose Dolphin *Tursiops truncatus*

**Identification:** "Typical" dolphin. Mature adults in Queensland waters reach 2–2.5 m. Body fairly robust; light grey, though almost brown in some light. As animal matures, underbody becomes spotted; spotting increases with age. Dorsal fin recurved at back. Breathing pattern — no exaggerated roll (see Indopacific Humpback Dolphin below).

**Habitat and Range:** Most common species near Brisbane. More than 350 in Moreton Bay. Temperate to tropical waters worldwide.

**Notes:** Bottlenose Dolphins can be seen from shore at Point Lookout on North Stradbroke Island. From a boat, dolphins can be seen about 40 m behind working prawn trawlers. Usually in groups of about six to 10 animals, although sometimes in groups of up to 100.

R. Slade

## Indopacific Humpback Dolphin
### *Sousa chinensis*

**Identification:** Body length and weight similar to Bottlenose. Humpbacks distinguished by longer rostrum (beak). Juveniles lighter grey than Bottlenose. Adults — white on dorsal fin, rostrum and "forehead"; upper back dark, almost black. Dorsal fin shaped like an equilateral triangle. Breathing pattern — dolphins poke rostrum (nose) out of water, followed by head and back in a rolling motion.

**Habitat and Range:** About 50 resident in Moreton Bay. Generally occur in shallower waters and closer to shore than Bottlenose Dolphins. Sometimes found at mouth of Brisbane River; near Luggage Point and container ship wharves; small boat harbour at Scarborough; and Point Lookout. Can also be seen off Bribie Island in Pumicestone Passage and on ocean beaches; off Amity Point; and feeding behind trawlers in Moreton Bay.

**Notes:** Some field guides show the Humpback Dolphin with a large hump on its back, on which dorsal fin is situated. Humpbacks in Queensland waters do not have this.

# About the Authors

**Dr Christine Cannon** grew up in England, gained her first degree in zoology there, a Master's degree, a husband and a family in Canada, and then a PhD from the University of Queensland where she studied feeding and ecology of rosellas. Since then she has researched diets, movements and disease in lorikeets on the Gold Coast and was, for a time, Curator-in-Charge of Wildlife at the Currumbin Sanctuary. She later trained as a librarian and is currently an information officer with the International Food Institute of Queensland. Christine retains her keen interest in parrots however, and she and her husband are researching the extent of the hybrid zone between Pale-headed Rosellas and Eastern Rosellas along the Queensland/NSW border.

**Dr Lester Cannon** is Senior Curator (Worms) at the Queensland Museum where he has been studying and writing about parasitic and free-living worms since 1976. As a boy he used to walk to and from school along the beach at Redcliffe. This triggered a life-long fascination for little creatures. He is especially interested in flatworms, good food, fine music and travel — though not necessarily in that order — and is the author of numerous publications, both scholarly and popular.

**Dr Peter Corkeron** researched the behaviour and ecology of inshore dolphins in the waters off Brisbane for his PhD and maintains a research interest in the dolphins of Moreton Bay. His current research interests include pelagic delphinids in the waters off Brisbane; molecular genetic studies of Humpback Whales in eastern Australia; and studies of the behaviour of Humpback Whales in Hervey Bay and Right Whales off the coast of southern Australia.

**Patrick Couper** is Curator (Vertebrates) at the Queensland Museum where his research is on the taxonomy and zoogeography of Queensland's reptiles. He has special expertise with species from southern Queensland including those from Moreton Bay. Sea snakes and freshwater turtles have received special attention in the research collections of the Museum recently.

**Jeanette Covacevich**, BA, MSc, is Senior Curator (Vertebrates) at the Queensland Museum. She has had a long research interest in the occurrence of reptiles in densely settled South-East Queensland. Snakes, particularly the potentially dangerous species, have been a special focus of her work.

**Greg Czechura** works as a Senior Museum Technician at the Queensland Museum. His qualifications include a Diploma in Teaching (Primary), an Associate Diploma in Applied Biology and a Bachelor of Education. His interests include birds of prey (about which he has published extensively), reptiles, amphibians and the history of the High Middle Ages. He is Queensland Area Coordinator and council member of the Australasian Raptor ✦

Association and is studying the distribution and status of the Red Goshawk, Australia's rarest bird of prey, in southern Queensland.

**Professor Tony Ewart** came to Queensland in 1967 from London, via New Zealand where he spent seven years. Although a geologist by profession, he has wide interests in natural history, especially in cicadas. Tony first became fascinated with these distinctive insects in New Zealand (which has a surprisingly varied number of species), but was even more intrigued by those he found in Queensland. He was further amazed to find so little was known about cicadas even though they are one of the most prominent insects of the summer months (noise-wise!). Tony's geological research is far removed from cicadas — in the fields of geochemistry and vulcanology!

**Dr Les Hall** has been studying bats for more than 30 years. His parents fostered an early interest in natural history which was carried through to his professional career. Bats appeal to Les because so little is known about them and to study them requires special techniques and plenty of travel. Les is Senior Lecturer in Anatomical Sciences at the University of Queensland.

**Jeff Johnson** has worked in the Ichthyology section of the Queensland Museum since 1977. During this time he has accrued a detailed and extensive knowledge of Queensland's fish fauna. His current projects include an annotated checklist of the fishes of Moreton Bay (approximately 700 species). Jeff is a keen fisherman, scuba diver and boat enthusiast.

**Dr Darryl Jones** is Lecturer in Ecology in the Faculty of Environmental Sciences at Griffith University. He has been studying the ecology of Australian Brush-turkeys in South-East Queensland since 1983 and received his PhD for work on the breeding of the species, He has a long-term interest in the ecology of urban areas and especially interactions between people and wildlife. He is currently researching crows, koels, brush-turkeys and lyrebirds.

**Dr Anne Kemp** teaches gross human anatomy at the University of Queensland. She is studying the development, habitat and biology of living Australian lungfish and comparing information on this species with related fossils. Her research includes analysis of pathological conditions in living and fossil lungfish. Dr Kemp, who is originally from Scotland, graduated with honours in zoology from the University of Edinburgh in 1963. She has lived in Queensland since 1968 and obtained her PhD in 1977, followed by a BVSc in 1984, from the University of Queensland.

**Dr Judith King** is Extension Officer for the Queensland Forest Research Institute, Department of Primary Industries Forest Service. She advises industry, government departments and the public on pests of trees and timber. She has been an entomologist since 1979 and her areas of research have included systematics of bees and pollination of leguminous and tree fruit crops. Judith retains her interest in, and publishes on, Hymenoptera, particularly bees. She watches and encourages bee and wasp activity in her garden.

**Dr Kevin Lambkin** graduated with a BSc (Hons) from the University of Queensland in 1976 and a PhD from the University of Sydney in 1980. Although employed in non-scientific pursuits since then, he has maintained an active interest in the systematics of the Neuroptera and Mecoptera and has published extensively. From 1992–1994 Kevin was a Senior Curator of Entomology at the Queensland Museum.

**Phil Lawless** grew up on a cattle property in Queensland's South Burnett. In 1980 he completed a BSc in zoology at the University of Queensland and joined the Queensland Museum in 1986. Phil worked in the Crustacea and Social History sections until 1991 when he settled in Arachnology where he is now Assistant Curator.

**Ray Leggett** has had a life-long interest in all aspects of natural history, with special emphasis on the study of freshwater fishes. He has bred and raised 246 species from around the world, many for the first time in aquariums. From 1970 till 1973, Ray worked in the aquarium industry in England and since his return to Australia has travelled to every state, collecting and studying our native fishes. He is well known as a senior judge and exhibitor and is the author of *Australian Native Fishes for Aquariums.*

**Dr Colin Limpus** is one of Australia's foremost authorities on marine turtles. He gained a BSc (physics and mathematics) and an MSc (sea snake toxicology) from the University of Queensland where he also completed his PhD on the ecology of marine turtles. His interest in marine turtles spans 27 years and his outstanding contributions to turtle conservation have been recognised with the award of a Public Service Medal. His special area of interest is the biology of long-lived animals.

**Dr Len Martin** graduated in zoology with First Class Honours from the University of Sydney in 1955. He researched female sex hormones in mice for his PhD in 1961 and mammalian sex hormones remain a unifying interest. Len worked at the Imperial Cancer Research Fund in London from 1965 to 1980, becoming Head of the Department of Hormone Physiology. He joined the University of Queensland in 1981 where he is Reader in Physiology. Sex hormones prompted Len's interest in flying foxes which he has been studying since 1982. He has the world's largest captive breeding colony of flying foxes and is inaugural president of the Australasian Bat Society.

**Rolly McKay** has been Curator of Fishes at the Queensland Museum since 1971. Before this he held positions in the Western Australian Museum and the WA Department of Fisheries. He has published widely on groups such as Whiting, Grunters and Sweetlips and on the aquarium industry. Rolly's other area of expertise is far removed from fish — Wolf Spiders!

**Dr Geoff Monteith** has BSc and PhD degrees from the University of Queensland where he worked in the Department of Entomology from 1963 to 1078. He then joined the Queensland Museum as Curator of Insects, a position he still occupies. Geoff has a special interest in rainforest insects and has surveyed them extensively in Australia and nearby countries. He has also been active in promoting public appreciation of insects through Museum displays and educational workshops.

**Ric Natrass** is a Wildlife Ranger in the National Parks and Wildlife Service, Central Moreton District which includes the Greater Brisbane Region. In 1990 he founded the Brisbane Frog Society, the first Australian organisation specifically concerned with the conservation of frogs. His interest in the Cane Toad is a natural extension of his passion for frogs with whom he has spent many long wet nights. He has authored and co-authored a number of papers and articles on a wide variety of native vertebrates and is heard Friday mornings on "Wildlife Talkback" on Brisbane's Radio 4QR.

**Dr Robert Paterson** is a diagnostic radiologist at the Royal Brisbane Hospital. He and his wife Patricia have documented the emerging recovery of the east Australian Humpback Whale population by means of annual shore-based surveys in the Cape Moreton/Point Lookout region since 1978. This interest resulted in Dr Paterson's appointment as an Honorary Research Fellow at the Queensland Museum. With Stephen Van Dyck from the Museum's mammal department, he has published papers on taxonomy and skeletal abnormalities of cetacean specimens in the Museum collection.

**Christoph Pavey** obtained his BSc (Hons) degree at the University of Queensland where he is now completing his PhD. Chris has researched the foraging ecology of five species of horseshoe bat in eastern Queensland. He has also carried out a number of projects on the Powerful Owl and is especially interested in their diet, breeding, biology and distribution. Chris has wide interests in Australian natural history, but is especially keen on owls, raptors, bats and arboreal marsupials.

**Brenton C. Peters** heads the survey and treatment program against the West Indian drywood termite for the Department of Primary Industries Forest Service. He has 20 years' professional experience in tropical and sub-tropical timber entomology research, development, extension and regulation. Brenton has worked on pest identification, prevention and remedial treatments of drywood and subterranean termites and borers. He is a member of the Australian Standards Association Committee on Termite Control and has published technical papers and book reviews in professional and industry journals.

**Stephen Poole,** BSc, is an Environment Officer with Brisbane City Council and is responsible for the Council's activities with respect to Bushland Acquisition, Ecotourism and Fauna Management. Before joining the Council, Stephen was a freelance environmental consultant. This experience and his work with the Council have given him an in-depth knowledge of the ecology of the Greater Brisbane Region. His interests are widespread, but he is particularly concerned about koala habitat management and planning in

South-East Queensland. His position with the Council has dual roles in terms of interacting with local fauna and planning for their protection.

**Dr Anthony Preen** has been studying dugongs from Moreton Bay, Hervey Bay, the Gulf of Carpentaria and the Arabian Gulf since 1985. His interests have covered many aspects of dugong ecology including movements, diet and the environmental factors affecting their distribution.

**Dr Robert Raven** is Senior Curator (Arachnology) at the Queensland Museum and an international authority on Trapdoor, Funnel-web and Tarantula Spiders. He has named more than 250 new species from Australia, Africa, the Pacific and Thailand. Dr Raven is also an authority on Redback Spiders in Australia and the Pacific. He has worked at the Queensland Museum since 1981.

**Deniss Reeves** is a pharmacist who has had a life-long interest in insects, particularly butterflies, and more recently, dragonflies. He is a foundation member of the Australian Entomological Society and President of the Queensland Naturalists' Club. In 1990 he received the prestigious J.C. Le Souef Award for amateur entomologists from the Victorian Entomological Society.

**John Short** is a Curatorial Assistant in the Crustacea section of the Queensland Museum. Through his collection responsibilities John has gained a detailed knowledge of the Queensland fauna. He is currently studying for a PhD on the systematics and evolution of Australian long-armed prawns and has also published on the taxonomy of freshwater crayfish, crabs and shrimps.

**Dr John Stanisic** is Senior Curator (Molluscs) at the Queensland Museum and is Australia's foremost expert on land snails. He gained his PhD at the University of Queensland with a thesis on minute rainforest snails and has written a number of publications on the systematics and biogeography of land snails. His main research interests are the distribution of the prolific Charopidae in eastern Australia, and the evolution of land snails in relation to the occurrence of rainforest and limestone outcrops. As a result of 15 years of collecting at more than 1200 sites (from the islands of the Torres Strait to far southern New South Wales), the Queensland Museum holds Australia's most significant land snail collection.

**Stephen Van Dyck** is Curator (Vertebrates) at the Queensland Museum where he has worked since 1975. His research interests include studies of carnivorous marsupials in New Guinea and Australia and documentation of rare and endangered mammals of Queensland.

**Ian Venables** has been interested in birds since childhood. He is an active member of the Queensland Ornithological Society, Royal Australasian Ornithologists Union, Australian Raptor Association, Australian Wader Study Group and several other naturalist groups. Ian is a guide and lecturer for many bird tours and activities and has acted as an environmental consultant on birds for government and business organisations. He has contributed to several major publications including the *Atlas of Australian Birds* and is preparing a guide to *Bird Sites Around Brisbane*. Ian is a member of the Queensland Museum Board of Trustees.

**Steven K. Wilson** found his first reptile about the time he could just walk and, according to Steve, things have gone downhill ever since. He now spends his time scouring the bushland of Australia and destinations beyond, studying and photographing reptiles. He is co-author of a photographic reference to Australia's reptiles and author of numerous popular articles on natural history. As an Interpretation Officer with the Queensland Museum, he deals with inquiries from members of the public about local reptiles, soothing their fears, educating and, hopefully, engendering an interest.

**Shaun Winterton** is an ecologist specialising in aquatic insect/plant inter-actions and limnology. He is currently researching the effects of eutrophica-tion on the biological control of water hyacinth for the Cooperative Research Centre for Tropical Pest Management based at CSIRO, Brisbane. Shaun also has a keen interest in lacewings, particularly in the taxonomy and biology of the Australian Chrysopidae (Green Lacewings).

**Dr Peter Woodall** was born in Zimbabwe and became interested in birds at an early age. He studied zoology, botany and ecology at the University of Rho-desia and obtained his doctorate from Oxford for a study of the Water Vole. Since moving to Brisbane 12 years ago, he has been involved in wide ranging research of local birds and has been President of the Queensland Ornitho-logical Society, the Queensland Naturalists' Club and was editor of *Emu*. He is now a senior lecturer in the Department of Anatomy at the University of Queensland.

# Index of Common Names

# Index of Scientific Names

# Useful Contacts

The information listed here is correct at time of printing. However, telephone numbers around Australia are being altered to incorporate an extra digit. This program will continue until 1999, please check numbers before dialling.

**Queensland Museum Reference Centre**
**Ph: (07) 3840 7635 Fax: (07) 3846 1918**

**Australian Affiliation of Herpetological Societies**
PO Box R307
SYDNEY NSW 2000

**Australian and New Guinea Fishes Association Inc.**
PO Box 535
WOOLOONGBABBA QLD 4102

**Australian Conservation Foundation**
340 Gore St
FITZROY VIC 3065
Contact: Information Services
Ph: (03) 9416 1166 Fax: (03) 9416 0767

**Australian Entomological Society**
c/- Department of Crop Protection
WAITE Campus
University of Adelaide
PO GLEN OSMOND SA 5064
Contact: Dr P.E. Madge
Ph: (08) 370 2987 Fax: (08) 370 2987

**Australian Fauna Ward**
37 Woodbine St
FORESTDALE QLD 4118
Contact: Stuart McNabb
Ph: (07) 3800 3601 Fax: (07) 3809 2901

**Australian Mammal Society**
Department of Zoology
James Cook University
TOWNSVILLE QLD 4811
Contact: Chris Johnson
Ph: (077) 81 4141 Fax: (077) 25 1570

**Australian Marine Conservation Society**
PO Box 49
MOOROOKA QLD 4105
Contact: Kath Martin
Ph: (07) 3848 5235 Fax: (07) 3892 5814

**Australian Rainforest Conservation Society**
19 Colorado Av
BARDON QLD 4065
Contact: Dr Aila Keto
Ph: (07) 3368 1318  Fax: (07) 3368 3938

**Australasian Raptor Association**
c/-Flora's Cottage
Fairy Glen Rd
COLLINSVALE TAS. 7012
Contact: Greg Czechura (Qld Rep.)
Ph: (07) 3840 7642 Fax: (07) 3846 1918

**Australian Whale Conservation Society**
PO Box 12046
ELIZABETH ST PO QLD 4002
Contact: Paul Hodda
Ph: (07) 3398 2928 or 018 98 4359

**Bayside Regional Park Advisory Committee**
GPO Box 1434
BRISBANE QLD 4001
Contact: Peter Shilton/Andrew Chamberlin
Ph: (07) 3225 6396 Fax: 3225 6413

**Beerwah Field Study Centre**
PO Box 117
BEERWAH QLD 4519
Contact: The Director
Ph: (074) 946 781 Fax: (074) 94 6781

**Boondall Wetlands Management Committee**
GPO Box 1434
BRISBANE QLD 4001
Contact: Peter Shilton/Ben McMullen
Ph: (07) 3225 6396  Fax: (07) 3225 6413

**Bribie Island Environmental Protection Association.**
PO Box 350
BRIBIE ISLAND QLD 4507
Contact: Shirley Elliot
Ph: (07) 3408 9286 Fax: (07) 3408 3577

**BRISBANE CITY COUNCIL**

**Bushland Care Program**
290 Lancaster Rd
ASCOT QLD 4007
Contact: Jenny Leask
Ph: (07) 3268 4697 Fax: (07) 3268 5772

**Environment Management Branch**
GPO Box 1434
BRISBANE QLD 4001
**Brisbane River:** Annette Magee (07) 3225 6554
**Bushland:** Ian Hislop (07) 3225 6776
   Frank Andrews (07) 3225 6724
**Ecotourism:** Stephen Poole (07) 3225 4527

**Energy:** Trevor Gleeson (07) 3225 3118
**Environmental Education:** Debra Beattie
(07) 3225 6490
**Fire Management:** Bryn Gullen
(07) 3225 6369
**Natural Area Management:** Peter Shilton
(07) 3225 6396
**Open Space Planning:**
Frank Andrews (07) 3255 6724,
Joe Mumford (07) 3225 6778
**Waterways:** Paul Mack (07) 3225 6882
**Wetlands:** Hugh Suttor (07) 3225 4142
Patrick Bourke (07) 3225 3096
**Vegetation Protection:** Carole Rayner
(07) 3225 6766

**Brisbane Valley Koala Preservation
Society**
c/- 9 Adelaide St
ESK QLD 4312
Contact: Jeny Calway
Ph: (074) 241 788

**Brisbane Frog Society**
PO Box 7017
EAST BRISBANE QLD 4169
Contact: Ruth Wait
PH: (07) 3286 1095

**Centre for Conservation Biology**
University of Queensland
ST LUCIA QLD 4072
Contact: Dr Peter Hale
Ph: (07) 3365 2527 Fax: (07) 3365 4828

**Currumbin Sanctuary**
Gold Coast Highway
CURRUMBIN QLD 4223
Ph: (07) 5534 1266 Fax: (07) 5534 7427

**Department of Environment and Heritage**
see **National Parks and Wildlife Service**

**Downfall Creek Bushland Centre**
815 Rode Road
MCDOWALL QLD 4053
Contact: Peter Armstrong
Ph: (07) 3353 3707 (07) 3353 3266
Fax: (07) 3353 2818

**Entomological Society of Queensland**
c/- Department of Entomology
University of Queensland
ST LUCIA QLD 4072
Contact: Prof. Gordon Gordh
Ph: (07) 3365 1747 Fax: 3365 1922

**Environmental Defenders Office
(Qld) Inc.**
2/133 George Street
BRISBANE QLD 4000
Contact: Jo Bragg
Ph: (07) 3210 0275 Fax: (07) 3210 0253

**Fleay's Wildlife Park**
West Burleigh Rd
BURLEIGH HEADS QLD 4220
Contact: Greg Thompson
Ph: (07) 5556 2194 (07) 5535 6623

**Greening Australia**
GPO Box 9868
BRISBANE QLD 4001
Contact: The Secretary
Ph: (07) 3844 0211 Fax: (07) 3844 0727

**Ipswich Envirocare Association Inc.**
PO Box 2230
NORTH IPSWICH QLD 4305
Contact: Rocco de Pierri
Ph: (07) 3202 2906

**Jacobs Well Environmental Education Centre**
MS 1372
BEENLEIGH QLD 4207
Contact: Glenn Leiper
Ph: (07) 5546 2317 Fax: (07) 5546 2317

**Karawatha Forest Advisory Committee**
GPO Box 1434
BRISBANE QLD 4001
Contact: Peter Shilton/Andrew Chamberlin
Ph: (07) 3225 6369 Fax: (07) 3408 3577

**Landcare — South East Region**
PO Box 96
IPSWICH 4305
Contact: Sam Brown
Ph: (07) 3280 1893 Fax: (07) 3812 1715

**Lota-Manly West Community
Association Inc.**
10 Boondarra Street
MANLY WEST QLD 4179
Contact: Ann Edwards
Ph: (07) 3393 5290

**Macleay Island Conservation Group**
Lot 27, Duncan Street
MACLEAY ISLAND QLD 4184
Contact: Leigh Abbot
Ph: (07) 3409 5642

**Malacological Society of Australia Inc.**
Queensland Branch
PO Box 64
BRISBANE ALBERT ST QLD 4002
Contact: The Secretary

**Men of the Trees**
PO Box 283
CLAYFIELD QLD 4011
Contact: Mrs Ngairetta Brennan
Ph: (07) 3262 1096

**Moreton Bay Environmental Education
Centre**
PO Box 5173
MANLY QLD 4179
Contact: Eileen Mitchell
Ph: (07) 3396 0754 Fax: (07) 3893 2713

**Moreton Island Protection Committee**
PO Box 544
INDOOROOPILLY QLD 4068
Contact: Kay Martin
Ph: (07) 3378 0822

**Mt Nebo and Mt Glorious Environmental Protection Association**
C/- Mt Nebo Post Office
MT NEBO QLD 4520
Contact: Peter Stevenson
Ph: (07) 3289 0223

**National Parks Association of Queensland**
PO Box 1040
MILTON QLD 4064
Contact: George Haddock
Ph: (07) 3367 0878  Fax: (07) 3367 0890

**National Parks and Wildlife Service**

Central Moreton District (Greater Brisbane)
Wildlife Ranger
National Parks and Wildlife Service
PO Box 42
KENMORE QLD 4069
Ph: (07) 3202 0200 (all hours)

Sunshine Coast District
Wildlife Ranger
National Parks and Wildlife Service
PO Box 168
COTTON TREE QLD 4558
Ph: (074) 438 944 (all hours)

Gold Coast District
Wildlife Ranger
National Parks and Wildlife Service
PO Box 612
BURLEIGH HEADS QLD 4220
Ph: (07) 5535 3714

**Native Frog Restoration Project**
78 Ninth Avenue
ST LUCIA QLD 4068
Contact: Martin and Hilary Boscott
Ph: (07) 3870 8815  Fax: (07) 3227 6386

**NatureSearch**
PO Box 155
ALBERT STREET PO QLD 4002
Contact: Liz Horler
Ph: (07) 3227 7836  Fax: (07) 3227 6386

**Noah's Ark Wildlife Emergency**
PO Box 1249
BEENLEIGH QLD 4207
Contact: Eva Newman
Ph: (07) 3807 3404

**Nudgee Beach Environmental Education Centre**
1588 Nudgee Road
NUDGEE BEACH QLD 4016
Contact: Mary-Anne Pattison
Ph: (07) 3267 7811

**Orphaned Native Animals Rear and Release (ONARR)**
PO Box 3015
DARRA QLD 4076
Contact: Helen Luckhoff
Ph: (07) 3375 4620 Fax: 3375 4620

**Queensland Conservation Council**
PO Box 12046
BRISBANE ELIZABETH STREET QLD 4000
Contact: Nicky Hungerford
Ph: (07) 3221 0188  Fax: (07) 3229 7992

**Queensland Naturalists Club**
PO Box 5663
WEST END QLD 4101
Contact: The Secretary
Ph: (07) 3844 4426

**Queensland Ornithological Society**
PO Box 97
ST LUCIA QLD 4067
Contact: Roy Sonnenburg
Ph: (07) 3261 2391

**Queensland Reptile and Amphibian Club**
c/- Lot 7 Crowson Lane
PARK RIDGE QLD 4125
Contact: Alma Searle
Ph: (07) 3200 0266

**Queensland Reptile and Fauna Park**
Glasshouse Mountain, Tourist Road
BEERWAH QLD 4519
Contact: Thelma Engle
Ph: (074) 94 1134 Fax: (074) 94 8604

**Queensland Wader Study Group**
Fahey Rd
MT GLORIOUS QLD 4502
Contact: Peter Driscoll
Ph: (07) 3289 0237 Fax: (03) 3289 0237

**Restoring Australian Native Amphibians (RANA)**
42 Poinsettia Street
INALA QLD 4077
Contact: Wayne Winter
Ph: (07) 3372 1490

**Royal Australasian Ornithologists Union**
415 Riversdale Rd
HAWTHORN EAST VIC. 3123
Contact: Dr David Baker-Gabb
Ph: (03) 9882 2622 Fax: (03) 9882 2677

**Royal Geographical Society of Queensland**
112 Brookes Street
FORTITUDE VALLEY QLD 4006
Contact: Kath Berg
Ph: (07) 3252 3856  Fax: (07) 3252 4096

**Rural Environment Planning Association**
41 Gap Creek Road
KENMORE HILLS  QLD  4069
Contact: Jenny Hacker
Ph: (07) 3374 1468

**School of Environmental Studies**
Griffith University
NATHAN QLD 4111
Ph: (07) 3875 7519 Fax: (07) 3875 7459

**School of Marine Science**
University of Queensland
ST LUCIA QLD 4072
Contact: The Executive Officer
Ph: (07) 3365 4333 Fax: (07) 3365 4755

**Stradbroke Island Management Organisation**
PO Box 8 Point Lookout
NORTH STRADBROKE ISLAND  QLD  4183
Contact: Ellie Durbidge
Ph: (07) 3409 8115

**Sunshine Coast Environment Council Inc.**
PO Box 269
NAMBOUR QLD 4560
Contact: Jenny De Hayr
Ph: (074) 41 5747 Fax: (074) 41 7478

**Tinchi Tamba Wetlands Advisory Committee**
GPO Box 1434
BRISBANE  QLD  4001
Contact: Peter Shilton/Annette Magee
Ph: (07) 3225 6396  Fax: (07) 3225 6413

**Toohey Forest Management Committee**
GPO Box 1434
BRISBANE  QLD  4001
Contact: Peter Shilton/Ben McMullen
Ph: (07) 3225 6396  Fax: (07) 3225 6413

**Wilderness Society**
97 Albert Street
BRISBANE  QLD  4000
Contact: Virginia Young
Ph: (07) 3229 4533  Fax: (07) 3210 0120

**Wildlife Preservation Society of Queensland**
2/133 George Street
BRISBANE  QLD  4000
Contact: Jean Tilly
Ph: (07) 3221 0194  Fax: (07) 3221 0701

Bayside
PO Box 427
CAPALABA  QLD  4157
Contact: Simon Batais
Ph: (07) 3821 0454

Brisbane Valley
Lot 72 Willaura Dr
COOMINYA QLD 4311
Contact: Coral Rishworth
Ph: (074) 26 4742

Brisbane West
559 Honour Av

SHERWOOD QLD 4075
Contact: Beth Smyth
Ph: (07) 3379 6850

Caboolture
PO Box 1415
CABOOLTURE  QLD  4510
Contact: Eileen Rigdon
Ph: (074) 96 6644

Caloundra
PO Box 275
CALOUNDRA  QLD  4551
Contact: Jill Chamberlain
Ph: (074) 442 707

East Logan
PO Box 1113
SPRINGWOOD  QLD  4127
Contact: Ted Fensom
Ph: (07) 3341 6790

Gold Coast/Hinterland
PO Box 2441
SOUTHPORT QLD 4215
Contact: Elaine Quickenden
Ph: (075) 533 1290

Pine Rivers
PO Box 377
STRATHPINE  QLD  4500
Contact: Judy Elliott
Ph: (07) 3221 0194  Fax: (07) 3221 0701

Samford Valley
PO Box 272
SAMFORD VALLEY  QLD  4520
Contact: Heather Holcroft
Ph: (07) 3289 7247  Fax: (07) 3289 7247

South Redlands
6 Kruger St
REDLAND BAY QLD 4165
Contact: Terri Guardala
Ph: (07) 3829 0809

**Woogaroo Creek Community Group**
2 Mill Street
GOODNA QLD 4300
Contact: Keith McCosh
Ph: (07) 3288 4709

**World Wide Fund for Nature**
GPO BOX 528
SYDNEY  NSW 2001
Contact: Dr Ray Nias
Ph: (02) 9247 6300 Fax: (02) 9247 8778